C.S.E. Mathematics

1   The Core Course

By the same author

ARITHMETIC FOR COMMERCE
BUSINESS CALCULATIONS FOR BEC
A COMPLETE 'O' LEVEL MATHEMATICS
STATISTICS TODAY

C.S.E. Mathematics

1   The Core Course

A Greer

**Senior Lecturer, City of Gloucester
College of Technology**

Stanley Thornes (Publishers) Ltd.

First published in December 1978 by:
Stanley Thornes (Publishers) Ltd
EDUCA House
32 Malmesbury Road
Kingsditch
CHELTENHAM GL51 9PL
England

ISBN 0 85950 072 1

Printed and bound in Great Britain at
The Pitman Press, Bath

Preface

This book contains all the topics required for the 'common core' of the Certificate of Secondary Education Examination in Mathematics. It is essentially a revision course but nothing has been assumed and the book starts from the very beginning with elementary arithmetic.

Because this is a revision course the sections on Arithmetic, Algebra, Geometry, Trigonometry and Modern Mathematics have been dealt with separately. The emphasis is on a simple approach and a teacher and his class may work, if desired, through the book chapter by chapter.

A very large number of exercises have been included. These have been graded by means of the letters A, B, C and D. A indicates that the problem is fairly easy and nearly every student should be able to do these. D indicates that the problem is difficult and only very few students would be expected to solve this type.

At the end of most chapters an exercise consisting of past examination questions has been included so that the students can gain in confidence by tackling and solving these questions.

In appendices at the back of the book I have included a large number of short answer, multi-choice and long answer questions all of which have been taken from past examination papers.

Gloucester 1978   A. Greer

Acknowledgements

The author and the publishers wish to thank the following examination boards for granting permission to use questions taken from their past examination papers. The letters in brackets after the name of the board show the abbreviations used in the text.

Associated Lancashire Schools Examining Board (*A.L.*)
East Anglian Examinations Board (*E.A.*)
East Midland Regional Examinations Board (*E.M.*)
Metropolitan Regional Examinations Board (*M.R.*)
Middlesex Regional Examinations Board (*M.*)
North Regional Examinations Board (*N.*)
North West Regional Examinations Board (*N.W.*)
Southern Regional Examinations Board (*S.*)
South-East Regional Examinations Board (*S.E.*)
South-Western Examinations Board (*S.W.*)
Welsh Joint Education Committee (*W.*)
West Midlands Examinations Board (*W.M.*)
West Yorkshire and Lindsey Regional Examining Board (*W.Y.*)
Yorkshire Regional Examinations Board (*Y.R.*)

Contents

and continuous variables —
The histogram — Histogram
for a grouped distribution —
Discrete distributions —
Statistical averages — The
arithmetic mean — The
mean of a frequency
distribution — The median
— The mode — Theoretical
probability — The
probability scale —
Empirical probability.

Chapter 1 Operations with Whole Numbers

Some Definitions

Numbers are represented by symbols which are called *digits*. There are nine digits which are 1, 2, 3, 4, 5, 6, 7, 8 and 9. We also use the symbol 0 (i.e. zero) where no digit exists. Digits and zero may be combined together to represent any number.

Numeration expresses numbers in words—zero, one, two, three, four, five, six, seven, eight and nine.

Notation expresses numbers in figures or symbols (0, 1, 2, 3, 4, 5, 6, 7, 8, 9). These are all unit figures. The next number, ten, is 10 which is a combination of one and zero. 11 (eleven) is the combination of one and one and it equals ten plus one. 20 (twenty) is the combination of two and zero and it equals two tens. Ten tens are one hundred and ten hundreds are one thousand and so on.

- 100 indicates one hundred
- 900 indicates nine hundreds
- 954 indicates nine hundreds, five tens and four units
- 1000 indicates one thousand
- 8000 indicates eight thousands
- 9999 indicates nine thousands, nine hundreds, nine tens and nine units

Note that in the case of the number 9999:

```
9 9 9 9
d c b a
```

a is a unit figure and equals		9
b is a tens figure and equals		90
c is a hundreds figure and equals		900
d is a thousands figure and equals		9000

In arithmetic the sign + means plus or add and the sign = means equals. Thus,

$$7+2=9$$

The number $9999 = 9000+900+90+9$

If we want to write six hundreds, five tens and seven units then we write 657. If we want to write four hundred and seven units we write 407; the zero keeps the place for the missing tens.

eight thousand and thirty five is written 8035
eight thousand and nine is written 8009
ten thousand is written 10 000
one hundred thousand is written 100 000
one thousand thousand is called one million which is written 1 000 000
8 000 000 indicates eight million
37 895 762 indicates thirty seven million, eight hundred and ninety five thousand, seven hundred and sixty two.

In the number 37 895 762 we have grouped the digits in threes with a space between them. This space takes the place of the comma which was traditionally used to group the figures of a number into threes. The change has taken place because many foreign countries use a comma instead of a decimal point.

Exercise 1 — *All type A*

Write the following in figures:

1) four hundred and fifty seven

1

2) nine thousand, five hundred and thirty six

3) seven thousand, seven hundred and seventy seven

4) three thousand and eight

5) seven hundred and five

6) thirty thousand and twenty eight

7) five thousand and ninety

8) four thousand nine hundred and four

9) one hundred and twenty five thousand, nine hundred and six

10) three million, eight hundred thousand and seven

11) ninety five million, eight hundred and twenty seven thousand

12) three hundred million and nine

Write the following numbers in words:

13)	225	**19)**	17 000
14)	8321	**20)**	198 376
15)	3017	**21)**	200 005
16)	3960	**22)**	7 365 231
17)	1807	**23)**	27 000 309
18)	20 004		

Addition

When adding numbers together place the figures in columns making sure that all the units figures are placed under one another, that all the tens figures are placed beneath each other and so on. Thus all the figures having the same place value fall in the same column.

Example 1

Add together 4219, 583, 98 and 1287.

```
  4219
   583
    98
  1287
 _____
  6187
 _____
```

Start off by adding the units column. Thus 7 and 8 make 15 and 3 makes 18 and 9 makes 27. Place the 7 in the units column of the answer and carry the 2 forward to the tens column. Adding this we have 2 and 8 is 10 and 9 is 19 and 8 is 27 and 1 is 28. Place the 8 in the tens column of the answer and carry the 2 forward to the hundreds column which we now add. 2 and 2 is 4 and 5 is 9 and 2 is 11. We write a 1 in the hundreds column of the answer and carry 1 forward to the thousands column which we now add. 1 and 1 is 2 and 4 is 6. Writing the 6 in the thousands column of the answer we see that the answer to the addition is 6187.

Example 2

Find the value of
17 638 + 108 749 + 1011 + 2 345 008.

The + sign simply means add the numbers together and our problem is to add the four numbers. As before we write them in a column so that digits having the same place values are written beneath each other.

```
    17 638
   108 749
     1 011
 2 345 008
 _____
 2 472 406
 _____
```

Add up the units column from bottom to top, saying audibly, 9, 18, 26. Write 6 in the units column of the answer and carry the 2 forward to the tens column. Add the tens column as 2, 3, 7 and 10. Write 0 in the tens column of the answer and carry the 1 forward to the hundreds column. Carry on in this way with the remaining columns until the answer is obtained.

The order in which numbers are added is not important. Thus:

$$2+3+7 = 3+7+2$$
$$= 7+2+3$$
$$= 12$$

Exercise 2 — *All type A*

Find the values of each of the following:

1) $96+247+8$

2) $109+57+3478+926$

3) $35\,068+21\,007+905+1178+32$

4) $23\,589+7\,987\,432+234\,068$
$$+9871+324\,689$$

5) $15\,437+1344+1626+107\,924$

Subtraction

Subtraction means taking away. Let us take 5 from 6. We know that 1 is left. We write $6-5=1$ which we read as six minus five equals 1.

Example 3

Subtract 17 from 59

59	Place 17 under 59. 7 from 9 leaves.
17	2. Write 2 in the units column of
—	the answer and then 1 from 5
42	leaves 4. Writing 4 in the tens
—	column of the answer we see

that $59-17=42$.

There are two methods by which subtraction can be performed. Consider

$$15-8=7$$

1st method: Take 8 from 15. We have 7 left.

2nd method: If to 7 we add 8 then we obtain 15. 7 is therefore the difference between 15 and 8.

Example 4

Find the difference between 32 and 17.

Which is the greater of 32 and 17? Clearly 32 is the greater. Therefore we subtract 17 from 32.

32	In the units column we cannot take
17	7 from 2. However if we borrow 1
—	from the tens place and put it
15	before the 2 we get 12, the 3 in
—	the tens column becoming 2. Now

7 from 12 leaves 5. We write 5 in the tens column of the answer and take 1 from 2 in the tens column leaving 1.

Many people find it easier to work the borrowing method the other way round and to write the subtraction out in this way:

32	We say that 7 from 2 will not go,
17	so we take 7 from 12 giving 5
1	which we write in the units column
—	of the answer. We now increase
15	the 1 in the tens column by 1
—	making it 2 (the small figure 1

is a useful aid to the memory until practice makes it unnecessary). Finally we take 2 from 3 leaving 1 which is written in the tens column of the answer.

Example 5

Subtract 1835 from 5423.

5423	In the units column 5 from 3
1835	will not go, so take 5 from
1 1 1	13 leaving 8. Increase the 3 on
	the bottom of the tens column
—	by 1 making it 4. 4 from 2 will
3588	not go, so take 4 from 12 leav-
—	ing 8 and increase the 8 on the

bottom of the hundreds column by 1 making it 9. 9 from 4 will not go, so take 9 from 14 leaving 5. Finally increase the 1 on the bottom of the thousands column and take 2 from 5 leaving 3.

Exercise 3 — *All type A*

1) Find the difference of 27 and 59.

2) Subtract 258 from 593.

3) Find the value of $53-39$.

4) Subtract 7693 from 9251.

5) What is the difference between 336 and 9562?

Exercise 4 — *All type A*

Find the value of each of the following:

1) $8-6+7-5+9-2$

2) $21+32-63-58+79+32-11$

3) $152-78+43-81$

4) $27+45+9+7-15-23-41-8+17$

Combined Addition and Subtraction

Suppose we want to find the value of,

$$18+7-5+3-16+8$$

we pick out all the numbers preceded by a plus sign and add them together. Thus:

$$18+7+3+8 = 36$$

(Note that the first number, it is 18, has no sign in front of it. When this happens a plus sign is always assumed.)

Next we pick out all the numbers preceded by a minus sign and add these together. Thus:

$$-5-16 = -21$$

Finally we subtract 21 from 36 to give 15.

Hence,

$$18+7-5+3-16+8 = 36-21 = 15$$

Example 6

Find the value of $2+6-3+9-5+11$

$$2+6+9+11 = +28$$
$$-3-5 = -8$$
$$\left.\begin{array}{r}+28 \\ -\ 8\end{array}\right\} \text{ Subtracting}$$
$$\overline{20}$$

Arithmetical Signs, Terms and Symbols

The result obtained by adding numbers is called the *sum*. Thus the sum of 9 and 6 is 15.

The result obtained by subtracting one number from another is called the *difference*. The difference between 19 and 8 is $19-8 = 11$.

The sign = is the sign of *equality* and means equal to. Thus 4 hours = 240 minutes.

$+$ is the *addition* sign meaning plus. Thus $4+5 = 9$

$-$ is the *subtraction* sign meaning minus. Thus $9-5 = 4$

$\times$ is the *multiplication* sign meaning multiplied by, or times. Thus $6\times8 = 48$

$\div$ is the *division* sign meaning divided by. There are several ways of indicating division which are as follows:

(1) $6\div3 = 2$ This reads six divided by three equals two.

(2) $\dfrac{6}{3} = 2$ This reads six over three (or six divided by three) equals two.

(3) $3\overline{)6}$ This reads three into six goes two or six divided by three equals two.

4

Multiplication

We can find the value of $6+6+6+6$ by adding the four sixes together. The answer is 24. We could, however, do this more rapidly by using the multiplication tables because we know that $4 \times 6 = 24$.

When two numbers are multiplied together the result is called the *product*. Thus the product of 5 and 9 is $5 \times 9 = 45$.

MULTIPLICATION TABLE

1	2	3	4	5	6	7	8	9	10
2	4	6	8	10	12	14	16	18	20
3	6	9	12	15	18	21	24	27	30
4	8	12	16	20	24	28	32	36	40
5	10	15	20	25	30	35	40	45	50
6	12	18	24	30	36	42	48	54	60
7	14	21	28	35	42	49	56	63	70
8	16	24	32	40	48	56	64	72	80
9	18	27	36	45	54	63	72	81	90
10	20	30	40	50	60	70	80	90	100

The multiplication table is shown above. The extreme left hand vertical column, 1 to 10, as well as the top horizontal row, give the numbers whose products we wish to find. Thus to find the product of 6 and 8 (i.e. 6×8) we find 6 in the extreme left hand column. We then run the eye, or a finger, horizontally along this row until we come to the column headed 8 and we find the number 48, which is the required product. Hence $6 \times 8 = 48$. Similarly we find that $5 \times 9 = 45$ and $9 \times 8 = 72$.

You should use this multiplication table to revise the tables you may previously have studied. Try to make sure that you know up to 10×10 without the need to refer to the table.

Exercise 5 — *All type A*

Write down the following products:

1) 3×2 **4)** 8×4 **7)** 9×9

2) 5×7 **5)** 7×9 **8)** 6×7

3) 9×6 **6)** 5×3

Long Multiplication

Example 7

Multiply 236 by 7.

$$\begin{array}{r} 236 \\ 7 \\ \hline 1652 \\ \hline \end{array}$$

7 times 6 is 42. Place the 2 in the answer and carry the 4. 7 times 3 is 21, plus the 4 carried, is 25. Place 5 in the answer and carry the 2. 7 times 2 is 14, plus the 2 carried is 16.

Example 8

Multiply 369 by 527.

$$\begin{array}{r} 369 \\ 527 \\ \hline 2583 \\ 738 \\ 1845 \\ \hline 194463 \\ \hline \end{array}$$

Write the two numbers with their respective units figures directly underneath each other. Start by multiplying 369 by 7 giving 2583. Write the 3 directly beneath the units figures of the two numbers to be multiplied together. Now multiply 369 by 2 (which is really 20) giving 738. Make sure that the figures obtained by multiplying are this time moved one place to the left. Finally, when multiplying by 5 (which is really 500) it is again necessary to move one further place to the left. We now add

5

the three sets of figures obtained by multiplication, the result being 194 463.

Alternatively if you wish, you can start with the left-hand figure in the multiplier as shown below.

369
527
———
184500
7380
2583
———
194463

First multiply 369 by 500 giving 184 500. Then multiply 369 by 20 giving 7380 and finally multiply 369 by 7 giving 2583. To obtain the product add these three sets of figures obtained by multiplication.

The order in which we multiply does not matter. Thus

$$8 \times 7 = 7 \times 8 = 56$$

$$5 \times 4 \times 7 = 4 \times 5 \times 7 = 7 \times 5 \times 4$$

$$= 5 \times 7 \times 4 = 4 \times 7 \times 5$$

$$= 7 \times 4 \times 5$$

$$= 140$$

Exercise 6 — *Questions 1 and 2 type A, remainder B*

Obtain the following products:

1) 29×32

2) 359×26

3) 3149×321

4) 5683×789

5) 17632×58

Division

Division consists of finding how many times one number is contained in another number.

The *dividend* is the number to be divided.

The *divisor* is the number by which the dividend is divided.

The *quotient* is the result of the division.

Thus, $\dfrac{\text{dividend}}{\text{divisor}} = \text{quotient}$

Short Division

If the divisor is less than 10 it is usual to work by short division.

Example 9

Divide 2625 by 7.

7)2625
375

7 will not divide into 2. Next try 7 into 26. It goes 3 and a remainder of 5. Carry the remainder so that the next number to be divided is 52. 7 goes into 52 7 times and remainder 3. Carry the 3 so that the next number to be divided is 35. 7 into 35 goes 5 exactly.

Example 10

Divide 1979 by 9.

9)1979
219 remainder 8

9 will not divide into 1 so try dividing 9 into 19. It goes 2 remainder 1. Carry the 1 so that the next number to be divided is 17. 9 into 17 goes 1 remainder 8. Carry the 8 so that the next number to be divided is 89. 9 goes into 89 9 times remainder 8. There are no more numbers to divide so the answer is 219 remainder 8.

Exercise 7 — *All type A*

Work out the answers to the following:

1) $1968 \div 8$

2) $392 \div 7$

3) $2168 : 5$

4) $7369 \div 4$

5) $5621 \div 9$

Long Division

The method is shown in the next example.

Example 11

Divide 3024 by 36.

```
36)3024(84
   288
   ───
   144
   144
   ───
    . . .
```

36 consists of two digits. Look at the first two digits in the dividend, i.e. 30. 36 will not divide into 30 because 36 is the larger number. Next look at the first three figures of the dividend. They are 302. Will 36 divide into 302? It will because 302 is the larger number. How many times will it go? Let us multiply 36 by 9 the result is 324 which is greater than 302. Now try 36×8. The result is 288 which is less than 302. Place 8 in the answer (i.e. the quotient) and write the 288 under the 302. Subtracting 288 from 302 we get a remainder of 14. Now bring down the next figure in the dividend, which is 4. Now divide 36 into 144. The result is 4 exactly because $4 \times 36 = 144$. Write 4 in the quotient and we see that $3024 \div 36 = 84$ exactly.

Example 12

Divide 1 000 000 by 250.

```
250)1000000(4000
    1000
    ────
     . . . .
```

250 will not divide into the first three figures of the dividend (100) so we try 250 into 1000. It goes 4 times exactly leaving no remainder. To obtain the quotient the remaining three zeros are written in the quotient giving 4000.

Tests for Divisibility

A number is divisible by:

2 if it is an even number,

3 if the sum of the digits is divisible by 3 (3156 is divisible by 3 because $3+1+5+6 = 15$ which is divisible by 3),

4 if its last two figures are divisible by 4 (3024 is divisible by 4 because 24 divided by 4 is 6 exactly),

5 if the last figure is a zero or a five (3265 and 4280 are both divisible by 5),

10 if the last figure is a zero (198 630 is divisible by 10).

Exercise 8 — *Questions 1–3 type A, remainder B*

Work out the answers to the following:

1)	$4918 \div 9$	**5)**	$15\,352 \div 17$
2)	$7584 \div 6$	**6)**	$45\,927 \div 27$
3)	$1237 \div 4$	**7)**	$2\,093\,595 \div 35$
4)	$10\,001 \div 11$	**8)**	$290\,227 \div 49$

Sequence of Arithmetical Operations

Numbers are often combined in a series of arithmetical operations. When this happens a definite sequence must be observed.

(1) Brackets are used if there is any danger of ambiguity. The contents of the bracket must be evaluated before performing any other operation. Thus:

$$2 \times (7+4) = 2 \times 11 = 22$$
$$15 - (8-3) = 15 - 5 = 10$$

7

(2) Multiplication and division must be done before addition and subtraction. Thus:

$$5 \times 8 + 7 = 40 + 7 = 47 \text{ (not } 5 \times 15)$$
$$8 \div 4 + 9 = 2 + 9 = 11 \text{ (not } 8 \div 13)$$
$$5 \times 4 - 12 \div 3 + 7 = 20 - 4 + 7$$
$$= 27 - 4 = 23$$

So far we have used the standard operations of add, subtract, multiply and divide. However if we wished we could make up some operations of our own.

Suppose we have an operation shown by the symbol ‡ which means double the first number and add the second number. Then,

$$3 ‡ 4 = 2 \times 3 + 4 = 6 + 4 = 10$$
$$5 ‡ 3 = 2 \times 5 + 3 = 10 + 3 = 13$$

Exercise 9 — *Questions 1–4 and 11–14 type A, remainder B*

Find values for the following:

1) $3 + 5 \times 2$

2) $3 \times 6 - 8$

3) $7 \times 5 - 2 + 4 \times 6$

4) $8 \div 2 + 3$

5) $7 \times 5 - 12 \div 4 + 3$

6) $11 - 9 \div 3 + 7$

7) $3 \times (8 + 7)$

8) $2 + 8 \times (3 + 6)$

9) $17 - 2 \times (5 - 3)$

10) $11 - 12 \div 4 + 3 \times (6 - 2)$

The operation * means divide the first number by 2 and add the second number. Use this operation to work out the following:

11) $2 * 4$

12) $6 * 7$

13) $8 * 3$

14) $10 * 2$

The operation † means add the first number to 3 times the second number. Use this operation to work out the following:

15) $8 † 2$

16) $9 † 4$

17) $2 † 5$

18) $4 † 3$

Factors and Multiples

If one number divides exactly into a second number the first number is said to be a *factor* of the second. Thus:

$35 = 5 \times 7$ ...5 is a factor of 35 and so is 7.

$240 = 3 \times 8 \times 10$ ...3, 8 and 10 are all factors of 240.

$63 = 3 \times 21 = 7 \times 9$

63 is said to be a *multiple* of any of the numbers 3, 7, 9 and 21 because each of them divides exactly into 63.

Every number has itself and 1 as factors. If a number has no other factors, apart from these, it is said to be a *prime number*. Thus 2, 3, 7, 11, 13, 17 and 19 are all prime numbers.

A factor which is a prime number is called a *prime factor*.

Factorials

Factorial 5 is written 5! and it equals $5 \times 4 \times 3 \times 2 \times 1 = 120$

Similarly, factorial 8 = 8!
$= 8 \times 7 \times 6 \times 5 \times 4 \times 3 \times 2 \times 1 = 40\,320$

Exercise 10 — *All type B*

1) What numbers are factors of:

    (a) 24   (b) 56   (c) 42?

2) Which of the following numbers are factors of 12:

    2, 3, 4, 5, 6, 12, 18 and 24?

Which of them are multiples of 6?

3) Write down all the multiples of 3 between 10 and 40.

4) Express as a product of prime factors:

(a) 24   (b) 36   (c) 56
(d) 132

5) Write down the two prime numbers next larger than 19.

6) Find the values of:

(a) 3!   (b) 6!   (c) 4!

7) Find the values of:

(a) 3!+4!   (b) 5!−2!
(c) 2!×3!

Sequences

A set of numbers which are connected by some definite law is called a series or a sequence of numbers. Each of the numbers in the series is called a term of the series. Here are some examples:

1, 3, 5, 7   ...(each term is obtained by adding 2 to the previous term)

2, 6, 18, 54 ...(each term is obtained by multiplying the previous term by 3)

Example 13

Write down the next two terms of the following series:

112, 56, 28, ...

The second term is found by dividing the first term by 2 and the third term is found by dividing the second term by 2. Hence:

$$\text{Fourth term} = \frac{28}{2} = 14$$

$$\text{Fifth term} = \frac{14}{2} = 7$$

Exercise 11 — *All type A*

Write down the next two terms of each of the following series of numbers:

1) 3, 12, 48, ...

2) 1, 4, 7, 10, ...

3) 5, 11, 17, 23, ...

4) 162, 54, 18, ...

5) 6, 12, 24, ...

Exercise 12 — *Questions 1–18(a) type A, remainder B*

The following questions are all taken from past C.S.E. examination papers.

1) Give the next number in the sequence: 1, 6, 11, 16, 21, ...   (*E.A.*)

2) Work out   (18+2)÷4   (*Y*)

3) Calculate:
(a) 9+7×3   (b) (9+7)×3   (*M*)

4) Find the sum of 10, 13, 15, 17 and 25   (*M*)

5) Work out   798−389   (*S*)

6) Subtract 376 from 5032   (*S*)

7) Multiply 329 by 207.   (*S*)

8) The sum of eleven thousand and eleven hundred is given by one of the following:

a 11 100   **b** 12 100
c 11 110   **d** 11 111
e 111 000

Which answer is correct?   (*W.Y.*)

9) Work out   12+68−35   (*N.W.*)

10) From the following set of numbers: 24, 33, 45, 61, 63, 27 and 49, write down:

(a) an even number
(b) an odd number
(c) a prime number
(d) a multiple of 7

9

(e)   numbers exactly divisible by 9

(f)   two numbers whose product is 1485.   (S)

11) Write down the next number in the sequence: 2, 6, 18, 54, . . . (Y.R.)

12) Ninety nine thousand and ninety nine written in figures is one of the following. Which?

    a 990 099   **b** 9999

    c 99 099

    e 90 999   (N.W.)

13) The value of $\dfrac{2000 \times 3000}{40}$ is

    a 1500   **b** 15 000

    c 150   **d** 150 000

    e 15   (N.W.)

14) Which of these numbers is a prime number?

    a 57   **b** 61   **c** 63

    d 65   **e** 69   (S.E.)

15) The Olympic Games have been held in 1964, 1968, 1972 and 1976. Assuming that the intervals remain the same, when will the next games take place?   (A.L.)

16) Find the value of $10 - (8 - 3)$.
                               (N.W.)

17) Write down the next two numbers in the series: 7, 14, 28, 56, 112 . . .   (S)

18) Write down the terms denoted by ? in the following series:

    (a) 0, 2, 4, ?, ?, 10, 12, 14

    (b) 5, 4, 6, 5, 7, 6, 8, ?, ?   (M)

19) Find the remainder when 2749 is divided by 15   (S)

20) What are the missing numbers in the addition:

$$
\begin{array}{r}
432 \\
254 \\
*** \\
\hline
1307 \\
\hline
\end{array}
$$
                               (W.M.)

21) Find $5! - 3!$ (N.W.)

22) To make $10 - 2 \times 7 = 56$ we use brackets and write $(10 - 2) \times 7 = 56$. Rewrite the following inserting brackets to make them true.

    (a) $1 + 4 \times 8 = 40$

    (b) $16 - 2 + 6 = 8$ (S)

23) Write down the missing numbers in the following subtraction:

$$
\begin{array}{r}
6325 \\
**** \\
\hline
1526 \\
\hline
\end{array}
$$
                               (Y.R.)

24) $8 + 5 \times (4 - 2)$ is equal to:

    a 12   **b** 50   **c** 2

    d 22   **e** 18   (N.W.)

25) Consider the numbers 11, 21, 31, 77, 112.

(a)   Two of these numbers are prime numbers. The number lying exactly half way between them is:

    a 16   **b** 21   **c** 26   **d** 54

(b)   Three of these numbers have a common factor. It is,

    a 2   **b** 7   **c** 11   **d** 14   (A.L.)

Chapter 2 Fractions

Vulgar Fractions

The circle in Fig. 2.1 has been divided into eight equal parts. Each part is called one-eighth of the circle and is written as $\frac{1}{8}$. The number 8 below the line shows how many equal parts there are and it is called the *denominator*. The number above the line shows how many of the equal parts are taken and it is called the *numerator*. If five of the eight equal parts are taken then we have taken $\frac{5}{8}$ of the circle.

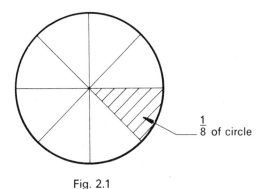

$\frac{1}{8}$ of circle

Fig. 2.1

From what has been said above we see that a fraction is always a part of something. The number below the line (the denominator) gives the fraction its name and tells us the number of equal parts into which the whole has been divided. The top number (the numerator) tells us the number of these equal parts that are to be taken. For example the fraction $\frac{3}{4}$ means that the whole has been divided into four equal parts and that three of these parts are to be taken.

The value of a fraction is unchanged if we multiply or divide both its numerator and denominator by the same amount.

$\frac{3}{5} = \frac{12}{20}$ (by multiplying the numerator (top number) and denominator (bottom number) by 4)

$\frac{2}{7} = \frac{10}{35}$ (by multiplying the numerator and denominator by 5)

$\frac{12}{32} = \frac{3}{8}$ (by dividing the numerator and denominator by 4)

$\frac{16}{64} = \frac{1}{4}$ (by dividing the numerator and denominator by 16)

Example 1

Write down the fraction $\frac{2}{7}$ with a denominator (bottom number) of 28.

In order to make the denominator (bottom number) 28, we must multiply the original denominator of 7 by 4 because $7 \times 4 = 28$. Remembering that to leave the value of the fraction unchanged we must multiply both numerator (top number) and denominator (bottom number) by the same amount, then

$$\frac{2}{7} = \frac{2 \times 4}{7 \times 4} = \frac{8}{28}$$

Exercise 13 — *All type A*

Write down the following fractions with the denominator (bottom number) stated:

1) $\frac{3}{4}$ with denominator 28

11

2) $\frac{3}{5}$ with denominator 20

3) $\frac{5}{6}$ with denominator 30

4) $\frac{1}{9}$ with denominator 63

5) $\frac{2}{3}$ with denominator 12

6) $\frac{1}{6}$ with denominator 24

7) $\frac{3}{8}$ with denominator 64

8) $\frac{5}{7}$ with denominator 35

Reducing a Fraction to its Lowest Terms

Fractions like $\frac{3}{8}$, $\frac{7}{16}$ and $\frac{3}{52}$ are said to be in their *lowest terms* because it is impossible to find a number which will divide exactly into both the top and bottom numbers. However, fractions like $\frac{9}{18}$, $\frac{8}{12}$ and $\frac{21}{24}$ are not in their lowest terms because they can be reduced further by dividing both the top and bottom numbers by some number which divides exactly into both of them. Thus,

$$\frac{9}{18} = \frac{1}{2} \quad \text{(by dividing both top and bottom by 9)}$$

$$\frac{8}{12} = \frac{2}{3} \quad \text{(by dividing both top and bottom by 4)}$$

$$\frac{21}{24} = \frac{7}{8} \quad \text{(by dividing both top and bottom by 3)}$$

Sometimes we can divide the top and bottom by the same number several times.

Example 2

Reduce $\frac{210}{336}$ to its lowest terms.

$$\frac{210}{336} = \frac{105}{168} \quad \text{(by dividing top and bottom by 2)}$$

$$= \frac{35}{56} \quad \text{(by dividing top and bottom by 3)}$$

$$= \frac{5}{8} \quad \text{(by dividing top and bottom by 7)}$$

Hence $\frac{210}{336}$ reduced to its lowest terms is $\frac{5}{8}$

Exercise 14 — *Questions 1–5 type A, remainder B*

Reduce the following fractions to their lowest terms:

1) $\frac{8}{16}$ **4)** $\frac{15}{25}$ **7)** $\frac{210}{294}$ **10)** $\frac{210}{315}$

2) $\frac{9}{15}$ **5)** $\frac{42}{48}$ **8)** $\frac{126}{245}$

3) $\frac{8}{64}$ **6)** $\frac{180}{240}$ **9)** $\frac{132}{198}$

Types of Fractions

If the top number of a fraction is less than its bottom number the fraction is called a *proper fraction*. Thus $\frac{2}{3}$, $\frac{5}{8}$ and $\frac{3}{4}$ are all proper fractions. Note that a proper fraction has a value which is less than 1.

If the top number of a fraction is greater than its bottom number then the fraction is called an *improper fraction* or a *top heavy fraction*. Thus $\frac{5}{4}$, $\frac{3}{2}$ and $\frac{9}{7}$ are all top heavy, or improper, fractions. Note that all top heavy fractions have a value which is greater than 1.

Every top heavy fraction can be expressed as a whole number and a proper fraction. These are sometimes called *mixed numbers*. Thus $1\frac{1}{2}$, $5\frac{1}{3}$ and $9\frac{3}{4}$ are all mixed numbers. In order to convert a top heavy fraction into a mixed number it must be remembered that

$$\frac{\text{top number}}{\text{bottom number}} = \text{top number} \div \text{bottom number}$$

Example 3

Express $\frac{15}{8}$ as a mixed number.

$$\frac{15}{8} = 1\frac{7}{8}$$

(because $15 \div 8 = 1$ and remainder 7)

From Example 3 we see that we convert a top heavy fraction into a mixed number by dividing the bottom number into the top number. Notice that the remainder becomes the top number in the fractional part of the mixed number. To change a mixed number into an improper fraction we multiply the whole number by the bottom number of the fractional part. To this we add the numerator of the fractional part and this sum then becomes the top number of the improper fraction. Its bottom number is the same as the bottom number of the fractional part of the mixed number.

Example 4

Express $3\frac{5}{8}$ as a top heavy fraction.

$$3\frac{5}{8} = \frac{(8 \times 3) + 5}{8} = \frac{24 + 5}{8} = \frac{29}{8}$$

Exercise 15 — *All type A*

Express each of the following as a mixed number:

1) $\frac{7}{2}$ 3) $\frac{22}{10}$ 5) $\frac{21}{8}$

2) $\frac{8}{4}$ 4) $\frac{12}{11}$

Express each of the following as top heavy fractions:

6) $2\frac{3}{8}$ 8) $8\frac{2}{3}$ 10) $4\frac{3}{7}$

7) $5\frac{1}{10}$ 9) $6\frac{7}{20}$

Lowest Common Multiple (LCM)

The LCM of a set of numbers is the *smallest* number into which each of the given numbers will divide. Thus the LCM of 4, 5 and 10 is 20 because 20 is the smallest number into which the numbers, 4, 5 and 10 will divide exactly.

The LCM of a set of numbers can usually be found by inspection.

Exercise 16 — *Questions 1–4 type A, remainder B*

Find the LCM of the following sets of numbers:

1) 8 and 12   5) 2, 8 and 10

2) 3, 4 and 5   6) 20 and 25

3) 2, 6 and 12   7) 20 and 32

4) 3, 6 and 8   8) 10, 15 and 40

9) 12, 42, 60 and 70

10) 18, 30, 42 and 48

Lowest Common Denominator

When we wish to compare the values of two or more fractions the easiest way is to express the fractions with the same bottom number. This common denominator should be the LCM

13

of the denominators of the fractions to be compared and it is called the *lowest common denominator*.

Example 5

Arrange the fractions $\frac{3}{4}, \frac{5}{8}, \frac{7}{10}$ and $\frac{11}{20}$ in order of size starting with the smallest.

The lowest common denominator of 4, 8, 10 and 20 is 40. Expressing each of the given fractions with a bottom number of 40 gives:

$$\frac{3}{4} = \frac{3 \times 10}{4 \times 10} = \frac{30}{40} \qquad \frac{5}{8} = \frac{5 \times 5}{8 \times 5} = \frac{25}{40}$$

$$\frac{7}{10} = \frac{7 \times 4}{10 \times 4} = \frac{28}{40} \qquad \frac{11}{20} = \frac{11 \times 2}{20 \times 2} = \frac{22}{40}$$

Therefore the order is

$$\frac{22}{40}, \frac{25}{40}, \frac{28}{40}, \frac{30}{40} \quad \text{or} \quad \frac{11}{20}, \frac{5}{8}, \frac{7}{10} \text{ and } \frac{3}{4}$$

Exercise 17 — *All type A*

Arrange the following sets of fractions in order of size, beginning with the smallest:

1) $\frac{1}{2}, \frac{5}{6}, \frac{2}{3}, \frac{7}{12}$ 4) $\frac{3}{4}, \frac{5}{8}, \frac{3}{5}, \frac{13}{20}$

2) $\frac{9}{10}, \frac{3}{4}, \frac{6}{7}, \frac{7}{8}$ 5) $\frac{11}{16}, \frac{7}{10}, \frac{9}{14}, \frac{3}{4}$

3) $\frac{13}{16}, \frac{11}{20}, \frac{7}{10}, \frac{3}{5}$ 6) $\frac{3}{8}, \frac{4}{7}, \frac{5}{9}, \frac{2}{5}$

Addition of Fractions

The steps when adding fractions are as follows:

(1) Find the lowest common denominator of the fractions to be added.

(2) Express each of the fractions with this common denominator.

(3) Add the numerators of the new fractions to give the numerator of the answer. The denominator of the answer is the lowest common denominator found in (1).

Example 6

Find the sum of $\frac{2}{7}$ and $\frac{3}{4}$.

First find the lowest common denominator (this is the LCM of 7 and 4). It is 28.

Now express $\frac{2}{7}$ and $\frac{3}{4}$ with a bottom number of 28.

$$\frac{2}{7} = \frac{2 \times 4}{7 \times 4} = \frac{8}{28} \qquad \frac{3}{4} = \frac{3 \times 7}{4 \times 7} = \frac{21}{28}$$

Adding the top numbers of the new fractions:

$$\frac{2}{7} + \frac{3}{4} = \frac{8}{28} + \frac{21}{28} = \frac{29}{28} = 1\frac{1}{28}$$

A better way of setting out the work is as follows:

$$\frac{2}{7} + \frac{3}{4} = \frac{2 \times 4 + 3 \times 7}{28}$$
$$= \frac{8 + 21}{28} = \frac{29}{28} = 1\frac{1}{28}$$

Example 7

Simplify $\frac{3}{4} + \frac{2}{3} + \frac{7}{10}$

The LCM of the bottom numbers 4, 3 and 10 is 60.

$$\frac{3}{4} + \frac{2}{3} + \frac{7}{10} = \frac{3 \times 15 + 2 \times 20 + 7 \times 6}{60}$$
$$= \frac{45 + 40 + 42}{60} = \frac{127}{60} = 2\frac{7}{60}$$

Example 8

Add together $5\frac{1}{2}, 2\frac{2}{3}$ and $3\frac{2}{5}$

First add the whole numbers together, $5+2+3=10$. Then add the fractional parts in the usual way. The LCM of 2, 3 and 5 is 30.

$$5\frac{1}{2}+2\frac{2}{3}+3\frac{2}{5}$$

$$=10+\frac{15\times1+10\times2+6\times2}{30}$$

$$=10+\frac{15+20+12}{30}$$

$$=10+\frac{47}{30}=10+1\frac{17}{30}=11\frac{17}{30}$$

Exercise 18 — *All type A*

Add together:

1) $\frac{1}{2}+\frac{1}{3}$

2) $\frac{2}{5}+\frac{9}{10}$

3) $\frac{3}{4}+\frac{3}{8}$

4) $\frac{3}{10}+\frac{1}{4}$

5) $\frac{1}{2}+\frac{3}{4}+\frac{7}{8}$

6) $\frac{1}{8}+\frac{2}{3}+\frac{3}{5}$

7) $1\frac{3}{8}+3\frac{9}{16}$

8) $7\frac{2}{3}+6\frac{3}{5}$

9) $3\frac{3}{8}+5\frac{2}{7}+4\frac{3}{4}$

10) $4\frac{1}{2}+3\frac{5}{6}+2\frac{1}{3}$

11) $7\frac{3}{8}+2\frac{3}{4}+\frac{7}{8}+\frac{5}{16}$

12) $7\frac{2}{3}+\frac{2}{5}+\frac{3}{10}+2\frac{1}{2}$

Subtraction of Fractions

The method is similar to that used in addition. Find the common denominator of the fractions and after expressing each fraction with this common denominator, subtract.

Example 9

Simplify $\frac{5}{8}-\frac{2}{5}$

The LCM of the bottom numbers is 40.

$$\frac{5}{8}-\frac{2}{5}=\frac{5\times5-8\times2}{40}=\frac{25-16}{40}=\frac{9}{40}$$

When mixed numbers have to be subtracted the best way is to turn the mixed numbers into top heavy fractions and then proceed in the way shown in Example 9.

Example 10

Simplify $3\frac{7}{10}-2\frac{3}{4}$

$$3\frac{7}{10}-2\frac{3}{4}=\frac{37}{10}-\frac{11}{4}$$

$$=\frac{37\times2-11\times5}{20}$$

$$=\frac{74-55}{20}=\frac{19}{20}$$

Example 11

Simplify $5\frac{2}{5}-3\frac{7}{8}$

$$5\frac{2}{5}-3\frac{7}{8}=\frac{27}{5}-\frac{31}{8}=\frac{27\times8-31\times5}{40}$$

$$=\frac{216-155}{40}=\frac{61}{40}=1\frac{21}{40}$$

Exercise 19 — *Questions 1–7 type A, remainder B*

Simplify the following:

1) $\frac{1}{2}-\frac{1}{3}$

2) $\frac{1}{3}-\frac{1}{5}$

3) $\frac{2}{3}-\frac{1}{2}$

4) $\frac{7}{8}-\frac{3}{8}$

5) $\frac{7}{8}-\frac{5}{6}$

6) $3-\frac{5}{7}$

7) $5-3\frac{4}{5}$

8) $3\frac{1}{4}-2\frac{3}{8}$

9) $5\frac{3}{8}-2\frac{9}{10}$

10) $4\frac{7}{32}-3\frac{9}{10}$

11) $1\frac{5}{16}-\frac{4}{5}$

Combined Addition and Subtraction

Example 12

Simplify $5\frac{3}{8}-1\frac{1}{4}+2\frac{1}{2}-\frac{7}{16}$

$$5\frac{3}{8}-1\frac{1}{4}+2\frac{1}{2}-\frac{7}{16}=\frac{43}{8}-\frac{5}{4}+\frac{5}{2}-\frac{7}{16}$$

$$=\frac{43\times2-5\times4+5\times8-7\times1}{16}$$

$$=\frac{86-20+40-7}{16}$$

$$=\frac{(86+40)-(20+7)}{16}$$

$$=\frac{126-27}{16}=\frac{99}{16}=6\frac{3}{16}$$

Exercise 20 — *All type B*

Simplify the following:

1) $2\frac{1}{2}+3\frac{1}{4}-4\frac{3}{8}$

2) $5\frac{1}{10}-3\frac{1}{2}-1\frac{1}{4}$

3) $4\frac{3}{8}-2\frac{1}{2}+5$

4) $6\frac{1}{2}-3\frac{1}{6}+2\frac{1}{12}-4\frac{3}{4}$

5) $1\frac{3}{16}-2\frac{2}{5}+3\frac{3}{4}+5\frac{5}{8}$

6) $12\frac{7}{10}-5\frac{1}{8}+3\frac{3}{20}+1\frac{1}{2}$

7) $2\frac{3}{16}-2\frac{3}{10}+\frac{5}{8}+1\frac{3}{4}$

8) $12\frac{3}{4}-6\frac{7}{8}+5\frac{21}{32}-2\frac{13}{16}$

9) $3\frac{9}{20}+1\frac{3}{8}-2\frac{7}{10}+1\frac{3}{4}$

10) $2\frac{9}{25}+3\frac{4}{5}-2\frac{7}{10}-\frac{3}{20}$

Multiplication

When multiplying together two or more fractions we first multiply all the top numbers together and then we multiply all the bottom numbers together. Mixed numbers must always be converted into top heavy fractions.

Example 13

Simplify $\frac{5}{8}\times\frac{3}{7}$

$$\frac{5}{8}\times\frac{3}{7}=\frac{5\times3}{8\times7}=\frac{15}{56}$$

Example 14

Simplify $\frac{2}{5}\times3\frac{2}{3}$

$$\frac{2}{5}\times3\frac{2}{3}=\frac{2}{5}\times\frac{11}{3}=\frac{2\times11}{5\times3}=\frac{22}{15}=1\frac{7}{15}$$

Example 15

Simplify $1\frac{3}{8}\times1\frac{1}{4}$

$$1\frac{3}{8}\times1\frac{1}{4}=\frac{11}{8}\times\frac{5}{4}=\frac{11\times5}{8\times4}=\frac{55}{32}=1\frac{23}{32}$$

Exercise 21 — *All type A*

Simplify the following:

1) $\frac{2}{3}\times\frac{4}{5}$ 4) $\frac{5}{9}\times\frac{11}{4}$ 7) $1\frac{2}{9}\times1\frac{2}{5}$

2) $\frac{3}{4}\times\frac{5}{7}$ 5) $1\frac{2}{5}\times3\frac{1}{2}$ 8) $1\frac{7}{8}\times1\frac{4}{7}$

3) $\frac{2}{9}\times1\frac{2}{3}$ 6) $2\frac{1}{2}\times2\frac{2}{3}$

Cancelling

Example 16

Simplify $\frac{2}{3} \times 1\frac{7}{8}$

$$\frac{2}{3} \times 1\frac{7}{8} = \frac{2}{3} \times \frac{15}{8} = \frac{2 \times 15}{3 \times 8}$$

$$= \frac{30}{24} = \frac{5}{4} = 1\frac{1}{4}$$

The step to reducing $\frac{30}{24}$ to its lowest terms has been done by dividing 6 into both the top and bottom numbers.

The work can be made easier by *cancelling* before multiplication as shown below.

$$\overset{1}{\underset{1}{\cancel{2}}} \times \frac{\overset{5}{\cancel{15}}}{\underset{4}{\cancel{8}}} = \frac{1 \times 5}{1 \times 4} = \frac{5}{4} = 1\frac{1}{4}$$

We have divided 2 into 2 (a top number) and 8 (a bottom number) and also we have divided 3 into 15 (a top number) and 3 (a bottom number). You will see that we have divided the top numbers and the bottom numbers by the same amount. Notice carefully that we can only cancel between a top number and a bottom number.

Example 17

Simplify $\frac{16}{25} \times \frac{7}{8} \times 8\frac{3}{4}$

$$\frac{\overset{1}{\overset{2}{\cancel{16}}}}{25} \times \frac{7}{\underset{1}{\cancel{8}}} \times \frac{\overset{7}{\cancel{35}}}{\underset{2}{\cancel{4}}} = \frac{1 \times 7 \times 7}{5 \times 1 \times 2} = \frac{49}{10} = 4\frac{9}{10}$$

Sometimes in calculations with fractions the word 'of' appears. It should always be taken as meaning multiply.

Thus

$$\frac{4}{5} \text{ of } 20 = \frac{4}{5} \times \frac{\overset{4}{\cancel{20}}}{\underset{1}{1}} = \frac{4 \times 4}{1 \times 1} = \frac{16}{1} = 16$$

Exercise 22 — *All type A*

Simplify the following:

1) $\frac{3}{4} \times 1\frac{7}{9}$ 7) $3\frac{3}{4} \times 1\frac{3}{5} \times 1\frac{1}{8}$

2) $5\frac{1}{5} \times \frac{10}{13}$ 8) $\frac{15}{32} \times \frac{8}{11} \times 24\frac{1}{5}$

3) $1\frac{5}{8} \times \frac{7}{26}$ 9) $\frac{3}{4}$ of 16

4) $1\frac{1}{2} \times \frac{2}{5} \times 2\frac{1}{2}$ 10) $\frac{5}{7}$ of 140

5) $\frac{5}{8} \times \frac{7}{10} \times \frac{2}{21}$ 11) $\frac{2}{3}$ of $4\frac{1}{2}$

6) $2 \times 1\frac{1}{2} \times 1\frac{1}{3}$ 12) $\frac{4}{5}$ of $2\frac{1}{2}$

Division of Fractions

To divide by a fraction, all we have to do is to invert it (i.e. turn it upside down) and multiply. Thus:

$$\frac{3}{5} \div \frac{2}{7} = \frac{3}{5} \times \frac{7}{2} = \frac{3 \times 7}{5 \times 2} = \frac{21}{10} = 2\frac{1}{10}$$

Example 18

Divide $1\frac{4}{5}$ by $2\frac{1}{3}$

$$1\frac{4}{5} \div 2\frac{1}{3} = \frac{9}{5} \div \frac{7}{3} = \frac{9}{5} \times \frac{3}{7} = \frac{27}{35}$$

Exercise 23 — *All type A*

Simplify the following:

1) $\frac{4}{5} \div 1\frac{1}{3}$ 2) $2 \div \frac{1}{4}$ 3) $\frac{5}{8} \div \frac{15}{32}$

4) $3\frac{3}{4} \div 2\frac{1}{2}$ **6)** $5 \div 5\frac{1}{5}$ **8)** $2\frac{3}{10} \div \frac{3}{5}$

5) $2\frac{1}{2} \div 3\frac{3}{4}$ **7)** $3\frac{1}{15} \div 2\frac{5}{9}$.

Operations with Fractions

The sequence of operations when dealing with fractions is the same as those used with whole numbers. They are, in order:

(1) Work out brackets.

(2) Multiply and divide.

(3) Add and subtract.

Example 19

Simplify $\frac{1}{5} \div \left(\frac{1}{3} \div \frac{1}{2}\right)$

$$\frac{1}{5} \div \left(\frac{1}{3} \div \frac{1}{2}\right) = \frac{1}{5} \div \left(\frac{1}{3} \times \frac{2}{1}\right)$$

$$= \frac{1}{5} \div \frac{2}{3} = \frac{1}{5} \times \frac{3}{2} = \frac{3}{10}$$

Example 20

Simplify $\dfrac{2\frac{4}{5} + 1\frac{1}{4}}{3\frac{3}{5}} - \dfrac{5}{16}$

With problems of this kind it is best to work in stages as shown below:

$$2\frac{4}{5} + 1\frac{1}{4} = 3\frac{16+5}{20} = 3\frac{21}{20} = 4\frac{1}{20}$$

$$\frac{4\frac{1}{20}}{3\frac{3}{5}} = \frac{81}{20} \div \frac{18}{5} = \frac{81}{20} \times \frac{5}{18} = \frac{9}{8}$$

$$\frac{9}{8} - \frac{5}{16} = \frac{18-5}{16} = \frac{13}{16}$$

Exercise 24 — *All type B*

Simplify the following:

1) $3\frac{3}{14} + \left(1\frac{1}{49} \times \frac{7}{10}\right)$

2) $\frac{1}{4} \div \left(\frac{1}{8} \times \frac{2}{5}\right)$

3) $1\frac{2}{3} \div \left(\frac{3}{5} \div \frac{9}{10}\right)$

4) $\left(1\frac{7}{8} \times 2\frac{2}{5}\right) - 3\frac{2}{3}$

5) $\dfrac{2\frac{2}{3} + 1\frac{1}{5}}{5\frac{4}{5}}$

6) $3\frac{2}{3} \div \left(\frac{2}{3} + \frac{4}{5}\right)$

7) $\dfrac{5\frac{3}{5} - 3\frac{1}{2} \times \frac{2}{3}}{2\frac{1}{3}}$

8) $\frac{2}{5} \times \left(\frac{2}{3} - \frac{1}{4}\right) + \frac{1}{2}$

9) $\dfrac{3\frac{9}{16} \times \frac{4}{9}}{2 + 6\frac{1}{4} \times 1\frac{1}{5}}$

10) $\dfrac{\frac{5}{9} - \frac{7}{15}}{1 - \left(\frac{5}{9} \times \frac{7}{15}\right)}$

Exercise 25 — *All type A*

The questions in this exercise have all been taken from past C.S.E. examination papers.

1)

(a) Divide $\frac{9}{16}$ by $\frac{5}{8}$ and give your answer in its simplest form.

(b) By how much is $\frac{8}{5}$ greater than $\frac{5}{8}$

(S)

2)

(a) Arrange the fractions $\frac{7}{8}$, $\frac{2}{3}$ and $\frac{7}{12}$ in order of size, smallest first.

(b) Calculate $\frac{5}{6} + \frac{7}{8}$

(c) Calculate $\frac{2}{3} \times \frac{5}{6}$ (*S*)

3) Calculate $\dfrac{7 \times (23 - 15)}{4 \times (12 + 9)}$ leaving the answer as a fraction.   (*E.M.*)

4) In the Treble Chance football pool, you have to select 8 matches which you think are going to end in a draw. If you select 12 matches and 'perm any 8 from 12', the number of lines required is given by the expression

$$\frac{12 \times 11 \times 10 \times 9 \times 8 \times 7 \times 6 \times 5}{8 \times 7 \times 6 \times 5 \times 4 \times 3 \times 2 \times 1}.$$

Work out the number of lines required. (The answer is a whole number less than 500.)   (*E.M.*)

5) Consider the fractions $\frac{1}{4}$, $\frac{2}{3}$, $\frac{7}{12}$, $\frac{5}{8}$ and $1\frac{3}{5}$:

(a) Add together the first three fractions

(b) Multiply $\frac{5}{8}$ by $1\frac{3}{5}$

(c) Work out $\frac{7}{12} \div \frac{1}{4}$ (*S*)

6) What is $\frac{42}{60}$ as a fraction in its lowest form?   (*S.W.*)

7) What is $\frac{2}{3}$rds of $1\frac{1}{2}$ hours   (*A.L.*)

8) Calculate $\frac{1}{2} + \frac{1}{3} + \frac{1}{4}$ (*M*)

9) Which is the largest of $\frac{3}{8}$, $\frac{1}{4}$, $\frac{9}{32}$ and $\frac{17}{64}$?   (*A.L.*)

10) Write as a single fraction:

(a) $\frac{1}{2} + \frac{1}{3}$ (b) $\frac{2}{3} \times \frac{3}{5}$

(c) $\frac{1}{4} \div \frac{2}{5}$ (*A.L.*)

11) The fraction $\frac{12}{16}$ is the same as one of the following. Which one?

a $\frac{2}{6}$ **b** $\frac{1}{4}$ **c** $\frac{3}{4}$

d $\frac{1}{3}$ **e** $\frac{4}{3}$ (*W.M.*)

12) What is the value of $\frac{3}{4} + \frac{1}{3}$?

a $1\frac{1}{12}$ **b** $1\frac{1}{7}$ **c** $\frac{7}{12}$

d $\frac{4}{7}$ **e** $\frac{3}{12}$ (*S.E.*)

13) The lowest number which can be divided exactly by 2, 3, 4, 5 is:

a 15   **b** 20   **c** 30

d 45   **e** 60   (*S.E.*)

14) What is $\frac{1}{2} + (\frac{1}{2} \times \frac{1}{2})$?

a $\frac{1}{8}$ **b** $\frac{1}{2}$ **c** $\frac{3}{4}$

d 1   **e** $1\frac{1}{2}$ (*S.E.*)

15) The value of $3 \times (\frac{1}{2} + \frac{1}{4})$ is:

a 1   **b** $\frac{3}{8}$ **c** $3\frac{3}{4}$

d $2\frac{1}{4}$ **e** $1\frac{3}{4}$ (*W.M.*)

16) The value of $\frac{1}{2} \times \frac{1}{3}$ is:

a $\frac{1}{5}$ **b** $\frac{5}{6}$ **c** $\frac{1}{6}$

d $\frac{2}{3}$ **e** $\frac{3}{2}$ (*W.M.*)

17) Which is the largest of the following fractions:

a $\frac{2}{3}$ **b** $\frac{1}{2}$ **c** $\frac{11}{15}$

d $\frac{7}{10}$ **e** $\frac{5}{6}$ (*W.M.*)

18) Work out:

(a) $\frac{5}{6} - \frac{1}{4}$ (b) $(\frac{7}{8} \times \frac{2}{5}) - \frac{3}{10}$ (*S*)

19) Calculate $3\frac{2}{5} + 2\frac{1}{4}$ (*Y.R.*)

20) Find the value of:

$1\frac{1}{4} + 2\frac{1}{8} - \frac{5}{8}$ (*Y.R.*)

Chapter 3   The Decimal System

The Decimal System

The decimal system is an extension of our ordinary number system. When we write the number 666 we mean 600+60+6. Reading from left to right each figure 6 is ten times the value of the next one.

We now have to decide how to deal with fractional quantities, that is, quantities whose values are less than one. If we regard 666.666 as meaning $600+60+6+\frac{6}{10}+\frac{6}{100}+\frac{6}{1000}$ then the dot, called the decimal point, separates the whole numbers from the fractional parts. Notice that with the fractional, or decimal parts, e.g. .666, each figure 6 is ten times the value of the following one, reading from left to right. Thus $\frac{6}{10}$ is ten times as great as $\frac{6}{100}$, and $\frac{6}{100}$ is ten times as great as $\frac{6}{1000}$ and so on.

Decimals then are fractions which have denominators of 10, 100, 1000 and so on, according to the position of the figure after the decimal point.

If we have to write six hundred and five we write 605; the zero keeps the place for the missing tens. In the same way if we want to write $\frac{3}{10}+\frac{5}{1000}$ we write .305; the zero keeps the place for the missing hundredths. Also $\frac{6}{100}+\frac{7}{1000}$ would be written .067; the zero in this case keeps the place for the missing tenths.

When there are no whole numbers it is usual to insert a zero in front of the decimal point so that, for instance, .35 would be written 0.35.

20

Read off as decimals:

1) $\dfrac{7}{10}$

2) $\dfrac{3}{10}+\dfrac{7}{100}$

3) $\dfrac{5}{10}+\dfrac{8}{100}+\dfrac{9}{1000}$

4) $\dfrac{9}{1000}$

5) $\dfrac{3}{100}$

6) $\dfrac{1}{100}+\dfrac{7}{1000}$

7) $8+\dfrac{6}{100}$

8) $24+\dfrac{2}{100}+\dfrac{9}{10\,000}$

9) $50+\dfrac{8}{1000}$

Read off the following with denominators (bottom numbers) 10, 100, 1000, etc.

10)	0.2	15)	0.036
11)	4.6	16)	400.029
12)	3.58	17)	0.001
13)	437.25	18)	0.0329
14)	0.004		

Addition and Subtraction of Decimals

Adding or subtracting decimals is done in exactly the same way as for whole numbers. Care must be taken, however, to write the decimal points directly underneath one another. This makes sure that all the figures having the same place value fall in the same column.

Example 1

Simplify $11.36 + 2.639 + 0.047$

```
  11.36
   2.639
   0.047
 ───────
  14.046
 ───────
```

Example 2

Subtract 8.567 from 19.126

```
  19.126
   8.567
 ───────
  10.559
 ───────
```

Exercise 27 — *All type A*

Write down the values of:

1) $2.375 + 0.625$

2) $4.25 + 7.25$

3) $3.196 + 2.475 + 18.369$

4) $38.267 + 0.049 + 20.3$

5) $27.418 + 0.967 + 25 + 1.467$

6) $12.48 - 8.36$

7) $19.215 - 3.599$

8) $2.237 - 1.898$

9) $0.876 - 0.064$

10) $5.48 - 0.069\ 1$

Multiplication and Division of Decimals

One of the advantages of decimals is the ease with which they may be multiplied or divided by 10, 100, 1000, etc.

Example 3

Find the value of 1.4×10

$$1.4 \times 10 = 1 \times 10 + 0.4 \times 10$$
$$= 10 + \frac{4}{10} \times 10 = 10 + 4 = 14$$

Example 4

Find the value of 27.532×10

$$27.532 \times 10 = 27 \times 10 + 0.5 \times 10$$
$$+ 0.03 \times 10 + 0.002 \times 10$$
$$= 270 + \frac{5}{10} \times 10 + \frac{3}{100} \times 10$$
$$+ \frac{2}{1000} \times 10$$
$$= 270 + 5 + \frac{3}{10} + \frac{2}{100}$$
$$= 275.32$$

In both of the above examples you will notice that the figures have not been changed by the multiplication; only the *positions* of the figures have been changed. Thus in Example 3, $1.4 \times 10 = 14$, that is the decimal point has been moved one place to the right. In Example 4, $27.532 \times 10 = 275.32$; again the decimal point has been moved one place to the right.

To multiply by 10, then, is the same as shifting the decimal point one place to the right. In the same way to multiply by 100 means shifting the decimal point two places to the right and so on.

Example 5

$17.369 \times 100 = 1736.9$

The decimal point has been moved two places to the right.

Example 6

$0.0789\,5 \times 1000 = 78.95$

The decimal point has been moved three places to the right.

Exercise 28 — *All type A*

Multiply each of the following numbers by 10, 100 and 1000.

1) 4.1 3) 0.046 5) 0.1486

2) 2.42 4) 0.35 6) 0.001 753

7) 0.4853×100

8) 0.009×1000

9) 170.06×10

10) $0.563\,96 \times 10\,000$

When dividing by 10 the decimal point is moved one place to the left, by 100, two places to the left and so on. Thus,

$$154.26 \div 10 = 15.426$$

The decimal point has been moved one place to the left.

$$9.432 \div 100 = 0.094\,32$$

The decimal point has been moved two places to the left.

$35 \div 1000 = 0.035$

The decimal point has been moved three places to the left.

In the above examples note carefully that use has been made of zeros following the decimal point to keep the places for the missing tenths.

Exercise 29 — *All type A*

Divide each of the following numbers by 10, 100 and 1000.

1) 3.6 3) 0.07 5) 0.352

2) 64.198 4) 510.4

Give the value of:

6) $5.4 \div 100$ 8) $0.04 \div 10$

7) $2.05 \div 1000$ 9) $0.0086 \div 1000$

10) $627.428 \div 10\,000$

Long Multiplication

Example 7

Find the value of 36.5×3.504.

First disregard the decimal points and multiply 365 by 3504

```
              365
            3 504
         ─────────
        1 095 000
          182 500
            1 460
         ─────────
        1 278 960
         ─────────
```

Now count up the total number of figures following the decimal points in both numbers (i.e. $1 + 3 = 4$). In the answer to the multiplication (the product), count this total number of figures from the right and insert the decimal point. The product is then 127.8960 or 127.896 since the zero does not mean anything.

Find the values of the following:

1) 25.42×29.23 4) 3.025×2.45

2) 0.3618×2.63 5) 0.043×0.032

3) 0.76×0.38

Long Division

Example 8

Find the value of $19.24 \div 2.6$

First convert the divisor (2.6) into a whole number by multiplying it by 10. To compensate multiply the dividend (19.24) by 10 also so that we now have $192.4 \div 26$. Now proceed as in ordinary division.

```
26)192.4(7.4
    182        —this line 26×7
    ───
     10 4   —4 brought down from
     10 4    above. Since 4 lies to
     ───     the right of the decimal
     . . .   point in the dividend
     ───     insert a decimal point
             in the answer (the
             quotient)
```

Notice carefully how the decimal point in the quotient was obtained. The 4 brought down from the dividend lies to the right of the decimal point. Before bringing this down put a decimal point in the quotient immediately following the 7.

The division in this case is exact (i.e. there is no remainder) and the answer is 7.4. Now let us see what happens when there is a remainder.

Example 9

Find the value of $15.187 \div 3.57$

As before make the divisor into a whole number by multiplying it by 100 so that it becomes 357. To compensate multiply the dividend also by 100 so that it becomes 1518.7. Now divide.

```
357)1518.7(4.254 06
    1428           —this line 357×4
    ───
     907           —7 brought down
     714            from the divi-
     ───            dend. Since it
                    lies to the right
                    of the decimal
                    point insert a
                    decimal point in
                    the quotient.
    1930           —bring down a
    1785            zero as all the
    ───             figures in the
    1450            dividend have
    1428            been used up.
    ───
    2200           —Bring down a
    2142            zero. The divisor
    ───             will not go into
      58            220 so place 0 in
                    the quotient and
                    bring down
                    another zero.
```

The answer to 5 decimal places is 4.254 06. This is not the correct answer because there is a remainder. The division can be continued in the way shown to give as many decimal places as desired, or until there is no remainder.

It is important to realise what is meant by an answer given to so many decimal places. It is the number of figures which follow the decimal point which give the number of decimal places. If the first figure to be dis-

23

carded is 5 or more then the previous figure is increased by 1. Thus:

$$85.7684 = 85.8 \text{ correct to 1 decimal place}$$
$$= 85.77 \text{ correct to 2 decimal places}$$
$$= 85.768 \text{ correct to 3 decimal places}$$

Notice carefully that zeros must be kept:

$$0.007362 = 0.007 \text{ correct to 3 decimal places}$$
$$= 0.01 \text{ correct to 2 decimal places}$$
$$7.601 = 7.60 \text{ correct to 2 decimal places}$$
$$= 7.6 \text{ correct to 1 decimal place}$$

If an answer is required correct to 3 decimal places the division should be continued to 4 decimal places and the answer corrected to 3 decimal places.

Exercise 31 — *All type B*

Find the value of:

1) $18.89 \div 14.2$ correct to 2 decimal places.

2) $0.0396 \div 2.51$ correct to 3 decimal places.

3) $7.21 \div 0.038$ correct to 2 decimal places.

4) $13.059 \div 3.18$ correct to 4 decimal places.

5) $0.1382 \div 0.0032$ correct to 1 decimal place.

Significant Figures

Instead of using the number of decimal places to express the accuracy of an answer, significant figures can be used. The number 39.38 is correct to 2 decimal places but it is also correct to 4 significant figures since the number contains four figures. The rules regarding significant figures are as follows:

(i) If the first figure to be discarded is 5 or more the previous figure is increased by 1.

$$8.1925 = 8.193 \text{ correct to 4 significant figures}$$
$$= 8.19 \text{ correct to 3 significant figures}$$
$$= 8.2 \text{ correct to 2 significant figures}$$

(ii) Zeros must be kept to show the position of the decimal point, or to indicate that the zero is a significant figure.

$$24392 = 24390 \text{ correct to 4 significant figures}$$
$$= 24400 \text{ correct to 3 significant figures}$$
$$0.0858 = 0.086 \text{ correct to 2 significant figures}$$
$$425.804 = 425.80 \text{ correct to 5 significant figures}$$
$$= 426 \text{ correct to 3 significant figures}$$

Exercise 32 — *All type B*

Write down the following numbers correct to the number of significant figures stated:

1) 24.86582 (i) to 6 (ii) to 4 (iii) to 2

2) 0.0083571 (i) to 4 (ii) to 3 (iii) to 2

3) 4.97848 (i) to 5 (ii) to 3 (iii) to 1

4) 21.987 to 2

5) 35.603 to 4

6) 28387617 (i) to 5 (ii) to 2

7) 4.149 76 (i) to 5 (ii) to 4 (iii) to 3

8) 9.204 8 to 3

Rough Checks for Calculations

The worst mistake that can be made in a calculation is that of misplacing the decimal point. To place it wrongly, even by one place, makes the answer ten times too large or ten times too small. To prevent this occurring it is always worth while doing a rough check by using approximate numbers. When doing these rough checks always try to select numbers which are easy to multiply or which will cancel.

Example 10

a) 0.23×0.56

For a rough check we will take
0.2×0.6
Product roughly $= 0.2 \times 0.6 = 0.12$
Correct product $= 0.128\,8$

(The rough check shows that the answer is 0.128 8 not 1.288 or 0.012 88)

b) $173.3 \div 27.8$

For a rough check we will take
$180 \div 30$
Quotient roughly $= 6$
Correct quotient $= 6.23$

(Note the rough check and the correct answer are of the same order)

c) $\dfrac{8.198 \times 19.56 \times 30.82 \times 0.198}{6.52 \times 3.58 \times 0.823}$

Answer roughly $= \dfrac{8 \times 20 \times 30 \times 0.2}{6 \times 4 \times 1} = 40$

Correct answer $= 50.94$

(Although there is a big difference between the rough answer and the correct answer, the rough check shows that the answer is 50.94 and not 509.4 or 5.094)

Exercise 33 — *All type B*

Find rough checks for the following:

1) $223.6 \times 0.004\,8$

2) 32.7×0.259

3) $0.682 \times 0.097 \times 2.38$

4) $78.41 \div 23.78$

5) $0.059 \div 0.002\,68$

6) $33.2 \times 29.6 \times 0.031$

7) $\dfrac{0.728 \times 0.006\,25}{0.028\,1}$

8) $\dfrac{27.5 \times 30.52}{11.3 \times 2.73}$

Fraction to Decimal Conversion

We found, when doing fractions, that the line separating the numerator and the denominator of a fraction takes the place of a division sign. Thus

$$\frac{17}{80} \text{ is the same as } 17 \div 80$$

Therefore to convert a fraction into a decimal we divide the denominator into the numerator.

Example 11

Convert $\dfrac{27}{32}$ to decimals.

$$\frac{27}{32} = 27 \div 32$$

```
32)27.0(0.843 75
   25 6
   ────
    1 40
    1 28
    ────
      120
       96
      ────
      240
      224
      ────
      160
      160
      ────
      . . .
      ────
```

Therefore $\dfrac{27}{32} = 0.843\,75$

Example 12

Convert $2\dfrac{9}{16}$ into decimals.

When we have a mixed number to convert into decimals we need only deal with the fractional part. Thus to convert $2\frac{9}{16}$ into decimals we only have to deal with $\frac{9}{16}$.

$$\frac{9}{16} = 9 \div 16$$

```
16)9.0(0.5625
   8 0
   ────
   1 00
     96
   ────
     40
     32
   ────
     80
     80
   ────
     ..
   ────
```

The division shows that $\frac{9}{16} = 0.5625$ and hence $2\frac{9}{16} = 2.5625$

Sometimes a fraction will not divide out exactly as shown in Example 13.

Example 13

Convert $\dfrac{1}{3}$ to decimals.

$$\frac{1}{3} = 1 \div 3$$

```
        3)1.0(0.333
          9
          ─
          10
           9
          ──
          10
           9
          ──
           1
```

It is clear that all we shall get from the division is a succession of threes.

This is an example of a *recurring decimal* and in order to prevent endless repetition the result is written $0.\dot{3}$. Therefore $\frac{1}{3} = 0.\dot{3}$.

Some further examples of recurring decimals are:

$\frac{2}{3} = 0.\dot{6}$ (meaning 0.6666 . . . etc.)

$\frac{1}{6} = 0.1\dot{6}$ (meaning 0.1666 . . . etc.)

$\frac{5}{11} = 0.\dot{4}\dot{5}$ (meaning 0.454545 . . . etc.)

$\frac{3}{7} = 0.\dot{4}2857\dot{1}$ (meaning 0.428571428571 . . . etc.)

For all practical purposes we never need recurring decimals; what we need is an answer given to so many significant figures or decimal places. Thus:

$\frac{2}{3} = 0.67$ (correct to 2 decimal places)

$\frac{5}{11} = 0.455$ (correct to 3 significant figures)

Exercise 34 — *Questions 1–6 and 11–15 type A, remainder B*

Convert the following to decimals correcting the answers, where necessary, to 4 decimal places:

1) $\dfrac{1}{4}$ 5) $\dfrac{1}{2}$ 9) $1\dfrac{5}{6}$

2) $\dfrac{3}{4}$ 6) $\dfrac{2}{3}$ 10) $2\dfrac{7}{16}$

3) $\dfrac{3}{8}$ 7) $\dfrac{21}{32}$

4) $\dfrac{11}{16}$ 8) $\dfrac{29}{64}$

Write down the following recurring decimals correct to 3 decimal places:

11) $0.\dot{3}$ 15) $0.3\dot{5}$ 19) $0.\dot{3}2\dot{8}$

12) $0.\dot{7}$ 16) $0.\dot{2}\dot{3}$ 20) $0.56\dot{7}\dot{1}$

13) $0.1\dot{3}$ 17) $0.5\dot{2}$

14) $0.1\dot{8}$ 18) $0.3\dot{8}$

Conversion of Decimals to Fractions

We know that decimals are fractions with denominators 10, 100, 1000, etc. Using this fact we can always convert a decimal to a fraction.

Example 14

Convert 0.32 to a fraction.

$$0.32 = \frac{32}{100} = \frac{8}{25}$$

When comparing decimals and fractions it is best to convert the fraction into a decimal.

Example 15

Find the difference between $1\dfrac{3}{16}$ and 1.1632

$$1\frac{3}{16} = 1.1875$$

$$1\frac{3}{16} - 1.1632 = 1.1875 - 1.1632$$

$$= 0.0243$$

Exercise 35 — *Questions 1 and 2 type A, remainder B*

Convert the following to fractions in their lowest terms:

1)   0.2   3)   0.3125   5)   0.0075

2)   0.45   4)   2.55   6)   2.125

7)   What is the difference between 0.28135 and $\frac{9}{32}$?

8)   What is the difference between $\frac{19}{64}$ and 0.295?

Exercise 36 — *Questions 1–26 type A, remainder B*

The questions in this exercise have all been taken from past C.S.E. examination papers.

1)   Calculate 0.568×100.   (*S.W.*)

2)   Calculate:
(a) $3.52 + 49.5$
(b) $10 \div 6$ to 2 places of decimals.
(*S.W.*)

3)
(a)   Work out $(18 + 12) \div 4$ giving your answer as a decimal fraction.
(b)   Now work out $(18 \div 4) + (12 \div 4)$ again giving your answer as a decimal fraction.   (*Y.R.*)

4)   Divide 0.06 by 20.   (*E.A.*)

5)   Write 0.02846 correct to three significant figures.   (*S*)

6)   Write 5.928:
(a)   correct to two decimal places,
(b)   correct to two significant figures.
(*S*)

7)   Write these fractions in decimal form:

(a) $\dfrac{1}{5}$ (b) $\dfrac{1}{3}$ (c) $\dfrac{1}{9}$ (*S*)

8)   Take 6.75 from the sum of 7.4 and 3.9.   (*S*)

9) Calculate the exact value of 0.019 6 ÷ 0.14. (*Y.R.*)

10) Write down the answers to:

(a) 3.6×0.3   (c) 3.6÷0.3

(b) 3.6×30   (d) 3.6÷30   (*W*)

11) Do the following calculations:

(a) 9.73×100   (c) 9.0×0.003

(b) 742÷100   (*S*)

12) 0.72 is equivalent to:

a $\dfrac{18}{25}$ **b** $\dfrac{7}{10}$ **c** $7\dfrac{1}{5}$

d $\dfrac{72}{1000}$ **e** $\dfrac{16}{25}$ (*W.M.*)

13) Using the approximate value of π as 3.141 59 express:

(a) the value of π to two significant figures,

(b) the value of 4π to two decimal places. (*S.W.*)

14) The value of 4.7−1.9+2.1 is:

a 5.9   **b** 0.7   **c** 8.7

d 1.7   **e** 4.9   (*W.Y.*)

15) 0.4×1.4 equals:

a 560   **b** 56   **c** 5.6

d 0.56   **e** 0.056   (*W.Y.*)

16) 0.064 76 correct to three decimal places is:

a 0.064   **b** 0.065   **c** 0.0647

d 0.0648   **e** none of these (*W.Y.*)

17) 6474 correct to three significant figures is:

a 647   **b** 648   **c** 6470

d 6480   **e** 7000   (*W.Y.*)

18) 24 866 written to the nearest hundred is:

a 24 800   **b** 25 000   **c** 24 900

d 24 870   **e** 24 860   (*W.M.*)

19) The value of $\dfrac{2.4}{4}$ is:

a 0.6   **b** 6   **c** 60

d 2.1   **e** 2.0   (*W.M.*)

20) 0.2×0.4 equals:

a 0.8   **b** 0.08   **c** 8

d 0.6   **e** 0.008   (*W.M.*)

21) In the number 8.6792 the value of the digit 7 is:

a 70   **b** $\dfrac{7}{10}$ **c** $\dfrac{7}{100}$

d 700   **e** $\dfrac{7}{1000}$

22) 5−0.003 equals:

a 0.002   **b** 4.003   **c** 4.007

d 4.997   **e** 5.003   (*S.E.*)

23) 0.93+0.08 is equal to:

a 1.01   **b** 1.1   **c** 1.11

d 0.101   **e** 0.91   (*W.M.*)

24) 0.1×0.2×0.3 is equal to:

a 0.06   **b** 0.006   **c** 0.05

d 0.005   **e** 0.6   (*N.W.*)

25) What must be added to 3.1476 to make 4.0? (*W*)

26) List these decimals in order of size, largest first:

0.22, 2.20, 0.022, 2.02.   (*A.L.*)

27) The value of 136×47 is 6392.

(a) The value of 1.36×4.7 is:

a 0.6392   **b** 6.392   **c** 63.92

d 639.2

(b) The value of $\dfrac{63.92}{13.6}$ is:

a 47   **b** 4.7   **c** 0.47

d 50.32   (*A.L.*)

28) Given that 225×35 = 7875 then:

22.5×0.35 is equal to:

a 787.5   **b** 7.875   **c** 0.7875

d 0.078 75   **e** 0.007 875   (*W.Y.*)

29) Approximations to the nearest whole number for 4.861, 14.295 and 7.407 are 5, 14 and 7 respectively.

Use these suggestions to obtain an approximate result for

$$\frac{4.861 \times 14.295}{7.407}$$

Applying the same method obtain an approximate result for

$$\frac{3.862 \times 19.8}{9.943} \qquad (M)$$

30) If $14.8 \times 36.8 = 544.64,$ write down in decimal form the value of:

(a) 1.48×3.68 (b) $54.464 \div 14.8$

$(Y.R.)$

Chapter 4　Decimal Currency

The British System

The British system of decimal currency uses the pound as the basic unit. The only sub-unit used is pence such that

$$100 \text{ pence} = 1 \text{ pound}$$

The abbreviation p is used for pence and the abbreviation £ is used for pounds. A decimal point is used to separate the pounds from the pence, for example

£3.58 meaning three pounds and fifty-eight pence

There are two ways of expressing amounts less than £1. For example 74 pence may be written as £0.74 or 74 p; 5 pence may be written as £0.05 or as 5 p.

The smallest unit used is the half-penny which is always written as a fraction i.e. as $\frac{1}{2}$. Thus £5.17$\frac{1}{2}$ means 5 pounds and 17$\frac{1}{2}$ pence. 53$\frac{1}{2}$ pence is written as either 53$\frac{1}{2}$ p or as £0.53$\frac{1}{2}$. Note carefully that $\frac{1}{2}$ p = £0.005, a fact which is useful when solving some problems with decimal currency.

Addition and Subtraction

The addition of sums of money is done in almost the same way as the addition of decimals. The exception occurs with the half pence piece.

Example 1

Add together £3.78, £5.23 and £8.19

£3.78
£5.23
£8.19
£17.20

Write down the amounts with the decimal points directly beneath one another. First add the pence which total 120. This is equal to £1.20 so we write 20 in the pence column and carry the £1. Now add the pounds $1+8+5+3 = 17$.

Example 2

Add together £2.58$\frac{1}{2}$, £3.27$\frac{1}{2}$ and 5.73$\frac{1}{2}$

£2.58$\frac{1}{2}$
£3.27$\frac{1}{2}$
£5.73$\frac{1}{2}$
£11.59$\frac{1}{2}$

First add the half-pence and we get 1$\frac{1}{2}$ p. Write $\frac{1}{2}$ in the answer and carry 1 p. Now add the whole pence: $1+73+27+58 = 159$ p. This is equal to £1.59 so write 59 in the answer and carry £1. Finally add the pounds thus: $1+2+3+5 = $ £11.

Example 3

Add together 39 p, 84$\frac{1}{2}$ p and £1.73

£0.39
£0.84$\frac{1}{2}$
£1.73
£2.96$\frac{1}{2}$

When amounts are given in pence it is best to write these as pounds. Thus 39 p is written £0.39, etc. The addition is then performed as previously described.

Example 4

Subtract £2.36$\frac{1}{2}$ from £3.08

£3.08	We cannot take 36$\frac{1}{2}$p
£2.36$\frac{1}{2}$	from 8 p so we borrow
	£1 = 100 p from the £3
£0.71$\frac{1}{2}$	on the top line. Then

108 − 36$\frac{1}{2}$ = 71$\frac{1}{2}$. The £3
becomes £2 and we have 2 − 2 = 0
thus giving an answer of £0.71$\frac{1}{2}$ or
71$\frac{1}{2}$ p.

Exercise 37 — *All type A*

1) Express the following amounts as pence:

£0.68, £0.63, £0.58$\frac{1}{2}$.

2) Express the following as pence:
£2.16, £3.59$\frac{1}{2}$, £17.68.

3) Express the following as pounds:
35 p, 78$\frac{1}{2}$ p, 6 p, 3 p.

4) Express the following as pounds:
246 p, 983$\frac{1}{2}$ p, 26 532 p.

5) Add the following sums of money together:

(a) £2.15, £3.28, £4.63
(b) £8.28, £109.17, £27.98, £70.15
(c) £0.17$\frac{1}{2}$, £1.63$\frac{1}{2}$, £1.71, £1.90$\frac{1}{2}$
(d) 82 p, 71 p, 82 p
(e) 17$\frac{1}{2}$ p, 27 p, 81$\frac{1}{2}$ p, 74$\frac{1}{2}$ p

6) Subtract the following:

(a) £7.60 from £9.84
(b) £3.49 from £11.42
(c) £18.73$\frac{1}{2}$ from £87.35
(d) £0.54$\frac{1}{2}$ from £1.32$\frac{1}{2}$
(e) 54 p from £2.63$\frac{1}{2}$

Multiplication and Division

The multiplication and division of decimal currency are very similar to the methods used with decimal numbers.

Example 5

Find the cost of 23 articles if each costs 27 p.

Now 27 p = £0.27

Cost of 23 articles @ £0.27
$$= 23 \times £0.27$$
$$= £6.21$$

Example 6

Find the cost of 19 articles costing 21$\frac{1}{2}$ p each.

Now 21$\frac{1}{2}$ p = £0.215

Cost of 19 articles @ £0.215 each
= £4.085 = £4.08$\frac{1}{2}$

(Note that $\frac{1}{2}$ p = £0.005 and hence
£4.085 = £4.08$\frac{1}{2}$)

Example 7

If 127 articles cost £14.60$\frac{1}{2}$ find the cost of each article.

Now £14.60$\frac{1}{2}$ is a mixture of decimals and fractions and the first step is to make it into a wholly decimal number by remembering that
$\frac{1}{2}$ p = £0.005. Hence:

£14.60$\frac{1}{2}$ = £14.605.

£14.605 ÷ 127 = £0.115 or 11$\frac{1}{2}$ p

Exercise 38 — *All type B*

1) Find the cost of 12 articles costing 15 p each.

2) Find the cost of 85 articles costing 7$\frac{1}{2}$ p each.

3) How much does 43 articles @ $39\frac{1}{2}$ p each cost?

4) What is the cost of 24 articles costing £7.03$\frac{1}{2}$ each?

5) If 12 identical articles cost £1.56, how much does each cost?

6) If 241 identical articles cost £51.81$\frac{1}{2}$, how much does each cost?

7) If 5000 articles cost £6525, find the cost of each article.

8) If 125 articles cost £270.62$\frac{1}{2}$, what is the cost of each article?

Exercise 39 — *All type A*

All the questions in this exercise have been taken from past C.S.E. examination papers.

1) Find the cost of 12 litres of petrol at 15 p per litre. (S)

2) Brian, Tom and David together have £18. How many records at £1.50 could they buy altogether. (Y.R.)

3)
(a) From £25 take £12.73.
(b) Work out £42.42 ÷ 6. (S)

4) Work out the answer to £7.29 + £13.26 + £1.88. (S)

5) Julie had £5. She spent £1.54, £2.07 and £1.10. How much money had she left? (Y.R.)

6) Find the cost of buying 5 litres of paint at 97 p per litre. How much is

saved by buying a 5 litre can at £4.30? (S)

7) Find the cost of $6\frac{1}{2}$ metres of material at 30 p per metre. (S.W.)

8) How many pence are there in £3.63? (Y)

9) How many 7 p stamps can be bought for £1.47? (Y)

10) The cost of 4 articles at $72\frac{1}{2}$ p each is:

   a £2.92   **b** £2.88   **c** £2.89
   d £2.90   **e** £2.95   (W.M.)

11) The cost of $2\frac{1}{2}$ kg of tomatoes at 36 p per kg is

   a 90 p   **b** 86 p   **c** 110 p
   d 72 p   **e** 84 p   (W.M.)

12) The cost of 2 metres of material at £1.20 per metre and 3 metres at £1.50 per metre is:

   a £6.90   **b** £13.50   **c** £6.60
   d £7.10   **e** £2.70   (N.W.)

13) The cost of 2000 articles at 25 p each is:

   a £50 000   **b** £2500   **c** £5000
   d £50   **e** £500   (W.M.)

14) The change from £1 after buying 18 buttons at $2\frac{1}{2}$ p each is:

   a 35 p   **b** $37\frac{1}{2}$ p   **c** 45 p
   d 52 p   **e** 55 p   (S.E.)

15) The cost of 200 articles at $3\frac{1}{2}$ p each is:

   a £3.50   **b** £70.00   **c** £7.00
   d £35.00   **e** £700.000   (S.E.)

Chapter 5   Ratio and Proportion

A *ratio* is a comparison between two similar quantities. If the length of a certain ship is 120 metres and a model of it is 1 metre long then the length of the model is $\frac{1}{120}$th of the length of the ship. In making the model the dimensions of the ship are all reduced in the ratio of 1 to 120. The ratio 1 to 120 is usually written $1:120$.

As indicated above a ratio may be expressed as a fraction and all ratios may be looked upon as fractions. Thus the ratio $2:5 = \frac{2}{5}$. The two terms of a ratio may be multiplied or divided without altering the value of the ratio. Hence $6:36 = 1:6 = \frac{1}{6}$. Again, $1:5 = 4:20$.

Before a ratio can be stated the units must be the same. We can state the ratio between 7 pence and £2 provided both sums of money are brought to the same units. Thus if we convert £2 to 200 p the ratio between the two amounts of money is $7:200$.

Example 1

Express the ratio 20 p to £4 in its simplest form.

$$£4 = 4 \times 100\,\text{p} = 400\,\text{p}$$

$$20:400 = \frac{20}{400} = \frac{1}{20}$$

Example 2

Express the ratio $4:\frac{1}{4}$ in its lowest terms.

$$4:\frac{1}{4} = 4 \div \frac{1}{4} = 4 \times \frac{4}{1} = \frac{16}{1}$$

$$4:\frac{1}{4} = 16:1$$

Example 3

Two lengths are in the ratio $8:5$. If the first length is 120 metres, what is the second length?

The second length $= \frac{5}{8}$ of the first length $= \frac{5}{8} \times 120 = 75$ metres.

Example 4

Two amounts of money are in the ratio of $12:7$. If the second amount is £21 what is the first amount?

First amount $= \frac{12}{7} \times £21 = £36$

Exercise 40 — *Questions 1–7 type A, remainder B*

Express the following ratios as fractions in their lowest terms:

1) $8:3$

2) $4:6$

3) $12:4$

4) $9:15$

5) $8:12$

6) Express the ratio of 30 p to £2 as a fraction in its lowest terms.

7) Express the ratio £5 : 80 p as a fraction in its lowest terms.

8) Two lengths are in the ratio $7:5$. If the first length is 210 metres, what is the second length?

9) Two amounts of money are in the ratio $8:5$. If the second amount is £120, what is the first amount?

10) Express $3:\frac{1}{2}$ in its lowest terms.

Proportional Parts

The diagram (Fig. 5.1) shows a line AB whose length is 16 centimetres divided into two parts in the ratio $3:5$. As can be seen in the diagram the line has been divided into a total of 8 parts.

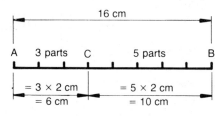

Fig. 5.1

The length AC contains 3 parts and the length BC contains 5 parts. Each part is $\frac{16}{8}=2$ centimetres long; hence AC is $3\times2=6$ centimetres long and BC is $5\times2=10$ centimetres long. We could tackle this problem in this way:

Total number of parts
$=3+5=8$ parts

Length of each part
$=\frac{16}{8}=2$ centimetres

Length of AC
$=3\times2=6$ centimetres

Length of BC
$=5\times2=10$ centimetres

Example 5

Divide £1100 into two parts in the ratio $7:3$.

Total number of parts $=7+3=10$

Amount of each part $=\frac{1100}{10}=£110$

Amount of first part
$=7\times110=£770$

Amount of second part
$=3\times110=£330$

Example 6

An aircraft carries 2880 litres of fuel distributed in three tanks in the ratio $3:5:4$. Find the quantity in each tank.

Total number of parts
$=3+5+4=12$

Amount of each part
$=\frac{2880}{12}=240$ litres

Amount of 3 parts
$=3\times240=720$ litres

Amount of 4 parts
$=4\times240=960$ litres

Amount of 5 parts
$=5\times240=1200$ litres

The three tanks contain 720, 1200 and 960 litres.

Exercise 41 — *Questions 1–3 type A, remainder B*

1) Divide £800 in the ratio $5:3$.

2) Divide £80 in the ratio $4:1$.

3) Divide £120 in the ratio $5:4:3$.

4) A sum of money is divided into two parts in the ratio $5:7$. If the smaller amount is £200, find the larger amount.

5) An alloy consists of copper, zinc and tin in the ratios $2:3:5$. Find the amount of each metal in 75 kilogrammes of the alloy.

6) A line is to be divided into three

34

parts in the ratios $2:7:11$. If the line is 840 millimetres long, calculate the length of each part.

7) Two villages have populations of 336 and 240 respectively. The two villages are to share a grant of £10 728 in proportion to their populations. Calculate how much each village receives.

8) Four friends contribute sums of money to a charitable organisation in the ratio of $2:4:5:7$. If the largest amount contributed is £1.40, calculate the total amount contributed by the four people.

Direct Proportion

Two quantities are said to vary directly, or be in direct proportion, if they increase or decrease at the same rate. Thus the quantity of petrol used and the distance travelled by a motor car are in direct proportion. Again if we buy potatoes at 20 pence for 2 kilogrammes then we expect to pay 40 p for 4 kilogrammes and 10 p for 1 kilogramme. That is if we double the amount bought then we double the cost; if we halve the amount bought we halve the cost.

In solving problems on direct proportion we can use either the unitary method or the fractional method. They are illustrated in Example 7.

Example 7

If 25 kilogrammes of butter cost £17 how much does 8 kilogrammes cost?

a) Using the unitary method:

25 kilogrammes cost £17 or 1700 pence

1 kilogramme costs $\frac{1700}{25} = 68$ pence

8 kilogrammes cost 8×68

$\qquad = 544$ pence or £5.44

b) Using the fractional method:

Cost of 8 kilogrammes

$$= \frac{8}{25} \times 1700 = \frac{8 \times 1700}{25}$$

$$= 544 \text{ pence or } £5.44$$

Example 8

A recipe for Boeuf Stroganoff quotes the following amounts to serve four people: 450 grammes of rump steak, 3 tablespoons flour, 4 tablespoons butter, 50 grammes of onion, 75 grammes of mushrooms, 140 grammes of sour cream. What amounts should be used for six people?

The quantities required and the number of people are in direct proportion. Hence the amounts must be increased in the ratio of $6:4$ or $3:2$.

Amount of rump steak
$\qquad = \frac{3}{2} \times 450$ 43 675 grammes

Amount of flour
$\qquad = \frac{3}{2} \times 3 = 4\frac{1}{2}$ tablespoons

Amount of butter
$\qquad = \frac{3}{2} \times 4 = 6$ tablespoons

Amount of onion
$\qquad = \frac{3}{2} \times 50 = 75$ grammes

Amount of mushrooms
$\qquad = \frac{3}{2} \times 75 = 112\frac{1}{2}$ grammes

Amount of sour cream
$\qquad = \frac{3}{2} \times 140 = 210$ grammes

Exercise 42 — *Questions 1–4 type A, remainder B*

1) If 7 kilogrammes of apples cost £2.80, how much does 12 kilogrammes cost?

2) If 74 exercise books cost £5.92, how much do 53 cost?

3) If 40 articles cost £35, how much does 1 article cost? What is the cost of 55 articles?

4) Eggs cost 70 p per 10. How much will 25 eggs cost?

5) A car travels 205 kilometres on 20 litres of petrol. How much petrol is needed for a journey of 340 kilometres?

6) The ingredients for a cake which will serve 12 people are as follows: 55 grammes of butter, 110 grammes of castor sugar, 6 egg yolks, 120 grammes plain flour and 3 tablespoons of milk. What quantities are needed to serve 4 people?

7) If 9 metres of carpet cost £21, how much will 96 metres cost?

8) A train travels 200 kilometres in 4 hours. How long will it take to complete a journey of 350 kilometres?

Inverse Proportion

Suppose that 8 men working on a certain job take 10 days to complete it. If we double the number of men then we should halve the time taken. If we halve the number of men then the job will probably take twice as long. This is an example of inverse proportion.

Example 9

20 men working in a factory produce 3000 articles in 12 working days. How long will it take 15 men to produce the 3000 articles?

The number of men is reduced in the ratio $\frac{15}{20} = \frac{3}{4}$

Since this is an example of inverse proportion the number of days required must be increased in the ratio $\frac{4}{3}$.

Number of days required
$$= \tfrac{4}{3} \times 12 = 16 \text{ days}$$

Exercise 43 — *All type B*

1) A farmer employs 12 men to harvest his potato crop. They take 9 days to do the job. If he had employed 8 men how long would it have taken them?

2) 10 men produce 500 articles in 5 working days. How long would it take 15 men to produce the same amount?

3) Two gear wheels mesh together. One has 40 teeth and the other has 25 teeth. If the larger wheel makes 100 revolutions per minute how many revolutions per minute does the smaller wheel make?

4) A bag contains sweets. When divided amongst 8 children each child receives 9 sweets. If the sweets were divided amongst 12 children how many sweets would each receive?

5) 4 men can do a piece of work in 30 hours. How many men would be required to do the work in 6 hours?

Foreign Exchange

Every country has its own monetary system. If there is to be trade and travel between any two countries there must be a rate at which the money of one country can be converted into money of the other country. This rate is called the rate of exchange.

The methods used for direct proportion are applicable to problems in foreign exchange.

Example 10

If £1 = 120 Spanish pesetas, find to the nearest whole pence the value in

Country	Monetary unit		Rate of exchange	
Belgium	100 centimes	= 1 franc	BF60.35	= £1
France	100 centimes	= 1 franc	F8.40	= £1
Germany	100 pfennig	= 1 mark	DM4.03	= £1
Greece	100 lepta	= 1 drachma	DR60	= £1
Italy	100 centesimi	= 1 lira	Lit1500	= £1
Spain	100 centimos	= 1 peseta	Ptas119	= £1
Switzerland	100 centimes	= 1 franc	SWF4.22	= £1
United States	100 cents	= 1 dollar	$1.70	= £1

British money of 1000 pesetas.

1) Using the unitary method:

$$120 \text{ pesetas} = £1$$

$$1 \text{ peseta } = £\frac{1}{120}$$

$$1000 \text{ pesetas} = £\frac{1}{120} \times 1000$$

$$= £\frac{1000}{120} = £8.33$$

b) Using the fractional method:

$$1000 \text{ pesetas} = £\frac{1000}{120} = £8.33$$

Example 11

A tourist changes travellers cheques for £40 into French francs at 8.40 francs to the pound. How many francs does he get?

$$£40 = 40 \times 8.40 \text{ francs} = 336 \text{ francs}$$

Exercise 44 — *Questions 1–6 type A, remainder B*

Where necessary give the answers to 2 places of decimals.

Using the exchange rates given above find:

1) The number of German marks equivalent to £15.

2) The number of Spanish pesetas equivalent to £25.

3) The number of United States dollars equivalent to £32.

4) The number of pounds equivalent to 223 United States dollars.

5) The number of pounds equivalent to 8960 Italian lire.

6) The number of Belgian francs equivalent to £98.50.

7) A transistor set costs £26.30 in the United Kingdom. An American visitor wants to purchase a set but wishes to pay in United States dollars. What is the equivalent price in dollars?

8) A tourist changes travellers cheques for £50 into Greek currency at 67 drachma to the £1. He spends 3120 drachma and changes the remainder back into sterling at the same rate. How much did the tourist receive?

9) Calculate the rate of exchange if a bank exchanges 810 Swedish krona for £90.

10) A person on holiday in France changed £100 into francs at a rate of 8.40 francs to the £1. His hotel expenses were 75 francs per day for eight days and his other expenses were 204 francs. On returning home he changed what francs he had left into sterling at a rate of 8.30 francs to the £1. Calculate.

(a) The number of francs received for the £100.

(b) The total expenses in francs.

(c) The number of francs left after

paying these expenses.

(d) The amount in £'s obtained for the francs he had left. (Give your answer to the nearest whole pence.)

Exercise 45 — *All type B*

The questions in this exercise have all been taken from past C.S.E. question papers.

1) In Holland there are 100 cents in a florin. There are 5 florins to a pound. How many pence is a 25 cent coin worth?

    a 4   **b** $2\frac{1}{2}$ **c** 5

    d 2   **e** 1   (*N.W.*)

2) Find the cost of 7 kg of potatoes when 3 kg cost $7\frac{1}{2}$ p.   (*W.Y.*)

3) The ratio of A's share to B's share in the profits of a business is 5 : 4. If the total profit is £450 then A's share is:

    a £90   **b** £200   **c** £225

    d £250   (*A.L.*)

4) If £120 is divided in the ratio 2 to 3 then the smaller share is:

    a £48   **b** £80   **c** £72

    d £60   **e** £40   (*W.M.*)

5) The ratio of the shares of two partners A and B in the profits of a business is 5 : 3.

(a) How much will B receive when the profit is £1200?

    a £300   **b** £360

    c £450   **d** £720

(b) How much will A receive when B receives £480?

    a £800   **b** £300

    c £288   **d** £216   (*A.L.*)

6) A car does 12 km per litre of petrol. How many complete litres of petrol will be needed to be sure of completing a journey of 100 km? (*A.L.*)

7) A councillor gets a car travel allowance of 8.7 p per kilometre. How much is he paid for a journey of 20 km?   (*A.L.*)

8) A vending machine needs 20 litres of orangeade to fill 50 cups. How many litres is needed to fill 60 cups? (*A.L.*)

9) Change £150 into dollars when the exchange rate is £1 = $1.75. (*E.M.*)

10) Change 2272 French francs into £ when £1 = 8.50 francs. (*E.M.*)

11) Divide £400 in the ratio 5 : 3.   (*E.M.*)

12) Ann and Jane have £20 shared between them, but Ann gets three times as much as Jane. How much does Ann receive?   (*A.L.*)

13) If two men can paint a fence in 6 hours, how long will it take three men to paint it, assuming they all work at the same rate?   (*A.L.*)

14) Ten explorers have rations enough to last for 30 days. Work out the answers to the items which follow, assuming that the rate of working per explorer is the same in each case:

(a) How many days would the rations have lasted one explorer?

(b) How many explorers would have eaten all the rations in 5 days?

(c) How long would the rations have lasted three explorers?

(d) If after 15 days of eating their rations the original ten explorers were joined by fifteen other explorers how much longer did the remaining rations last these twenty-five explorers?   (*M*)

15) 2 dratt equal 1 assam and 1 dratt is the same as 4 yeda. How many yeda to an assam?   (*N.W.*)

Chapter 6 **Percentages**

When comparing fractions it is often convenient to express them with a denominator of a hundred. Thus:

$$\frac{1}{2} = \frac{50}{100}$$

$$\frac{2}{5} = \frac{40}{100}$$

Fractions with a denominator of 100 are called *percentages*. Thus:

$$\frac{1}{4} = \frac{25}{100} = 25 \text{ per cent}$$

$$\frac{3}{10} = \frac{30}{100} = 30 \text{ per cent}$$

The sign % is usually used instead of the words per cent.

To convert a fraction into a percentage we multiply it by 100.

Examples 1

$$\frac{3}{4} = \frac{3}{4} \times 100\% = 75\%$$

$$\frac{17}{20} = \frac{17}{20} \times 100\% = 85\%$$

Exercise 46 — *All type A*

Convert the following fractions to percentages:

1) $\frac{7}{10}$ 4) $\frac{4}{5}$ 7) $\frac{9}{10}$

2) $\frac{11}{20}$ 5) $\frac{31}{50}$ 8) $\frac{19}{20}$

3) $\frac{9}{25}$ 6) $\frac{1}{4}$

Decimal numbers may be converted into percentages by using the same rule. Thus:

$$0.3 = \frac{3}{10} = \frac{3}{10} \times 100 = 30\%$$

The same result is produced if we omit the intermediate step of turning 0.3 into a vulgar fraction and just multiply 0.3 by 100. Thus:

$$0.3 = 0.3 \times 100\% = 30\%$$

Examples 2

$$0.56 = 0.56 \times 100\% = 56\%$$

$$0.683 = 0.683 \times 100\% = 68.3\%$$

Exercise 47 — *All type A*

Convert the following decimal numbers into percentages:

1) 0.7   4) 0.813   7) 0.819

2) 0.73   5) 0.927

3) 0.68   6) 0.333

To convert a percentage into a fraction we divide by 100.

Examples 3

$$45\% = \frac{45}{100} = 0.45$$

$$3.9\% = \frac{3.9}{100} = 0.039$$

Note that all we have done is to move the decimal point 2 places to the left.

Exercise 48 — *All type A*

Convert the following percentages into decimal fractions:

1) 32%   5) 31.5%   9) 3.95%

2) 78%   6) 48.2%   10) 20.1%

3) 6%   7) 2.5%

4) 24%   8) 1.25%

Percentage of a Quantity

It is easy to find the percentage of a quantity if we first express the percentage as a fraction.

Examples 4

a) What is 10% of 40?

Expressing 10% as a fraction it is $\frac{10}{100}$ and the problem then becomes: what is $\frac{10}{100}$ of 40?

$$10\% \text{ of } 40 = \frac{10}{100} \times 40 = 4$$

b) What is 25% of £50?

$$25\% \text{ of } £50 = \frac{25}{100} \times £50 = £12.50$$

c) 22% of a certain length is 55 cm. What is the complete length?

We have that 22% of the length
$$= 55 \text{ cm}$$

$$1\% \text{ of the length} = \frac{55}{22} \text{ cm} = 2.5 \text{ cm}$$

Now the complete length will be 100%, hence:

Complete length $= 100 \times 2.5$ cm
$$= 250 \text{ cm}$$

Alternatively

22% of the length $= 55$ cm

Complete length $= \frac{100}{22} \times 55$

$$= \frac{100 \times 55}{22} = 250 \text{ cm}$$

d) What percentage is 37 of 264? Give the answer correct to 5 significant figures.

$$\text{Percentage} = \frac{37}{264} \times 100$$

$$= \frac{37 \times 100}{264} = 14.015\%$$

1) What is:

(a) 20% of 50   (b) 30% of 80
(c) 5% of 120   (d) 12% of 20
(e) 20.3% of 105   (f) 3.7% of 68?

2) What percentage is:

(a) 25 of 200   (b) 30 of 150
(c) 24 of 150   (d) 29 of 178
(e) 15 of 33?

Where necessary give the answer correct to 4 significant figures.

3) A girl scores 36 marks out of 60 in an examination. What is her percentage mark? If the percentage needed to pass the examination is 45% how many marks are needed to pass?

4) If 20% of a length is 23 cm what is the complete length?

5) Given that 13.3 cm is 15% of a certain length, what is the complete length?

6) What is:

(a) 9% of £80   (b) 12% of £110
(c) 75% of £250?

7) Express the following statements in the form of a percentage:

(a) 3 eggs are bad in a box containing 144 eggs.
(b) In a school of 650 pupils, 20 are absent.
(c) In a school of 980 pupils, 860 eat school lunches.

8) In a certain county the average number of children eating lunches at school was 29 336 which represents 74% of the total number of children attending school. Calculate the total number of children attending school in that county.

9) 23% of a consignment of bananas is bad. There are 34.5 kg of bad bananas. How many kilograms were there in the consignment?

10) A retailer accepts a consignment of 5000 ball point pens. He finds that 12% are faulty. How many faulty pens were there?

Percentage Profit and Loss

When a dealer buys or sells goods, the cost price is the price at which he buys the goods and the selling price is the price at which he sells the goods. If the selling price is greater than the cost price then a profit is made. The amount of profit is the difference between the selling price and the cost price. That is:

Profit = selling price − cost price

The profit per cent is always calculated on the cost price. That is:

Profit %
$$= \frac{\text{selling price} - \text{cost price}}{\text{cost price}} \times 100$$

If a loss is made the cost price is greater than the selling price. The loss is the difference between the cost price and the selling price. That is:

Loss = cost price − selling price

$$\text{Loss}\% = \frac{\text{cost price} - \text{selling price}}{\text{cost price}} \times 100$$

Examples 5

a) A shopkeeper buys an article for £5.00 and sells it for £6.00. What is his profit per cent?

We are given:
cost price = £5 and selling price = £6

$$\text{Profit \%} = \frac{6-5}{5} \times 100$$

$$= \frac{1}{5} \times 100 = 20\%$$

b) A dealer buys 20 articles at a total cost of £5. He sells them for 30 p each. What is his profit per cent?

Since £5 = 500 p, cost price per article

$$= \frac{500}{20} = 25\,\text{p}$$

$$\text{Profit \%} = \frac{30-25}{25} \times 100$$

$$= \frac{5}{25} \times 100 = 20\%$$

c) A man buys a car for £1600 and sells it for £1200. Calculate his percentage loss.

Loss = cost price − selling price
$$= £1600 - £1200 = £400$$

$$\text{Loss \%} = \frac{400}{1600} \times 100 = 25\%$$

Exercise 50 — *Questions 1–4 type A, remainder B*

1) A shopkeeper buys an article for 80 p and sells it for £1. Calculate the percentage profit.

2) Calculate the profit per cent when:
(a) Cost price is £1.50 and selling price is £1.80.
(b) Cost price is 30 p and selling price is 35 p.

3) Calculate the loss per cent when:
(a) Cost price is 75 p and selling price is 65 p.
(b) Cost price is £6.53 and selling price is £5.88.

4) The price of coal has increased from £20 to £22 per 1000 kilogrammes. What is the percentage increase in the price of coal?

5) A greengrocer buys a box of 200 oranges for £5. He sells them for 3 p each. Calculate his percentage profit.

6) A dealer buys 100 similar articles for £60 and sells them for 80 p each. Find his profit per cent.

7) A retailer buys 30 articles at 8 p each. Three are damaged and unsale-able but he sells the others at 10 p each. What is the profit per cent?

8) A car is bought for £1700 and sold for £1400. What is the loss per cent?

Discount

When a customer buys an article from a retailer for cash he will often ask the retailer for a discount. This discount, which is usually a percentage of the selling price, is the amount which the retailer will take off his selling price thus reducing his profit.

Example 6

A radiogram is offered for sale at £60. A customer is offered a 10% discount for cash. How much does the customer actually pay?

Discount = 10% of £60

$$= \frac{10}{100} \times £60 = £6$$

Amount paid by customer

$$= £60 - £6 = £54$$

(*Alternatively:* since only 90% of the selling price is paid,

Amount customer pays

$$= 90\% \text{ of } £60 = \frac{90}{100} \times £60 = £54)$$

Sometimes discounts are quoted as so much in the pound, for instance 5 p in the £1. If we remember that 5 p in the £1 is the same as 5% then the cal-culation of discounts is the same as that shown in Example 6.

Example 7

How much will a girl pay for goods priced at £12.50 if a discount of 8 p in the £1 is offered for cash?

8 p in the £1 is the same as 8%

$$\text{Discount} = \frac{8}{100} \times £12.50 = £1.00$$

Amount paid by the girl

$$= £12.50 - £1.00 = £11.50$$

Exercise 51 — *All type A*

1) A chair marked for sale at £14 is sold for cash at a discount of 10%. What price did the customer pay?

2) A tailor charges £30 for a suit of clothes but allows a discount of 5% for cash. What is the cash price?

3) A grocer offers a discount of $2\frac{1}{2}\%$ to his customers provided their bills are paid within one week. If a bill of £7.25 is paid within one week, how much discount will the grocer allow?

4) A shop offers a discount of 5 p in the £1. How much discount will be allowed on a washing machine costing £85?

5) A furniture store offers a discount of 7 p in the £1 for cash sales. A cus-tomer buys a three piece suite priced at £285. How much will she actually pay?

Exercise 52 — *Questions 1–18 type A, remainder B*

All the questions in this exercise have been taken from past C.S.E. examina-tion papers.

1) What percentage is £2.40 of £5.00?
(*S*)

2) A radio originally bought for £11.56 four years ago is sold for 25% of its cost. For how much is it sold? (*S*)

3) Last year I spent, on average, £24 per week on my weekly shopping. This year I spent £28.80 per week. Find the

percentage increase in my weekly
shopping bill. (S)

4) Find 8% of £6.55 giving the
answer to the nearest penny. (S)

5) Express $\frac{1}{4}$ as a percentage. (S)

6) A case of apples weighing 15 kg
costs £3.30. At what price per kilogram must they be sold in order to
make a profit of £1.50 on the case? (S)

7) Find 35% of 1500 grams. (E.M.)

8) What is 0.75% of £1600? (E.M.)

9) Deduct 10% discount from a coat
priced at £80.60. (E.M.)

10) In a sale all prices are reduced by
5 p in the £. Calculate the sale price of
an article which would normally cost
£28. (A.L.)

11) $\frac{9}{10}$ as a percentage is:

    a 0.9%   **b** 9%   **c** 99%
    d 90%   (A.L.)

12) The word *discount* means:

a Money put down on an article
    bought on H.P.
b Money taken out of your wage.
c Money taken off the price of an
    article.
d Money owed to someone. (A.L.)

13) $\frac{3}{40}$ as a percentage is:

    a 3%   **b** $7\frac{1}{2}$%   **c** 40%
    d 75%   **e** 97%   . (W.Y.)

14) A boy scored 70% in a test. If the
maximum mark was 40, then the boy's
mark was

    a 4   **b** 10   **c** 28
    d 30   **e** 35   (W.Y.)

15) During a sale, a shop reduced the
price of everything by 10%. What was

the sale price of an article originally
priced at £4.30?

    a £0.43   **b** £3.40   **c** £3.87
    d £3.97   **e** £4.73   (W.Y.)

16) For his holidays a man put aside
10% of his £50 weekly wage for 40
weeks in the year. How much did he
save for his holiday?

    a £200   **b** £100   **c** £50
    d £500   **e** £150   (N.W.)

17) A special offer of 2 p off the nor-
mal selling price of 25 p for a packet of
biscuits is made. What percentage
reduction does this represent? (S)

18) In a sale, a discount of 10 p in the
£ is allowed off all marked prices. The
price of a pair of girl's shoes is marked
at £6.50. For how much can the shoes
be bought in the sale? (M)

19) A girl bought a record for 75 p
and sold it for 60 p.

(a) Her loss, as a percentage of the
    cost price, is:
    a 15%   **b** 20%   **c** 60%
    d 75%

(b) For what price should she have
    sold the record to make a profit of
    20% on her cost price of 75%?
    a 95 p   **b** 90 p   **c** 80 p
    d 72 p

(c) The shopkeeper from whom she
    bought the record made a profit of
    50% on his cost price. How much
    did the record cost him?
    a 25 p   **b** $37\frac{1}{2}$ p   **c** 50 p
    d £1.25   (A.L.)

20) 8% of a sum of money is equal to
£9.60. Find:

(a) 1% of the sum of money.
(b) The sum of money.
(c) 92% of the sum of money. (W)

Chapter 7 Averages

To find the average of a set of quantities, add the quantities together and divide by the number of quantities in the set. Thus:

$$\text{average} = \frac{\text{sum of the quantities}}{\text{number of quantities}}$$

Example 1

A batsman makes the following scores at cricket: 8, 20, 3, 0, 5, 9, 15 and 12. What is his average score.

Average score

$$= \frac{8+20+3+0+5+9+15+12}{8}$$

$$= \frac{72}{8} = 9$$

Thus the batsman has an average score of 9 runs per innings.

Example 2

The apples in a box have a mass of 4.68 kg. If each apple has a mass of 97.5 g on the average, how many apples are there in the box?

Total mass = average mass of an apple × number of apples in the box

Number of apples in the box

$$= \frac{\text{total mass}}{\text{average mass of an apple}}$$

$$= \frac{4680}{97.5} = 48$$

Example 3

Find the average age of a team of girls given that 4 of them are each 15 years 4 months and the other three girls are each 14 years 9 months old.

Total age of 4 girls at 15 years 4 months each

$= 4 \times 15$ years 4 months

$= 61$ years 4 months

Total age of 3 girls at 14 years 9 months

$= 3 \times 14$ years 9 months

$= 44$ years 3 months

Total age of 7 girls

$= 61$ years 4 months

$\quad + 44$ years 3 months

$= 105$ years 7 months

Average age $= \dfrac{105 \text{ years 7 months}}{7}$

$\qquad\quad = 15$ years 1 month

Example 4

200 candidates sat for an examination and the average mark was 62. If the top 70 gained an average mark of 87 and the bottom 50 gained an average mark of 42 what was the average mark for the remainder of the candidates?

Total marks gained by all the candidates $= 200 \times 62 = 12\,400$

Marks gained by the top 70 candidates $= 70 \times 87 = 6090$

Marks gained by the bottom 50 candidates $= 50 \times 42 = 2100$

Marks gained by remaining 80 candidates $= 12\,400 - 6090 - 2100$

$\qquad = 4210$

Average mark gained by the remaining 80 candidates

$$= \frac{4210}{80} = 52.625$$

Exercise 53 — *Questions 1–4 type A, remainder B*

1) Find the average of the following measurements: 22.3, 22.5, 22.6, 21.8 and 22.0 mm.

2) Find the average of the following numbers: 95, 128, 38, 97 and 217.

3) A business employs 125 people. The wage bill for a certain week was £3537.50. What was the average wage?

4) A batsman's average for 20 innings is 16.2 runs. How many runs did he score altogether?

5) 12 metal castings have a mass of 12 kg each and 8 have a mass of $12\frac{1}{2}$ kg. Find the average mass of the 20 castings.

6) In an office 5 people earn a wage of £36 each, 3 earn a wage of £40 each and 2 earn a wage of £42 each. Calculate the average wage.

7) The average of nine numbers is 72 and the average of four of them is 40. What is the average of the other five?

8) Find the average of a team of boys if 5 of them are each 15 years old and the other 6 are each 14 years 1 month old.

9) The average of three numbers is 58 and the average of two of them is 49. Calculate the third number.

10) A grocer sells 40 tins of soup at 8 p per tin, 50 at 9 p per tin and 60 tins at 10 p per tin. Find the average price per tin.

Exercise 54 — *Questions 1–7 type A, remainder B*

All the questions in this exercise have been taken from past C.S.E. examination papers.

1) What is the average of 0, 1, 6, 7, 9 and 19?

2) The average weight of four parcels is 8.5 kg. Three of these parcels weigh 7.6 kg, 7.8 kg and 8.3 kg respectively.

(a) What is the average weight of the three parcels whose weights are given?
(b) What is the weight of the fourth parcel? (*A.L.*)

3) Calculate the average age of four people whose ages are 16 years 6 months, 16 years 0 months, 17 years 2 months and 16 years 8 months. (*A.L.*)

4) A cricketer bats seven times and makes the following scores: 0, 3, 3, 6, 20, 21 and 24. Calculate his mean (average) score. (*A.L.*)

5) What is the average of 21, 23, 25, 27 and 29? (*E.M.*)

6) Find the average of the numbers 1.2, 2.3, 4.5 and 5.6. (*S*)

7) A group of four people measured themselves and found that their heights were 1.38 m, 1.71 m, 1.23 m and 1.40 m. Their average height (in metres) is:

     a 1.145   **b** 1.18   **c** 1.39

     d 1.405   **e** 1.43   (*M*)

8) After nine mathematics tests, a girl had an average mark of exactly 12. If in her tenth test she obtained a mark of 17, what was her average mark for the ten tests? (*M*)

9) In three weeks a man earns £60, £50 and £58. His average weekly earnings for four weeks is £54. How much did he earn on the fourth week? (*S.W.*)

10) A group of four workmen had an average wage of £75. When a fifth man joined the group the average wage fell to £72. If the four original members were still being paid the same wages, how much was the newcomer earning? (*E.M.*)

Chapter 8 Squares, Square Roots, Reciprocals

Squares of Numbers

When a number is multiplied by itself the result is called the square of the number. The square of 9 is $9 \times 9 = 81$. Instead of writing 9×9 it is usual to write 9^2 which is read as the square of 9. Thus

$$12^2 = 12 \times 12 = 144$$
$$(1.3)^2 = 1.3 \times 1.3 = 1.69$$

The square of any number can be

Table of Squares

x	0	1	2	3	4	5	6	7	8	9	1	2	3	4	5	6	7	8	9
1.0	1.000	1.020	1.040	1.061	1.082	1.103	1.124	1.145	1.166	1.188	2	4	6	8	10	13	15	17	19
1.1	1.210	1.232	1.254	1.277	1.300	1.323	1.346	1.369	1.392	1.416	2	5	7	9	11	14	16	18	21
1.2	1.440	1.464	1.488	1.513	1.538	1.563	1.588	1.613	1.638	1.664	2	5	7	10	12	15	17	20	22
1.3	1.690	1.716	1.742	1.769	1.796	1.823	1.850	1.877	1.904	1.932	3	5	8	11	13	16	19	22	24
1.4	1.960	1.988	2.016	2.045	2.074	2.103	2.132	2.161	2.190	2.220	3	6	9	12	14	17	20	23	26
1.5	2.250	2.280	2.310	2.341	2.372	2.403	2.434	2.465	2.496	2.528	3	6	9	12	15	19	22	25	28
1.6	2.560	2.592	2.624	2.657	2.690	2.723	2.756	2.789	2.822	2.856	3	7	10	13	16	20	23	26	30
1.7	2.890	2.924	2.958	2.993	3.028	3.063	3.098	3.133	3.168	3.204	3	7	10	14	17	21	24	28	31
1.8	3.240	3.276	3.312	3.349	3.386	3.423	3.460	3.497	3.534	3.572	4	7	11	15	18	22	26	30	33
1.9	3.610	3.648	3.686	3.725	3.764	3.803	3.842	3.881	3.920	3.960	4	8	12	16	19	23	27	31	35
2.0	4.000	4.040	4.080	4.121	4.162	4.203	4.244	4.285	4.326	4.368	4	8	12	16	20	25	29	33	37
2.1	4.410	4.452	4.494	4.537	4.580	4.623	4.666	4.709	4.752	4.796	4	9	13	17	21	26	30	34	39
2.2	4.840	4.884	4.928	4.973	5.018	5.063	5.108	5.153	5.198	5.244	4	9	13	18	22	27	31	36	40
2.3	5.290	5.336	5.382	5.429	5.476	5.523	5.570	5.617	5.664	5.712	5	9	14	19	23	28	33	38	42
2.4	5.760	5.808	5.856	5.905	5.954	6.003	6.052	6.101	6.150	6.200	5	10	15	20	24	29	34	39	44
2.5	6.250	6.300	6.350	6.401	6.452	6.503	6.554	6.605	6.656	6.708	5	10	15	20	25	31	36	41	46
2.6	6.760	6.812	6.864	6.917	6.970	7.023	7.076	7.129	7.182	7.236	5	11	16	21	26	32	37	42	48
2.7	7.290	7.344	7.398	7.453	7.508	7.563	7.618	7.673	7.728	7.784	5	11	16	22	27	33	38	44	49
2.8	7.840	7.896	7.952	8.009	8.066	8.123	8.180	8.237	8.294	8.352	6	11	17	23	28	34	40	46	51
2.9	8.410	8.468	8.526	8.585	8.644	8.703	8.762	8.821	8.880	8.940	6	12	18	24	29	35	41	47	53
3.0	9.000	9.060	9.120	9.181	9.242	9.303	9.364	9.425	9.486	9.548	6	12	18	24	30	37	43	49	55
3.1	9.610	9.672	9.734	9.797	9.860	9.923	9.986	10.05	10.11	10.18	6	13	19	25	31	38	44	50	57
3.2	10.24	10.30	10.37	10.43	10.50	10.56	10.63	10.69	10.76	10.82	1	1	2	3	3	4	5	5	6
3.3	10.89	10.96	11.02	11.09	11.16	11.22	11.29	11.36	11.42	11.49	1	1	2	3	3	4	5	5	6
3.4	11.56	11.63	11.70	11.76	11.83	11.90	11.97	12.04	12.11	12.18	1	1	2	3	3	4	5	6	6
3.5	12.25	12.32	12.39	12.46	12.53	12.60	12.67	12.74	12.82	12.89	1	1	2	3	4	4	5	6	6
3.6	12.96	13.03	13.10	13.18	13.25	13.32	13.40	13.47	13.54	13.62	1	1	2	3	4	4	5	6	7
3.7	13.69	13.76	13.84	13.91	13.99	14.06	14.14	14.21	14.29	14.36	1	2	2	3	4	4	5	6	7
3.8	14.44	14.52	14.59	14.67	14.75	14.82	14.90	14.98	15.05	15.13	1	2	2	3	4	5	5	6	7
3.9	15.21	15.29	15.37	15.44	15.52	15.60	15.68	15.76	15.84	15.92	1	2	2	3	4	5	6	6	7
4.0	16.00	16.08	16.16	16.24	16.32	16.40	16.48	16.56	16.65	16.73	1	2	2	3	4	5	6	6	7
4.1	16.81	16.89	16.97	17.06	17.14	17.22	17.31	17.39	17.47	17.56	1	2	2	3	4	5	6	7	7
4.2	17.64	17.72	17.81	17.89	17.98	18.06	18.15	18.23	18.32	18.40	1	2	3	3	4	5	6	7	8
4.3	18.49	18.58	18.66	18.75	18.84	18.92	19.01	19.10	19.18	19.27	1	2	3	3	4	5	6	7	8
4.4	19.36	19.45	19.54	19.62	19.71	19.80	19.89	19.98	20.07	20.16	1	2	3	4	4	5	6	7	8
4.5	20.25	20.34	20.43	20.52	20.61	20.70	20.79	20.88	20.98	21.07	1	2	3	4	5	5	6	7	8
4.6	21.16	21.25	21.34	21.44	21.53	21.62	21.72	21.81	21.90	22.00	1	2	3	4	5	6	7	7	8
4.7	22.09	22.18	22.28	22.37	22.47	22.56	22.66	22.75	22.85	22.94	1	2	3	4	5	6	7	8	9
4.8	23.04	23.14	23.23	23.33	23.43	23.52	23.62	23.72	23.81	23.91	1	2	3	4	5	6	7	8	9
4.9	24.01	24.11	24.21	24.30	24.40	24.50	24.60	24.70	24.80	24.90	1	2	3	4	5	6	7	8	9
5.0	25.00	25.10	25.20	25.30	25.40	25.50	25.60	25.70	25.81	25.91	1	2	3	4	5	6	7	8	9
5.1	26.01	26.11	26.21	26.32	26.42	26.52	26.63	26.73	26.83	26.94	1	2	3	4	5	6	7	8	9
5.2	27.04	27.14	27.25	27.35	27.46	27.56	27.67	27.77	27.88	27.98	1	2	3	4	5	6	7	8	9
5.3	28.09	28.20	28.30	28.41	28.52	28.62	28.73	28.84	28.94	29.05	1	2	3	4	5	6	7	9	10
5.4	29.16	29.27	29.38	29.48	29.59	29.70	29.81	29.92	30.03	30.14	1	2	3	4	5	7	8	9	10

found by multiplication but a great deal of time and effort is saved by using printed tables. Either three or four figure tables may be used. In the three figure tables the squares of numbers are given correct to three significant figures, but in the four figure tables the squares are given correct to four significant figures. Hence the four figure tables are more accurate.

Although the tables only give the squares of numbers from 1 to 10 they can be used to find the squares of numbers outside this range. The method is shown in the examples which follow.

Example 1

Find $(168.8)^2$

$(168.8)^2 = 168.8 \times 168.8$

$\qquad = 1.688 \times 100 \times 1.688 \times 100$

$\qquad = (1.688)^2 \times 100^2$

From the tables of squares,
$\qquad (1.688)^2 = 2.848$

Table of Squares

x	0	1	2	3	4	5	6	7	8	9	1	2	3	4	5	6	7	8	9
5.5	30.25	30.36	30.47	30.58	30.69	30.80	30.91	31.02	31.14	31.25	1	2	3	4	6	7	8	9	10
5.6	31.36	31.47	31.58	31.70	31.81	31.92	32.04	32.15	32.26	32.38	1	2	3	5	6	7	8	9	10
5.7	32.49	32.60	32.72	32.83	32.95	33.06	33.18	33.29	33.41	33.52	1	2	3	5	6	7	8	9	10
5.8	33.64	33.76	33.87	33.99	34.11	34.22	34.34	34.46	34.57	34.69	1	2	4	5	6	7	8	9	11
5.9	34.81	34.93	35.05	35.16	35.28	35.40	35.52	35.64	35.76	35.88	1	2	4	5	6	7	8	10	11
6.0	36.00	36.12	36.24	36.36	36.48	36.60	36.72	36.84	36.97	37.09	1	2	4	5	6	7	9	10	11
6.1	37.21	37.33	37.45	37.58	37.70	37.82	37.95	38.07	38.19	38.32	1	2	4	5	6	7	9	10	11
6.2	38.44	38.56	38.69	38.81	38.94	39.06	39.19	39.31	39.44	39.56	1	3	4	5	6	8	9	10	11
6.3	39.69	39.82	39.94	40.07	40.20	40.32	40.45	40.58	40.70	40.83	1	3	4	5	6	8	9	10	11
6.4	40.96	41.09	41.22	41.34	41.47	41.60	41.73	41.86	41.99	42.12	1	3	4	5	6	8	9	10	12
6.5	42.25	42.38	42.51	42.64	42.77	42.90	43.03	43.16	43.30	43.43	1	3	4	5	7	8	9	10	12
6.6	43.56	43.69	43.82	43.96	44.09	44.22	44.36	44.49	44.62	44.76	1	3	4	5	7	8	9	11	12
6.7	44.89	45.02	45.16	45.29	45.43	45.56	45.70	45.83	45.97	46.10	1	3	4	5	7	8	9	11	12
6.8	46.24	46.38	46.51	46.65	46.79	46.92	47.06	47.20	47.33	47.47	1	3	4	5	7	8	10	11	12
6.9	47.61	47.75	47.89	48.02	48.16	48.30	48.44	48.58	48.72	48.86	1	3	4	6	7	8	10	11	13
7.0	49.00	49.14	49.28	49.42	49.56	49.70	49.84	49.98	50.13	50.27	1	3	4	6	7	8	10	11	13
7.1	50.41	50.55	50.69	50.84	50.98	51.12	51.27	51.41	51.55	51.70	1	3	4	6	7	9	10	11	13
7.2	51.84	51.98	52.13	52.27	52.42	52.56	52.71	52.85	53.00	53.14	1	3	4	6	7	9	10	12	13
7.3	53.29	53.44	53.58	53.73	53.88	54.02	54.17	54.32	54.46	54.61	1	3	4	6	7	9	10	12	13
7.4	54.76	54.91	55.06	55.20	55.35	55.50	55.65	55.80	55.95	56.10	1	3	4	6	7	9	10	12	13
7.5	56.25	56.40	56.55	56.70	56.85	57.00	57.15	57.30	57.46	57.61	2	3	5	6	8	9	11	12	14
7.6	57.76	57.91	58.06	58.22	58.37	58.52	58.68	58.83	58.98	59.14	2	3	5	6	8	9	11	12	14
7.7	59.29	59.44	59.60	59.75	59.91	60.06	60.22	60.37	60.53	60.68	2	3	5	6	8	9	11	12	14
7.8	60.84	61.00	61.15	61.31	61.47	61.62	61.78	61.94	62.09	62.25	2	3	5	6	8	9	11	13	14
7.9	62.41	62.57	62.73	62.88	63.04	63.20	63.36	63.52	63.68	63.84	2	3	5	6	8	10	11	13	14
8.0	64.00	64.16	64.32	64.48	64.64	64.80	64.96	65.12	65.29	65.45	2	3	5	6	8	10	11	13	14
8.1	65.61	65.77	65.93	66.10	66.26	66.42	67.59	66.75	66.91	67.08	2	3	5	7	8	10	11	13	15
8.2	67.24	67.40	67.57	67.73	67.90	68.06	68.23	68.39	68.56	68.72	2	3	5	7	8	10	12	13	15
8.3	68.89	69.06	69.22	69.39	69.56	69.72	69.89	70.06	70.22	70.39	2	3	5	7	8	10	12	13	15
8.4	70.56	70.73	70.90	71.06	71.23	71.40	71.57	71.74	71.91	72.08	2	3	5	7	8	10	12	14	15
8.5	72.25	72.42	72.59	72.76	72.93	73.10	73.27	73.44	73.62	73.79	2	3	5	7	9	10	12	14	15
8.6	73.96	74.13	74.30	74.48	74.65	74.82	75.00	75.17	75.34	75.52	2	3	5	7	9	10	12	14	16
8.7	75.69	75.86	76.04	76.21	76.39	76.56	76.74	76.91	77.09	77.26	2	4	5	7	9	11	12	14	16
8.8	77.44	77.62	77.79	77.97	78.15	78.32	78.50	78.68	78.85	79.03	2	4	5	7	9	11	12	14	16
8.9	79.21	79.39	79.57	79.74	79.92	80.10	80.28	80.46	80.64	80.82	2	4	5	7	9	11	13	14	16
9.0	81.00	81.18	81.36	81.54	81.72	81.90	82.08	82.26	82.45	82.63	2	4	5	7	9	11	13	14	16
9.1	82.81	82.99	83.17	83.36	83.54	83.72	83.91	84.09	84.27	84.46	2	4	5	7	9	11	13	15	16
9.2	84.64	84.82	85.01	85.19	85.38	85.56	85.75	85.93	86.12	86.30	2	4	6	7	9	11	13	15	17
9.3	86.49	86.68	86.86	87.05	87.24	87.42	87.61	87.80	87.98	88.17	2	4	6	7	9	11	13	15	17
9.4	88.36	88.55	88.74	88.92	89.11	89.30	89.49	89.68	89.87	90.06	2	4	6	8	9	11	13	15	17
9.5	90.25	90.44	90.63	90.82	91.01	91.20	91.39	91.58	91.78	91.97	2	4	6	8	10	11	13	15	17
9.6	92.16	92.35	92.54	92.74	92.93	93.12	93.32	93.51	93.70	93.90	2	4	6	8	10	12	14	15	17
9.7	94.09	94.28	94.48	94.67	94.87	95.06	95.26	95.45	95.65	95.84	2	4	6	8	10	12	14	16	18
9.8	96.04	96.24	96.43	96.63	96.83	97.02	97.22	97.42	97.61	97.81	2	4	6	8	10	12	14	16	18
9.9	98.01	98.21	98.41	98.60	98.80	99.00	99.20	99.40	99.60	99.80	2	4	6	8	10	12	14	16	18

Hence $(168.8)^2 = 2.848 \times 100^2$

$\qquad = 28\,480$

Example 2

Find $(0.2388)^2$

$(0.2388)^2 = 2.388 \times \dfrac{1}{10} \times 2.388 \times \dfrac{1}{10}$

$\qquad = (2.388)^2 \times \dfrac{1}{100} = (2.388)^2 \div 100$

From the tables $\quad (2.388)^2 = 5.702$

Hence $\quad (0.2388)^2 \qquad = 5.702 \div 100$

$\qquad\qquad\qquad\qquad = 0.057\,02$

Exercise 55 — *Questions 1–12 type A, remainder B*

Find the square of the following numbers.

1) 1.5	**8)** 7.916	**15)** 98.12
2) 2.1	**9)** 8.017	**16)** 0.019
3) 8.6	**10)** 8.704	**17)** 0.7292
4) 3.15	**11)** 23	**18)** 0.004 219
5) 7.68	**12)** 40.6	**19)** 0.2834
6) 5.23	**13)** 3093	**20)** 0.000 578 4
7) 4.263	**14)** 112.3	

Table of Square Roots from 1–10

	0	1	2	3	4	5	6	7	8	9	1	2	3	4	5	6	7	8	9
1.0	1.000	1.005	1.010	1.015	1.020	1.025	1.030	1.034	1.039	1.044	0	1	1	2	2	3	3	4	4
1.1	1.049	1.054	1.058	1.063	1.068	1.072	1.077	1.082	1.086	1.091	0	1	1	2	2	3	3	4	4
1.2	1.095	1.100	1.105	1.109	1.114	1.118	1.122	1.127	1.131	1.136	0	1	1	2	2	3	3	4	4
1.3	1.140	1.145	1.149	1.153	1.158	1.162	1.166	1.170	1.175	1.179	0	1	1	2	2	3	3	3	4
1.4	1.183	1.187	1.192	1.196	1.200	1.204	1.208	1.212	1.217	1.221	0	1	1	2	2	3	3	3	4
1.5	1.225	1.229	1.233	1.237	1.241	1.245	1.249	1.253	1.257	1.261	0	1	1	2	2	2	3	3	4
1.6	1.265	1.269	1.273	1.277	1.281	1.285	1.288	1.292	1.296	1.300	0	1	1	2	2	2	3	3	3
1.7	1.304	1.308	1.311	1.315	1.319	1.323	1.327	1.330	1.334	1.338	0	1	1	1	2	2	3	3	3
1.8	1.342	1.345	1.349	1.353	1.356	1.360	1.364	1.367	1.371	1.375	0	1	1	1	2	2	3	3	3
1.9	1.378	1.382	1.386	1.389	1.393	1.396	1.400	1.404	1.407	1.411	0	1	1	1	2	2	3	3	3
2.0	1.414	1.418	1.421	1.425	1.428	1.432	1.435	1.439	1.442	1.446	0	1	1	1	2	2	2	3	3
2.1	1.449	1.453	1.456	1.459	1.463	1.466	1.470	1.473	1.476	1.480	0	1	1	1	2	2	2	3	3
2.2	1.483	1.487	1.490	1.493	1.497	1.500	1.503	1.507	1.510	1.513	0	1	1	1	2	2	2	3	3
2.3	1.517	1.520	1.523	1.526	1.530	1.533	1.536	1.539	1.543	1.546	0	1	1	1	2	2	2	2	3
2.4	1.549	1.552	1.556	1.559	1.562	1.565	1.568	1.572	1.575	1.578	0	1	1	1	2	2	2	2	3
2.5	1.581	1.584	1.587	1.591	1.594	1.597	1.600	1.603	1.606	1.609	0	1	1	1	2	2	2	2	3
2.6	1.612	1.616	1.619	1.622	1.625	1.628	1.631	1.634	1.637	1.640	0	1	1	1	2	2	2	2	3
2.7	1.643	1.646	1.649	1.652	1.655	1.658	1.661	1.664	1.667	1.670	0	1	1	1	2	2	2	2	3
2.8	1.673	1.676	1.679	1.682	1.685	1.688	1.691	1.694	1.697	1.700	0	1	1	1	2	2	2	2	3
2.9	1.703	1.706	1.709	1.712	1.715	1.718	1.720	1.723	1.726	1.729	0	1	1	1	1	2	2	2	3
3.0	1.732	1.735	1.738	1.741	1.744	1.746	1.749	1.752	1.755	1.758	0	1	1	1	1	2	2	2	3
3.1	1.761	1.764	1.766	1.769	1.772	1.775	1.778	1.780	1.783	1.786	0	1	1	1	1	2	2	2	3
3.2	1.789	1.792	1.794	1.797	1.800	1.803	1.806	1.808	1.811	1.814	0	1	1	1	1	2	2	2	2
3.3	1.817	1.819	1.822	1.825	1.828	1.830	1.833	1.836	1.838	1.841	0	1	1	1	1	2	2	2	2
3.4	1.844	1.847	1.849	1.852	1.855	1.857	1.860	1.863	1.865	1.868	0	1	1	1	1	2	2	2	2
3.5	1.871	1.873	1.876	1.879	1.881	1.884	1.887	1.889	1.892	1.895	0	1	1	1	1	2	2	2	2
3.6	1.897	1.900	1.903	1.905	1.908	1.910	1.913	1.916	1.918	1.921	0	1	1	1	1	2	2	2	2
3.7	1.924	1.926	1.929	1.931	1.934	1.936	1.939	1.942	1.944	1.947	0	1	1	1	1	2	2	2	2
3.8	1.949	1.952	1.954	1.957	1.960	1.962	1.965	1.967	1.970	1.972	0	1	1	1	1	2	2	2	2
3.9	1.975	1.977	1.980	1.982	1.985	1.987	1.990	1.992	1.995	1.997	0	0	1	1	1	1	2	2	2
4.0	2.000	2.002	2.005	2.007	2.010	2.012	2.015	2.017	2.020	2.022	0	0	1	1	1	1	2	2	2
4.1	2.025	2.027	2.030	2.032	2.035	2.037	2.040	2.042	2.045	2.047	0	0	1	1	1	1	2	2	2
4.2	2.049	2.052	2.054	2.057	2.059	2.062	2.064	2.066	2.069	2.071	0	0	1	1	1	1	2	2	2
4.3	2.074	2.076	2.078	2.081	2.083	2.086	2.088	2.090	2.093	2.095	0	0	1	1	1	1	1	2	2
4.4	2.098	2.100	2.102	2.105	2.107	2.110	2.112	2.114	2.117	2.119	0	0	1	1	1	1	1	2	2
4.5	2.121	2.124	2.126	2.128	2.131	2.133	2.135	2.138	2.140	2.142	0	0	1	1	1	1	1	2	2
4.6	2.145	2.147	2.149	2.152	2.154	2.156	2.159	2.161	2.163	2.166	0	0	1	1	1	1	1	2	2
4.7	2.168	2.170	2.173	2.175	2.177	2.179	2.182	2.184	2.186	2.189	0	0	1	1	1	1	1	2	2
4.8	2.191	2.193	2.195	2.198	2.200	2.202	2.205	2.207	2.209	2.211	0	0	1	1	1	1	1	2	2
4.9	2.214	2.216	2.218	2.220	2.223	2.225	2.227	2.229	2.232	2.234	0	0	1	1	1	1	1	2	2
5.0	2.236	2.238	2.241	2.243	2.245	2.247	2.249	2.252	2.254	2.256	0	0	1	1	1	1	1	2	2
5.1	2.258	2.261	2.263	2.265	2.267	2.269	2.272	2.274	2.276	2.278	0	0	1	1	1	1	1	2	2
5.2	2.280	2.283	2.285	2.287	2.289	2.291	2.293	2.296	2.298	2.300	0	0	1	1	1	1	1	2	2
5.3	2.302	2.304	2.307	2.309	2.311	2.313	2.315	2.317	2.319	2.322	0	0	1	1	1	1	1	2	2
5.4	2.324	2.326	2.328	2.330	2.332	2.335	2.337	2.339	2.341	2.343	0	0	1	1	1	1	1	2	2

Square Roots

The square root of a number is the number whose square equals the given number. Thus since $5^2 = 25$, the square root of $25 = 5$. The sign $\sqrt{}$ is used to denote a square root and hence we write $\sqrt{25} = 5$.

Similarly, since $9^2 = 81$, $\sqrt{81} = 9$.

The square root of a number can usually be found with sufficient accuracy by using the printed tables of square roots. There are two of these tables.

One gives the square roots of numbers 1 to 10 (*see pages 48 and 49*) and the other gives the square roots of numbers from 10 to 100 (*see pages 50 and 51*). The reason for having two tables is as follows:

$$\sqrt{2.5} = 1.581$$

$$\sqrt{25} = 5$$

Thus there are two square roots for the same figures, depending upon the position of the decimal point. The square root tables are used in the same way as the table of squares.

Table of Square Roots from 1–10

	0	1	2	3	4	5	6	7	8	9	1	2	3	4	5	6	7	8	9
5.5	2.345	2.347	2.349	2.352	2.354	2.356	2.358	2.360	2.362	2.364	0	0	1	1	1	1	1	2	2
5.6	2.366	2.369	2.371	2.373	2.375	2.377	2.379	2.381	2.383	2.385	0	0	1	1	1	1	1	2	2
5.7	2.387	2.390	2.392	2.394	2.396	2.398	2.400	2.402	2.404	2.406	0	0	1	1	1	1	1	2	2
5.8	2.408	2.410	2.412	2.415	2.417	2.419	2.421	2.423	2.425	2.427	0	0	1	1	1	1	1	2	2
5.9	2.429	2.431	2.433	2.435	2.437	2.439	2.441	2.443	2.445	2.447	0	0	1	1	1	1	1	2	2
6.0	2.449	2.452	2.454	2.456	2.458	2.460	2.462	2.464	2.466	2.468	0	0	1	1	1	1	1	2	2
6.1	2.470	2.472	2.474	2.476	2.478	2.480	2.482	2.484	2.486	2.488	0	0	1	1	1	1	1	2	2
6.2	2.490	2.492	2.494	2.496	2.498	2.500	2.502	2.504	2.506	2.508	0	0	1	1	1	1	1	2	2
6.3	2.510	2.512	2.514	2.516	2.518	2.520	2.522	2.524	2.526	2.528	0	0	1	1	1	1	1	2	2
6.4	2.530	2.532	2.534	2.536	2.538	2.540	2.542	2.544	2.546	2.548	0	0	1	1	1	1	1	2	2
6.5	2.550	2.551	2.553	2.555	2.557	2.559	2.561	2.563	2.565	2.567	0	0	1	1	1	1	1	2	2
6.6	2.569	2.571	2.573	2.575	2.577	2.579	2.581	2.583	2.585	2.587	0	0	1	1	1	1	1	2	2
6.7	2.588	2.590	2.592	2.594	2.596	2.598	2.600	2.602	2.604	2.606	0	0	1	1	1	1	1	2	2
6.8	2.608	2.610	2.612	2.613	2.615	2.617	2.619	2.621	2.623	2.625	0	0	1	1	1	1	1	2	2
6.9	2.627	2.629	2.631	2.632	2.634	2.636	2.638	2.640	2.642	2.644	0	0	1	1	1	1	1	2	2
7.0	2.646	2.648	2.650	2.651	2.653	2.655	2.657	2.659	2.661	2.663	0	0	1	1	1	1	1	2	2
7.1	2.665	2.666	2.668	2.670	2.672	2.674	2.676	2.678	2.680	2.681	0	0	1	1	1	1	1	2	2
7.2	2.683	2.685	2.687	2.689	2.691	2.693	2.694	2.696	2.698	2.700	0	0	1	1	1	1	1	2	2
7.3	2.702	2.704	2.706	2.707	2.709	2.711	2.713	2.715	2.717	2.718	0	0	1	1	1	1	1	2	2
7.4	2.720	2.722	2.724	2.726	2.728	2.729	2.731	2.733	2.735	2.737	0	0	1	1	1	1	1	2	2
7.5	2.739	2.740	2.742	2.744	2.746	2.748	2.750	2.751	2.753	2.755	0	0	1	1	1	1	1	2	2
7.6	2.757	2.759	2.760	2.762	2.764	2.766	2.768	2.769	2.771	2.773	0	0	1	1	1	1	1	2	2
7.7	2.775	2.777	2.778	2.780	2.782	2.784	2.786	2.787	2.789	2.791	0	0	1	1	1	1	1	2	2
7.8	2.793	2.795	2.796	2.798	2.800	2.802	2.804	2.805	2.807	2.809	0	0	1	1	1	1	1	2	2
7.9	2.811	2.812	2.814	2.816	2.818	2.820	2.821	2.823	2.825	2.827	0	0	1	1	1	1	1	2	2
8.0	2.828	2.830	2.832	2.834	2.835	2.837	2.839	2.841	2.843	2.844	0	0	1	1	1	1	1	2	2
8.1	2.846	2.848	2.850	2.851	2.853	2.855	2.857	2.858	2.860	2.862	0	0	1	1	1	1	1	2	2
8.2	2.864	2.865	2.867	2.869	2.871	2.872	2.874	2.876	2.877	2.879	0	0	1	1	1	1	1	2	2
8.3	2.881	2.883	2.884	2.886	2.888	2.890	2.891	2.893	2.895	2.897	0	0	1	1	1	1	1	2	2
8.4	2.898	2.900	2.902	2.903	2.905	2.907	2.909	2.910	2.912	2.914	0	0	1	1	1	1	1	2	2
8.5	2.915	2.917	2.919	2.921	2.922	2.924	2.926	2.927	2.929	2.931	0	0	1	1	1	1	1	2	2
8.6	2.933	2.934	2.936	2.938	2.941	2.943	2.944	2.946	2.948		0	0	1	1	1	1	1	2	2
8.7	2.950	2.951	2.953	2.955	2.956	2.958	2.960	2.961	2.963	2.965	0	0	1	1	1	1	1	2	2
8.8	2.966	2.968	2.970	2.972	2.973	2.975	2.977	2.978	2.980	2.982	0	0	1	1	1	1	1	2	2
8.9	2.983	2.985	2.987	2.988	2.990	2.992	2.993	2.995	2.997	2.998	0	0	1	1	1	1	1	2	2
9.0	3.000	3.002	3.003	3.005	3.007	3.008	3.010	3.012	3.013	3.015	0	0	0	1	1	1	1	1	1
9.1	3.017	3.018	3.020	3.022	3.023	3.025	3.027	3.028	3.030	3.032	0	0	0	1	1	1	1	1	1
9.2	3.033	3.035	3.036	3.038	3.040	3.041	3.043	3.045	3.046	3.048	0	0	0	1	1	1	1	1	1
9.3	3.050	3.051	3.053	3.055	3.056	3.058	3.059	3.061	3.063	3.064	0	0	0	1	1	1	1	1	1
9.4	3.066	3.068	3.069	3.071	3.072	3.074	3.076	3.077	3.079	3.081	0	0	0	1	1	1	1	1	1
9.5	3.082	3.084	3.085	3.087	3.089	3.090	3.092	3.094	3.095	3.097	0	0	0	1	1	1	1	1	1
9.6	3.098	3.100	3.102	3.103	3.105	3.106	3.108	3.110	3.111	3.113	0	0	0	1	1	1	1	1	1
9.7	3.114	3.116	3.118	3.119	3.121	3.122	3.124	3.126	3.127	3.129	0	0	0	1	1	1	1	1	1
9.8	3.130	3.132	3.134	3.135	3.137	3.138	3.140	3.142	3.143	3.145	0	0	0	1	1	1	1	1	1
9.9	3.146	3.148	3.150	3.151	3.153	3.154	3.156	3.158	3.159	3.161	0	0	0	1	1	1	1	1	1

Example 3

a) $\sqrt{2.748} = 1.657$ (directly from the tables from 1 to 10)

b) $\sqrt{92.65} = 9.626$ (directly from the tables from 10 to 100)

c) To find $\sqrt{836.3}$

Mark off the figures in pairs to the *left* of the decimal point. Each pair of figures is called a *period*. Thus 836.3 becomes 8'36.3. The first period is 8 so we use the table of square roots from 1 to 10 and look up $\sqrt{8.363} = 2.892$. To

position the decimal point in the answer remember that for each period to the left of the decimal point in the original number there will be one figure to the left of the decimal point in the answer. Thus

$$\frac{2\ 8.92}{8'36.3}$$

$$\sqrt{836.3} = 28.92$$

d) To find $\sqrt{173\,900}$

Marking off in periods $173\,900$ becomes $17'39'00$. The first period is 17

Table of Square Roots from 10–100

x	0	1	2	3	4	5	6	7	8	9	1	2	3	4	5	6	7	8	9
10	3.162	3.178	3.194	3.209	3.225	3.240	3.256	3.271	3.286	3.302	2	3	5	6	8	10	11	13	14
11	3.317	3.332	3.347	3.362	3.376	3.391	3.406	3.421	3.435	3.450	1	3	4	6	7	9	10	12	13
12	3.464	3.479	3.493	3.507	3.521	3.536	3.550	3.564	3.578	3.592	1	3	4	6	7	8	10	11	13
13	3.606	3.619	3.633	3.647	3.661	3.674	3.688	3.701	3.715	3.728	1	3	4	5	7	8	10	11	12
14	3.742	3.755	3.768	3.782	3.795	3.808	3.821	3.834	3.847	3.860	1	3	4	5	7	8	9	10	12
15	3.873	3.886	3.899	3.912	3.924	3.937	3.950	3.962	3.975	3.987	1	3	4	5	6	8	9	10	11
16	4.000	4.012	4.025	4.037	4.050	4.062	4.074	4.087	4.099	4.111	1	2	4	5	6	7	9	10	11
17	4.123	4.135	4.147	4.159	4.171	4.183	4.195	4.207	4.219	4.231	1	2	4	5	6	7	8	10	11
18	4.243	4.254	4.266	4.278	4.290	4.301	4.313	4.324	4.336	4.347	1	2	3	5	6	7	8	9	10
19	4.359	4.370	4.382	4.393	4.405	4.416	4.427	4.438	4.450	4.461	1	2	3	5	6	7	8	9	10
20	4.472	4.483	4.494	4.506	4.517	4.528	4.539	4.550	4.561	4.572	1	2	3	4	6	7	8	9	10
21	4.583	4.593	4.604	4.615	4.626	4.637	4.648	4.658	4.669	4.680	1	2	3	4	5	6	8	9	10
22	4.690	4.701	4.712	4.722	4.733	4.743	4.754	4.764	4.775	4.785	1	2	3	4	5	6	7	8	10
23	4.796	4.806	4.817	4.827	4.837	4.848	4.858	4.868	4.879	4.889	1	2	3	4	5	6	7	8	9
24	4.899	4.909	4.919	4.930	4.940	4.950	4.960	4.970	4.980	4.990	1	2	3	4	5	6	7	8	9
25	5.000	5.010	5.020	5.030	5.040	5.050	5.060	5.070	5.079	5.089	1	2	3	4	5	6	7	8	9
26	5.099	5.109	5.119	5.128	5.138	5.148	5.158	5.167	5.177	5.187	1	2	3	4	5	6	7	8	9
27	5.196	5.206	5.215	5.225	5.235	5.244	5.254	5.263	5.273	5.282	1	2	3	4	5	6	7	8	9
28	5.292	5.301	5.310	5.320	5.329	5.339	5.348	5.357	5.367	5.376	1	2	3	4	5	6	7	7	8
29	5.385	5.394	5.404	5.413	5.422	5.431	5.441	5.450	5.459	5.468	1	2	3	4	5	5	6	7	8
30	5.477	5.486	5.495	5.505	5.514	5.523	5.532	5.541	5.550	5.559	1	2	3	4	5	5	6	7	8
31	5.568	5.577	5.586	5.595	5.604	5.612	5.621	5.630	5.639	5.648	1	2	3	4	4	5	6	7	8
32	5.657	5.666	5.675	5.683	5.692	5.701	5.710	5.718	5.727	5.736	1	2	3	4	4	5	6	7	8
33	5.745	5.753	5.762	5.771	5.779	5.788	5.797	5.805	5.814	5.822	1	2	3	3	4	5	6	7	8
34	5.831	5.840	5.848	5.857	5.865	5.874	5.882	5.891	5.899	5.908	1	2	3	3	4	5	6	7	8
35	5.916	5.925	5.933	5.941	5.950	5.598	5.967	5.975	5.983	5.992	1	2	2	3	4	5	6	7	8
36	6.000	6.008	6.017	6.025	6.033	6.042	6.050	6.058	6.066	6.075	1	2	2	3	4	5	6	7	7
37	6.083	6.091	6.099	6.107	6.116	6.124	6.132	6.140	6.148	6.156	1	2	2	3	4	5	6	6	7
38	6.164	6.173	6.181	6.189	6.197	6.205	6.213	6.221	6.229	6.237	1	2	2	3	4	5	6	6	7
39	6.245	6.253	6.261	6.269	6.277	6.285	6.293	6.301	6.309	6.317	1	2	2	3	4	5	6	6	7
40	6.325	6.332	6.340	6.348	6.356	6.364	6.372	6.380	6.387	6.395	1	2	2	3	4	5	6	6	7
41	6.403	6.411	6.419	6.427	6.434	6.442	6.450	6.458	6.465	6.473	1	2	2	3	4	5	5	6	7
42	6.481	6.488	6.496	6.504	6.512	6.519	6.527	6.535	6.542	6.550	1	2	2	3	4	5	5	6	7
43	6.557	6.565	6.573	6.580	6.588	6.595	6.603	6.611	6.618	6.626	1	2	2	3	4	5	5	6	7
44	6.633	6.641	6.648	6.656	6.663	6.671	6.678	6.686	6.693	6.701	1	2	2	3	4	4	5	6	7
45	6.708	6.716	6.723	6.731	6.738	6.745	6.753	6.760	6.768	6.775	1	1	2	3	4	4	5	6	7
46	6.782	6.790	6.797	6.804	6.812	6.819	6.826	6.834	6.841	6.848	1	1	2	3	4	4	5	6	7
47	6.856	6.863	6.870	6.877	6.885	6.892	6.899	6.907	6.914	6.921	1	1	2	3	4	4	5	6	6
48	6.928	6.935	6.943	6.950	6.957	6.964	6.971	6.979	6.986	6.993	1	1	2	3	4	4	5	6	6
49	7.000	7.007	7.014	7.021	7.029	7.036	7.043	7.050	7.057	7.064	1	1	2	3	4	4	5	6	6
50	7.071	7.078	7.085	7.092	7.099	7.106	7.113	7.120	7.127	7.134	1	1	2	3	4	4	5	6	6
51	7.141	7.148	7.155	7.162	7.169	7.176	7.183	7.190	7.197	7.204	1	1	2	3	4	4	5	6	6
52	7.211	7.218	7.225	7.232	7.239	7.246	7.253	7.259	7.266	7.273	1	1	2	3	3	4	5	6	6
53	7.280	7.287	7.294	7.301	7.308	7.314	7.321	7.328	7.335	7.342	1	1	2	3	3	4	5	5	6
54	7.348	7.355	7.362	7.369	7.376	7.382	7.389	7.396	7.403	7.409	1	1	2	3	3	4	5	5	6

so we use the table of square roots from 10 to 100 and look up

$$\sqrt{17.3900} = 4.170$$

$$\frac{4\ 1\quad 7.0}{17'39'00}$$

$$\sqrt{173\,900} = 417.0$$

e) To find $\sqrt{0.000\,094\,31}$

In the case of numbers less than 1 mark off the periods to the right of the decimal point. 0.000 094 31 become 0.00'00'94'31. Apart from the zero pairs the first period is 94 so we use

the tables from 10 to 100 to look up $\sqrt{94.31} = 9.712$. For each zero pair in the original number there will be one zero following the decimal point in the answer. Thus

$$\frac{0.\ 0\ \ 0\,9\quad 712}{0.00'00'94'31}$$

$$\sqrt{0.000\,094\,31} = 0.009\,712$$

f) To find $\sqrt{0.073\,65}$

Marking off in periods to the right of the decimal point 0.073 65 becomes 07'36'50. Since the first period is 07 we

Table of Square Roots from 10–100

x	0	1	2	3	4	5	6	7	8	9	1	2	3	4	5	6	7	8	9
55	7.416	7.423	7.430	7.436	7.443	7.450	7.457	7.463	7.470	7.477	1	1	2	3	3	4	5	5	6
56	7.483	7.490	7.497	7.503	7.510	7.517	7.523	7.530	7.537	7.543	1	1	2	3	3	4	5	5	6
57	7.550	7.556	7.563	7.570	7.576	7.583	7.589	7.596	7.603	7.609	1	1	2	3	3	4	5	5	6
58	7.616	7.622	7.629	7.635	7.642	7.649	7.655	7.662	7.668	7.675	1	1	2	3	3	4	5	5	6
59	7.681	7.688	7.694	7.701	7.707	7.714	7.720	7.727	7.733	7.740	1	1	2	3	3	4	5	5	6
60	7.746	7.752	7.759	7.765	7.772	7.778	7.785	7.791	7.797	7.804	1	1	2	3	3	4	4	5	6
61	7.810	7.817	7.823	7.829	7.836	7.842	7.849	7.855	7.861	7.868	1	1	2	2	3	4	4	5	5
62	7.874	7.880	7.887	7.893	7.899	7.906	7.912	7.918	7.925	7.931	1	1	2	2	3	4	4	5	5
63	7.937	7.944	7.950	7.956	7.962	7.969	7.975	7.981	7.987	7.994	1	1	2	2	3	4	4	5	5
64	8.000	8.006	8.012	8.019	8.025	8.031	8.037	8.044	8.050	8.056	1	1	2	2	3	4	4	5	5
65	8.062	8.068	8.075	8.081	8.087	8.093	8.099	8.106	8.112	8.118	1	1	2	2	3	4	4	5	5
66	8.124	8.130	8.136	8.142	8.149	8.155	8.161	8.167	8.173	8.179	1	1	2	2	3	4	4	5	5
67	8.185	8.191	8.198	8.204	8.210	8.216	8.222	8.228	8.234	8.240	1	1	2	2	3	4	4	5	5
68	8.246	8.252	8.258	8.264	8.270	8.276	8.283	8.289	8.295	8.301	1	1	2	2	3	4	4	5	5
69	8.307	8.313	8.319	8.325	8.331	8.337	8.343	8.349	8.355	8.361	1	1	2	2	3	4	4	5	5
70	8.367	8.373	8.379	8.385	8.390	8.396	8.402	8.408	8.414	8.420	1	1	2	2	3	4	4	5	5
71	8.426	8.432	8.438	8.444	8.450	8.456	8.462	8.468	8.473	8.479	1	1	2	2	3	3	4	5	5
72	8.485	8.491	8.497	8.503	8.509	8.515	8.521	8.526	8.532	8.538	1	1	2	2	3	3	4	5	5
73	8.544	8.550	8.556	8.562	8.567	8.573	8.579	8.585	8.591	8.597	1	1	2	2	3	3	4	5	5
74	8.602	8.608	8.614	8.620	8.626	8.631	8.637	8.643	8.649	8.654	1	1	2	2	3	3	4	5	5
75	8.660	8.666	8.672	8.678	8.683	8.689	8.695	8.701	8.706	8.712	1	1	2	2	3	3	4	4	5
76	8.718	8.724	8.729	8.735	8.741	8.746	8.752	8.758	8.764	8.769	1	1	2	2	3	3	4	4	5
77	8.775	8.781	8.786	8.792	8.798	8.803	8.809	8.815	8.820	8.826	1	1	2	2	3	3	4	4	5
78	8.832	8.837	8.843	8.849	8.854	8.860	8.866	8.871	8.877	8.883	1	1	2	2	3	3	4	4	5
79	8.888	8.894	8.899	8.905	8.911	8.916	8.922	8.927	8.933	8.939	1	1	2	2	3	3	4	4	5
80	8.944	8.950	8.955	8.961	8.967	8.972	8.978	8.983	8.989	8.994	1	1	2	2	3	3	4	4	5
81	9.000	9.006	9.011	9.017	9.022	9.028	9.033	9.039	9.044	9.050	1	1	2	2	3	3	4	4	5
82	9.055	9.061	9.066	9.072	9.077	9.083	9.088	9.094	9.099	9.105	1	1	2	2	3	3	4	4	5
83	9.110	9.116	9.121	9.127	9.132	9.138	9.143	9.149	9.154	9.160	1	1	2	2	3	3	4	4	5
84	9.165	9.171	9.176	9.182	9.187	9.192	9.198	9.203	9.209	9.214	1	1	2	2	3	3	4	4	5
85	9.220	9.225	9.230	9.236	9.241	9.247	9.252	9.257	9.263	9.268	1	1	2	2	3	3	4	4	5
86	9.274	9.279	9.284	9.290	9.295	9.301	9.306	9.311	9.317	9.322	1	1	2	2	3	3	4	4	5
87	9.327	9.333	9.338	9.343	9.849	9.354	9.359	9.365	9.370	9.375	1	1	2	2	3	3	4	4	5
88	9.381	9.386	9.391	9.397	9.402	9.407	9.413	9.418	9.423	9.429	1	1	2	2	3	3	4	4	5
89	9.434	9.439	9.445	9.450	9.455	9.460	9.466	9.471	9.476	9.482	1	1	2	2	3	3	4	4	5
90	9.487	9.492	9.497	9.503	9.508	9.513	9.518	9.524	9.529	9.534	1	1	2	2	3	3	4	4	5
91	9.539	9.545	9.550	9.555	9.560	9.566	9.571	9.576	9.581	9.586	1	1	2	2	3	3	4	4	5
92	9.592	9.597	9.602	9.607	9.612	9.618	9.623	9.628	9.633	9.638	1	1	2	2	3	3	4	4	5
93	9.644	9.649	9.654	9.659	9.664	9.670	9.675	9.680	9.685	9.690	1	1	2	2	3	3	4	4	5
94	9.695	9.701	9.706	9.711	9.716	9.721	9.726	9.731	9.737	9.742	1	1	2	2	3	3	4	4	5
95	9.747	9.752	9.757	9.762	9.767	9.772	9.778	9.783	9.788	9.793	1	1	2	2	3	3	4	4	5
96	9.798	9.803	9.808	9.813	9.818	9.823	9.829	9.834	9.839	9.844	1	1	2	2	3	3	4	4	5
97	9.849	9.854	9.859	9.864	9.869	9.874	9.879	9.884	9.889	9.894	1	1	2	2	3	3	4	4	5
98	9.899	9.905	9.910	9.915	9.920	9.925	9.930	9.935	9.940	9.945	1	1	2	2	3	3	4	4	5
99	9.950	9.955	9.960	9.965	9.970	9.975	9.980	9.985	9.990	9.995	0	1	1	2	2	3	4	4	4

use the tables between 1 and 10 and look up $\sqrt{7.365} = 2.714$

$$
\begin{array}{r}
0. \ 2 \ \ 7\,14 \\
\overline{0.07'36'50}
\end{array}
$$

$$\sqrt{0.073\,65} = 0.2714$$

Exercise 56 — *Questions 1–12 type A, remainder B*

Find the square roots of the following numbers:

1)	3.4	13)	900
2)	8.19	14)	725.3
3)	5.264	15)	7142
4)	9.239	16)	89 000
5)	7.015	17)	3945
6)	3.009	18)	893 400 000
7)	35	19)	0.1537
8)	89.2	20)	0.001 698
9)	53.17	21)	0.039 47
10)	82.99	22)	0.000 783 1
11)	79.23	23)	0.001 978
12)	50.01		

The Square Root of a Product

The square root of a product is the product of the square roots. For example

$$\sqrt{4\times9} = \sqrt{4}\times\sqrt{9} = 2\times3 = 6$$

Also, $\sqrt{25\times16\times49}$

$$= \sqrt{25}\times\sqrt{16}\times\sqrt{49}$$

$$= 5\times4\times7$$

$$= 140$$

Exercise 57 — *All type A*

Find the values of the following:

1)	$\sqrt{4\times25}$	4)	$\sqrt{16\times36}$
2)	$\sqrt{9\times25}$	5)	$\sqrt{16\times25\times36}$
3)	$\sqrt{49\times49}$	6)	$\sqrt{4\times9\times25}$

7) $\sqrt{36\times49\times64}$

8) $\sqrt{4\times16\times25\times49\times81}$

The Square Root of a Fraction

To find the square root of a fraction, find the square roots of the numerator and denominator separately as shown in Example 4.

Example 4

Find the square root of $\dfrac{16}{25}$

$$\sqrt{\frac{16}{25}} = \frac{\sqrt{16}}{\sqrt{25}} = \frac{4}{5}$$

If the numbers under a square root sign are connected by a plus or a minus sign then we cannot find the square root by the methods used for products and quotients. We cannot say that $\sqrt{9+16} = \sqrt{9}+\sqrt{16} = 3+4 = 7$. We must add before finding the square root. Thus

$$\sqrt{9+16} = \sqrt{25} = 5$$

and $\qquad \sqrt{25-9} = \sqrt{16} = 4$

Exercise 58 — *Questions 1–5 type A, remainder B*

Find the square roots of the following:

1) $\dfrac{4}{9}$ 　　　　　 2) $\dfrac{9}{16}$

3) $\dfrac{25}{49}$ 10) $\dfrac{10}{360}$

4) $\dfrac{36}{81}$ 11) $25+144$

5) $\dfrac{81}{100}$ 12) $169-25$

6) $\dfrac{12}{27}$ 13) $25-16$

7) $\dfrac{100}{256}$ 14) $43+38$

8) $\dfrac{125}{245}$ 15) $65-29$

9) $\dfrac{48}{75}$

Reciprocals of Numbers

The reciprocal of a number is $\dfrac{1}{\text{number}}$.

Thus the reciprocal of $\ 5=\dfrac{1}{5}$

and the reciprocal of 21.3 is $\ \dfrac{1}{21.3}$.

The table of reciprocals of numbers is used in much the same way as the table of squares of numbers, except that the proportional parts are subtracted and not added. The table gives the reciprocals of numbers from 1 to 10 in decimal form.

From the tables (*see pages 54 and 55*):

the reciprocal of $\ 6=0.1667$

the reciprocal of $\ 3.157=0.3168$

The method of finding the reciprocals of numbers less than 1 or greater than 10 is shown in Example 5.

Example 5

a) To find the reciprocal of 639.2.

$$\dfrac{1}{639.2}=\dfrac{1}{6.392}\times\dfrac{1}{100}$$

From the table of reciprocals we find that the reciprocal of 6.392 is 0.1565

$$\dfrac{1}{639.2}=0.1565\times\dfrac{1}{100}$$

$$=\dfrac{0.1565}{100}=0.001\,565$$

b) To find the reciprocal of 0.039 82

$$\dfrac{1}{0.039\,82}=\dfrac{1}{3.982}\times\dfrac{100}{1}$$

From the table of reciprocals we find the reciprocal of 3.982 to be 0.2512.

$$\dfrac{1}{0.039\,82}=0.2512\times100=25.12$$

Exercise 59 — *Questions 1–8 type A, remainder B*

Find the reciprocals of the following numbers:

1) 3.4   9) 900

2) 8.19   10) 7142

3) 5.264   11) 0.1537

4) 9.239   12) 0.001 698

5) 7.015   13) 0.039 47

6) 35   14) 0.000 783 1

7) 89.2   15) 0.001 978

8) 53.17

Use of Tables in Calculations

Calculations may often be speeded up by making use of the tables of squares, square roots and reciprocals.

Example 6

Find the value of $\ \sqrt{(8.135)^2+(12.36)^2}$

53

By using the table of squares

$$\sqrt{(8.135)^2+(12.36)^2} = \sqrt{66.18+152.8}$$

$$= \sqrt{218.98}$$

Then by using the table of square roots

$$\sqrt{218.98} = 14.80$$

Example 7

Find the value of

$$\frac{1}{\sqrt{7.517}}+\frac{1}{(3.625)^2}$$

By using the square and square root tables

$$\frac{1}{\sqrt{7.517}}+\frac{1}{(3.625)^2} \quad = \frac{1}{2.741}+\frac{1}{13.14}$$

Then by using the reciprocal table

$$= 0.3649+0.0761$$

$$= 0.4410$$

Table of Reciprocals of Numbers from 1–10   Subtract

	0	1	2	3	4	5	6	7	8	9	1	2	3	4	5	6	7	8	9
1.0	1.0000	0.9901	0.9804	0.9709	0.9615	0.9524	0.9434	0.9346	0.9259	0.9174									
1.1	0.9091	0.9009	0.8929	0.8850	0.8772	0.8696	0.8621	0.8547	0.8475	0.8403									
1.2	0.8333	0.8264	0.8197	0.8130	0.8065	0.8000	0.7937	0.7874	0.7813	0.7752									
1.3	0.7692	0.7634	0.7576	0.7519	0.7463	0.7407	0.7353	0.7299	0.7246	0.7194									
1.4	0.7143	0.7092	0.7042	0.6993	0.6944	0.6897	0.6849	0.6803	0.6757	0.6711									
1.5	0.6667	0.6623	0.6579	0.6536	0.6494	0.6452	0.6410	0.6369	0.6329	0.6289	4	8	12	17	21	25	29	33	37
1.6	0.6250	0.6211	0.6173	0.6135	0.6098	0.6061	0.6024	0.5988	0.5952	0.5917	4	7	11	15	18	22	26	29	33
1.7	0.5882	0.5848	0.5814	0.5780	0.5747	0.5714	0.5682	0.5650	0.5618	0.5587	3	7	10	13	16	20	23	26	29
1.8	0.5556	0.5525	0.5495	0.5464	0.5435	0.5405	0.5376	0.5348	0.5319	0.5291	3	6	9	12	15	18	20	23	26
1.9	0.5263	0.5236	0.5208	0.5181	0.5155	0.5128	0.5102	0.5076	0.5051	0.5025	3	5	8	11	13	16	18	21	24
2.0	0.5000	0.4975	0.4950	0.4926	0.4902	0.4878	0.4854	0.4831	0.4808	0.4785	2	5	7	10	12	14	17	19	21
2.1	0.4762	0.4739	0.4717	0.4695	0.4673	0.4651	0.4630	0.4608	0.4587	0.4566	2	4	6	9	11	13	15	17	19
2.2	0.4545	0.4525	0.4505	0.4484	0.4464	0.4444	0.4425	0.4405	0.4386	0.4367	2	4	6	8	10	12	14	16	18
2.3	0.4348	0.4329	0.4310	0.4292	0.4274	0.4255	0.4237	0.4219	0.4202	0.4184	2	4	5	7	9	11	13	14	16
2.4	0.4167	0.4149	0.4132	0.4115	0.4098	0.4082	0.4065	0.4049	0.4032	0.4016	2	3	5	7	8	10	12	13	15
2.5	0.4000	0.3984	0.3968	0.3953	0.3937	0.3922	0.3906	0.3891	0.3876	0.3861	2	3	5	6	8	9	11	12	14
2.6	0.3846	0.3831	0.3817	0.3802	0.3788	0.3774	0.3759	0.3745	0.3731	0.3717	1	3	4	6	7	9	10	11	13
2.7	0.3704	0.3690	0.3676	0.3663	0.3650	0.3636	0.3623	0.3610	0.3597	0.3584	1	3	4	5	7	8	9	11	12
2.8	0.3571	0.3559	0.3546	0.3534	0.3521	0.3509	0.3497	0.3484	0.3472	0.3460	1	2	4	5	6	7	9	10	11
2.9	0.3448	0.3436	0.3425	0.3413	0.3401	0.3390	0.3378	0.3367	0.3356	0.3344	1	2	3	5	6	7	8	9	10
3.0	0.3333	0.3322	0.3311	0.3300	0.3289	0.3279	0.3268	0.3257	0.3247	0.3236	1	2	3	4	5	6	8	9	10
3.1	0.3226	0.3215	0.3205	0.3195	0.3185	0.3175	0.3165	0.3155	0.3145	0.3135	1	2	3	4	5	6	7	8	9
3.2	0.3125	0.3115	0.3106	0.3096	0.3086	0.3077	0.3067	0.3058	0.3049	0.3040	1	2	3	4	5	6	7	8	9
3.3	0.3030	0.3021	0.3012	0.3003	0.2994	0.2985	0.2976	0.2967	0.2959	0.2950	1	2	3	4	4	5	6	7	8
3.4	0.2941	0.2933	0.2924	0.2915	0.2907	0.2899	0.2890	0.2882	0.2874	0.2865	1	2	3	3	4	5	6	7	8
3.5	0.2857	0.2849	0.2841	0.2833	0.2825	0.2817	0.2809	0.2801	0.2793	0.2786	1	2	2	3	4	5	6	6	7
3.6	0.2778	0.2770	0.2762	0.2755	0.2747	0.2740	0.2732	0.2725	0.2717	0.2710	1	2	2	3	4	5	5	6	7
3.7	0.2703	0.2695	0.2688	0.2681	0.2674	0.2667	0.2660	0.2653	0.2646	0.2639	1	1	2	3	4	4	5	6	6
3.8	0.2632	0.2625	0.2618	0.2611	0.2604	0.2597	0.2591	0.2584	0.2577	0.2571	1	1	2	3	3	4	5	5	6
3.9	0.2564	0.2558	0.2551	0.2545	0.2538	0.2532	0.2525	0.2519	0.2513	0.2506	1	1	2	3	3	4	4	5	6
4.0	0.2500	0.2494	0.2488	0.2481	0.2475	0.2469	0.2463	0.2457	0.2451	0.2445	1	1	2	2	3	4	4	5	5
4.1	0.2439	0.2433	0.2427	0.2421	0.2415	0.2410	0.2404	0.2398	0.2392	0.2387	1	1	2	2	3	3	4	4	5
4.2	0.2381	0.2375	0.2370	0.2364	0.2358	0.2353	0.2347	0.2342	0.2336	0.2331	1	1	2	2	3	3	4	4	5
4.3	0.2326	0.2320	0.2315	0.2309	0.2304	0.2299	0.2294	0.2288	0.2283	0.2278	1	1	2	2	3	3	4	4	5
4.4	0.2273	0.2268	0.2262	0.2257	0.2252	0.2247	0.2242	0.2237	0.2232	0.2227	1	1	2	2	3	3	4	4	5
4.5	0.2222	0.2217	0.2212	0.2208	0.2203	0.2198	0.2193	0.2188	0.2183	0.2179	0	1	1	2	2	3	3	4	4
4.6	0.2174	0.2169	0.2165	0.2160	0.2155	0.2151	0.2146	0.2141	0.2137	0.2132	0	1	1	2	2	3	3	4	4
4.7	0.2128	0.2123	0.2119	0.2114	0.2110	0.2105	0.2101	0.2096	0.2092	0.2088	0	1	1	2	2	3	3	4	4
4.8	0.2083	0.2079	0.2075	0.2070	0.2066	0.2062	0.2058	0.2053	0.2049	0.2045	0	1	1	2	2	3	3	3	4
4.9	0.2041	0.2037	0.2033	0.2028	0.2024	0.2020	0.2016	0.2012	0.2008	0.2004	0	1	1	2	2	2	3	3	4
5.0	0.2000	0.1996	0.1992	0.1988	0.1984	0.1980	0.1976	0.1972	0.1969	0.1965	0	1	1	2	2	2	3	3	4
5.1	0.1961	0.1957	0.1953	0.1949	0.1946	0.1942	0.1938	0.1934	0.1931	0.1927	0	1	1	2	2	2	3	3	3
5.2	0.1923	0.1919	0.1916	0.1912	0.1908	0.1905	0.1901	0.1898	0.1894	0.1890	0	1	1	1	2	2	3	3	3
5.3	0.1887	0.1883	0.1880	0.1876	0.1873	0.1869	0.1866	0.1862	0.1859	0.1855	0	1	1	1	2	2	2	3	3
5.4	0.1852	0.1848	0.1845	0.1842	0.1838	0.1835	0.1832	0.1828	0.1825	0.1821	0	1	1	1	2	2	2	3	3

Exercise 60 — *All type B*

Find the values of:

1) $\dfrac{1}{(15.28)^2}$

2) $\dfrac{1}{(0.1372)^2}$

3) $\dfrac{1}{(250)^2}$

4) $\dfrac{1}{\sqrt{8.406}}$

5) $\dfrac{1}{\sqrt{18.73}}$

6) $\dfrac{1}{\sqrt{0.01798}}$

7) $\dfrac{1}{(30.15)^2+(8.29)^2}$

8) $\dfrac{1}{(11.26)^2+(8.18)^2}$

9) $\sqrt{(2.65)^2+(5.16)^2}$

10) $\sqrt{(11.18)^2-(5.23)^2}$

11) $\dfrac{1}{8.2}+\dfrac{1}{9.9}$

12) $\dfrac{1}{0.7325}-\dfrac{1}{0.9817}$

13) $\dfrac{1}{\sqrt{7.517}}+\dfrac{1}{(8.209)^2}+\dfrac{1}{0.0749}$

14) $\dfrac{1}{71.36}+\dfrac{1}{\sqrt{863.5}}+\dfrac{1}{(7.589)^2}$

Table of Reciprocals of Numbers from 1–10   Subtract

	0	1	2	3	4	5	6	7	8	9	1	2	3	4	5	6	7	8	9
5.5	0.1818	0.1815	0.1812	0.1808	0.1805	0.1802	0.1799	0.1795	0.1792	0.1789	0	1	1	1	2	2	2	3	3
5.6	0.1786	0.1783	0.1779	0.1776	0.1773	0.1770	0.1767	0.1764	0.1761	0.1757	0	1	1	1	2	2	2	3	3
5.7	0.1754	0.1751	0.1748	0.1745	0.1742	0.1739	0.1736	0.1733	0.1730	0.1727	0	1	1	1	2	2	2	2	3
5.8	0.1724	0.1721	0.1718	0.1715	0.1712	0.1709	0.1706	0.1704	0.1701	0.1698	0	1	1	1	2	2	2	2	3
5.9	0.1695	0.1692	0.1689	0.1686	0.1684	0.1681	0.1678	0.1675	0.1672	0.1669	0	1	1	1	1	2	2	2	3
6.0	0.1667	0.1664	0.1661	0.1658	0.1656	0.1653	0.1650	0.1647	0.1645	0.1642	0	1	1	1	1	2	2	2	2
6.1	0.1639	0.1637	0.1634	0.1631	0.1629	0.1626	0.1623	0.1621	0.1618	0.1616	0	1	1	1	1	2	2	2	2
6.2	0.1613	0.1610	0.1608	0.1605	0.1603	0.1600	0.1597	0.1595	0.1592	0.1590	0	1	1	1	1	2	2	2	2
6.3	0.1587	0.1585	0.1582	0.1580	0.1577	0.1575	0.1572	0.1570	0.1567	0.1565	0	0	1	1	1	1	2	2	2
6.4	0.1563	0.1560	0.1558	0.1555	0.1553	0.1550	0.1548	0.1546	0.1543	0.1541	0	0	1	1	1	1	2	2	2
6.5	0.1538	0.1536	0.1534	0.1531	0.1529	0.1527	0.1524	0.1522	0.1520	0.1517	0	0	1	1	1	1	2	2	2
6.6	0.1515	0.1513	0.1511	0.1508	0.1506	0.1504	0.1502	0.1499	0.1497	0.1495	0	0	1	1	1	1	2	2	2
6.7	0.1493	0.1490	0.1488	0.1486	0.1484	0.1481	0.1479	0.1477	0.1475	0.1473	0	0	1	1	1	1	2	2	2
6.8	0.1471	0.1468	0.1466	0.1464	0.1462	0.1460	0.1458	0.1456	0.1453	0.1451	0	0	1	1	1	1	1	2	2
6.9	0.1449	0.1447	0.1445	0.1443	0.1441	0.1439	0.1437	0.1435	0.1433	0.1431	0	0	1	1	1	1	1	2	2
7.0	0.1429	0.1427	0.1425	0.1422	0.1420	0.1418	0.1416	0.1414	0.1412	0.1410	0	0	1	1	1	1	1	2	2
7.1	0.1408	0.1406	0.1404	0.1403	0.1401	0.1399	0.1397	0.1395	0.1393	0.1391	0	0	1	1	1	1	1	2	2
7.2	0.1389	0.1387	0.1385	0.1383	0.1381	0.1379	0.1377	0.1376	0.1374	0.1372	0	0	1	1	1	1	1	2	2
7.3	0.1370	0.1368	0.1366	0.1364	0.1362	0.1361	0.1359	0.1357	0.1355	0.1353	0	0	1	1	1	1	1	1	2
7.4	0.1351	0.1350	0.1348	0.1346	0.1344	0.1342	0.1340	0.1339	0.1337	0.1335	0	0	1	1	1	1	1	1	2
7.5	0.1333	0.1332	0.1330	0.1328	0.1326	0.1325	0.1323	0.1321	0.1319	0.1318	0	0	1	1	1	1	1	1	2
7.6	0.1316	0.1314	0.1312	0.1311	0.1309	0.1307	0.1305	0.1304	0.1302	0.1300	0	0	1	1	1	1	1	1	2
7.7	0.1299	0.1297	0.1295	0.1294	0.1292	0.1290	0.1289	0.1287	0.1285	0.1284	0	0	0	1	1	1	1	1	1
7.8	0.1282	0.1280	0.1279	0.1277	0.1276	0.1274	0.1272	0.1271	0.1269	0.1267	0	0	0	1	1	1	1	1	1
7.9	0.1266	0.1264	0.1263	0.1261	0.1259	0.1258	0.1256	0.1255	0.1253	0.1252	0	0	0	1	1	1	1	1	1
8.0	0.1250	0.1248	0.1247	0.1245	0.1244	0.1242	0.1241	0.1239	0.1238	0.1236	0	0	0	1	1	1	1	1	1
8.1	0.1235	0.1233	0.1232	0.1230	0.1229	0.1227	0.1225	0.1224	0.1222	0.1221	0	0	0	1	1	1	1	1	1
8.2	0.1220	0.1218	0.1217	0.1215	0.1214	0.1212	0.1211	0.1209	0.1208	0.1206	0	0	0	1	1	1	1	1	1
8.3	0.1205	0.1203	0.1202	0.1200	0.1199	0.1198	0.1196	0.1195	0.1193	0.1192	0	0	0	1	1	1	1	1	1
8.4	0.1190	0.1189	0.1188	0.1186	0.1185	0.1183	0.1182	0.1181	0.1179	0.1178	0	0	0	1	1	1	1	1	1
8.5	0.1176	0.1175	0.1174	0.1172	0.1171	0.1170	0.1168	0.1167	0.1166	0.1164	0	0	0	1	1	1	1	1	1
8.6	0.1163	0.1161	0.1160	0.1159	0.1157	0.1156	0.1155	0.1153	0.1152	0.1151	0	0	0	1	1	1	1	1	1
8.7	0.1149	0.1148	0.1147	0.1145	0.1144	0.1143	0.1142	0.1140	0.1139	0.1138	0	0	0	1	1	1	1	1	1
8.8	0.1136	0.1135	0.1134	0.1133	0.1131	0.1130	0.1129	0.1127	0.1126	0.1125	0	0	0	1	1	1	1	1	1
8.9	0.1124	0.1122	0.1121	0.1120	0.1119	0.1117	0.1116	0.1115	0.1114	0.1112	0	0	0	0	1	1	1	1	1
9.0	0.1111	0.1110	0.1109	0.1107	0.1106	0.1105	0.1104	0.1103	0.1101	0.1100	0	0	0	0	1	1	1	1	1
9.1	0.1099	0.1098	0.1096	0.1095	0.1094	0.1093	0.1092	0.1091	0.1089	0.1088	0	0	0	0	1	1	1	1	1
9.2	0.1087	0.1086	0.1085	0.1083	0.1082	0.1081	0.1080	0.1079	0.1078	0.1076	0	0	0	0	1	1	1	1	1
9.3	0.1075	0.1074	0.1073	0.1072	0.1071	0.1070	0.1068	0.1067	0.1066	0.1065	0	0	0	0	1	1	1	1	1
9.4	0.1064	0.1063	0.1062	0.1060	0.1059	0.1058	0.1057	0.1056	0.1055	0.1054	0	0	0	0	1	1	1	1	1
9.5	0.1053	0.1052	0.1050	0.1049	0.1048	0.1047	0.1046	0.1045	0.1044	0.1043	0	0	0	0	1	1	1	1	1
9.6	0.1042	0.1041	0.1040	0.1038	0.1037	0.1036	0.1035	0.1034	0.1033	0.1032	0	0	0	0	1	1	1	1	1
9.7	0.1031	0.1030	0.1029	0.1028	0.1027	0.1026	0.1025	0.1024	0.1022	0.1021	0	0	0	0	1	1	1	1	1
9.8	0.1020	0.1019	0.1018	0.1017	0.1016	0.1015	0.1014	0.1013	0.1012	0.1011	0	0	0	0	1	1	1	1	1
9.9	0.1010	0.1009	0.1008	0.1007	0.1006	0.1005	0.1004	0.1003	0.1002	0.1001	0	0	0	0	1	1	1	1	1

Exercise 61 — *All type A*

The questions in this exercise have all been taken from past C.S.E. examination papers.

1) Use tables to find, as accurately as they will allow the values of:

(a) 6.75^2 (b) $\sqrt{6.75}$ (*M*)

2) Calculate: $(12.5)^2-(7.5)^2$ (*E.M.*)

3) Does $\sqrt{16}=8$?   (*S*)

4) Find $\sqrt{3.142}$ correct to 2 places of decimals.   (*E.M.*)

5) Find the value of $(3.142)^2$ correct to 2 places of decimals.   (*E.M.*)

6) Work out $(6.3)^2-(3.7)^2$.   (*E.M.*)

7) The difference between the squares of the numbers 11 and 21 is

    a 20   **b** 100
    c 220   **d** 320   (*A.L.*)

8) Find the value of $(0.7)^2$.   (*W*)

9) By means of tables, or otherwise, find correct to 3 decimal places the values of:

(a) $\dfrac{3}{2.5}+\dfrac{4}{3.5}$ (b) $\sqrt{0.0089}$ (*M*)

10) $\sqrt{2.25}$ is equal to

    a 1.5   **b** 15   **c** 4.74
    d 0.15   **e** none of these
                            (*W.M.*)

11) What is the reciprocal of 21?

    a 21^2 **b** 0.21   **c** $\sqrt{21}$
    d $\frac{1}{21}$ **e** 1.3222   (*N.W.*)

12) What is the value of 13^2-12^2?

    a 25   **b** 5   **c** 1^2
    d 125   **e** 2   (*N.W.*)

13) Find the value of $\sqrt{36\times25}$.
                                 (*N.W.*)

14) $(0.12)^2$ is equal to

    a 1.44   **b** 0.144   **c** 0.0144
    d 0.24   **e** 0.14   (*W.M.*)

15) Find the value of $3\sqrt{169}$. (*Y.R.*)

16) Given that $\dfrac{1}{18.27}=0.054\,734\,5$ correct to 6 significant figures find the reciprocal of 3.654 correct to 5 significant figures.   (*Y.R.*)

17) Express $\sqrt{900}$ as a product of its prime factors.   (*W*)

18) The value of $\dfrac{1}{0.2}+\dfrac{1}{0.25}$ is

    a 2   **b** 45   **c** 4.5
    d 2.5   **e** 9   (*N.W.*)

19) Find, without using tables, the value of:

(a) $\sqrt{1.21}$ (b) $\sqrt{0.09}$ (c) $\sqrt{6\frac{1}{4}}$
                                   (*W*)

20) Find the value of $\left(\dfrac{0.75}{0.15}\right)^2$ (*S*)

Chapter 9 Directed Numbers

Introduction

Directed numbers are numbers which have either a plus or a minus sign attached to them such as +7 and −5. In this chapter we shall study the rules for the addition, subtraction, multiplication and division of directed numbers. We need these rules in connection with logarithms which will be dealt with in Chapter 12.

Positive and Negative Numbers

Fig. 9.1 shows part of a centigrade thermometer. The freezing point of water is 0°C (nought degrees celsius). Temperatures above freezing point may be read off the scale directly and so may those below freezing. We now have to decide on a method for showing whether a temperature is above or below zero. We may say that a temperature is 6 degrees above zero or 5

degrees below zero but these statements are not compact enough for calculations. Therefore we say that a temperature of +6° is a temperature which is 6° above zero and a temperature of 5 degrees below zero would be written −5°. We have thus used the signs + and − to indicate a change of direction.

Again if starting from a given point, distances measured to the right are regarded as being positive then distances measured to the left are regarded as being negative. As stated in the introduction, numbers which have a sign attached to them are called directed numbers. Thus +7 is a positive number and −7 is a negative number.

The Addition of Directed Numbers

In Fig. 9.2 a movement from left to right (i.e. in the direction 0A) is regarded as positive, whilst a movement from right to left (i.e. in the direction 0B) is regarded as negative.

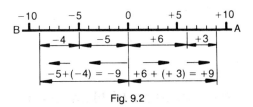

Fig. 9.2

To find the value of   +6+(+3)

Measure 6 units to the right of 0 (Fig. 9.2) and then measure a further 3

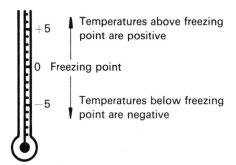

Fig. 9.1

units to the right. The final position is 9 units to the right of 0. Hence,

$$+6+(+3) = +9$$

To find the value of $-5+(-4)$

Again in Fig. 9.2, measure 5 units to the left of 0 and then measure a further 4 units to the left. The final position is 9 units to the left of 0. Hence,

$$-5+(-4) = -9$$

From these results we obtain the rule:

To add several numbers together whose signs are the same add the numbers together. The sign of the sum is the same as the sign of each of the numbers.

When a + sign means "add" it is usually omitted. When a calculation begins with a + sign this is also omitted. Positive signs are frequently omitted as shown in the following examples.

1) $+5+9 = +14$

    More often this is written

    $5+9 = 14$

2) $-7+(-9) = -16$

    More often this is written

    $-7-9 = -16$

3) $-7-6-4 = -17$

Exercise 62 — *All type A*

Find the values of the following:

1) $+8+7$ 5) $-9-6-5-4$

2) $-7-5$ 6) $3+6+8+9$

3) $-15-17$ 7) $-2-5-8-3$

4) $8+6$ 8) $9+6+5+3$

The Addition of Numbers Having Different Signs

To find the value of $-4+11$

Measure 4 units to the left of 0 (Fig.

9.3) and from this point measure 11 units to the right. The final position is 7 units to the right of 0. Hence,

$$-4+11 = 7$$

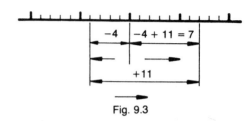

Fig. 9.3

To find the value of 8−15

Measure 8 units to the right of 0 (Fig. 9.4) and from this point measure 15 units to the left. The final position is 7 units to the left of 0. Hence,

$$8-15 = -7$$

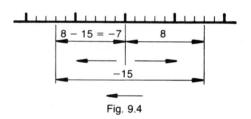

Fig. 9.4

From these results we obtain the rule:

To add two numbers together whose signs are different, subtract the numerically smaller from the larger. The sign of the result will be the same as the sign of the numerically larger number.

Examples

1) $-12+6 = -6$

2) $11-16 = -5$

When dealing with several numbers having mixed signs add the positive and negative numbers together separately. The set of numbers is then reduced to two numbers, one positive and the other negative, which are added in the way shown above.

58

Example

$$-16+11-7+3+8 = -23+22 = -1$$

Exercise 63 — *All type A*

Find the values for the following:

1) $6-11$	**4)** $12-7$
2) $7-16$	**5)** $-8+9-2$
3) $-5+10$	**6)** $15-7-8$

7) $23-21-8+2$

8) $-7+11-9-3+15$

Subtraction of Directed Numbers

To find the value of $-4-(+7)$

To represent $+7$ we measure 7 units to the right of 0 (Fig. 9.5). Therefore to represent $-(+7)$ we must reverse direction and measure 7 units to the left of 0 and hence $-(+7)$ is the same as -7. Hence,

$$-4-(+7) = -4-7 = -11$$

To find the value of $+3-(-10)$

To represent -10 we measure 10 units to the left of 0 (Fig. 9.5). Therefore to represent $-(-10)$ we measure 10 units to the right of 0 and hence $-(-10)$ is the same as $+10$. Hence,

$$+3-(-10) = 3+10 = 13$$

The rule is:

To subtract a directed number change its sign and add the resulting number.

Examples

1) $-10-(-6) = -10+6 = -4$

2) $7-(+8) = 7-8 = -1$

3) $8-(-3) = 8+3 = 11$

Exercise 64 — *All type A*

Find the values for the following:

1) $8-(+6)$	**5)** $-4-(-5)$
2) $-5-(-8)$	**6)** $-2-(+3)$
3) $8-(-6)$	**7)** $-10-(-5)$
4) $-3-(-7)$	**8)** $7-(-9)$

Multiplication of Directed Numbers

Now	$5+5+5 = 15$
That is,	$3 \times 5 = 15$

Thus two positive numbers multiplied together give a positive product.

Now	$(-5)+(-5)+(-5) = -15$
That is,	$3 \times (-5) = -15$

Thus a positive number multiplied by a negative number gives a negative product. Suppose, now, that we wish to find the value of $(-3) \times (-5)$. We can write (-3) as $-(+3)$ and hence

$$(-3) \times (-5) = -(+3) \times (-5)$$
$$= -(-15) = +15$$

Thus a negative number multiplied by a negative number gives a positive product.

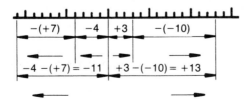

Fig. 9.5

We may summarise the above results as follows:

$$(+)\times(+) = (+) \quad (-)\times(+) = (-)$$

$$(+)\times(-) = (-) \quad (-)\times(-) = (+)$$

and the rule is:

The product of two numbers with like signs is positive whilst the product of two numbers with unlike signs is negative.

Examples

1) $7\times4 = 28$

2) $7\times(-4) = -28$

3) $(-7)\times4 = -28$

4) $(-7)\times(-4) = 28$

Exercise 65 — *All type A*

Find the values of the following:

1) $7\times(-6)$

2) $(-6)\times7$

3) 7×6

4) $(-7)\times(-6)$

5) $(-2)\times(-4)\times(-6)$

6) $(-2)^2$

7) $3\times(-4)\times(-2)\times5$

8) $(-3)^2$

Division of Directed Numbers

The rules for division must be very similar to those used for multiplication, since if $3\times(-5) = -15$,

then $\dfrac{-15}{3} = -5$. Also $\dfrac{-15}{-5} = 3$.

The rule is:

When dividing, numbers with like

signs give a positive quotient and numbers with unlike signs give a negative quotient.

The rule may be summarised as follows:

$$(+)\div(+) = (+) \quad (+)\div(-) = (-)$$

$$(-)\div(+) = (-) \quad (-)\div(-) = (+)$$

Examples

1) $\dfrac{20}{4} = 5$

2) $\dfrac{20}{-4} = -5$

3) $\dfrac{-20}{4} = -5$

4) $\dfrac{-20}{-4} = 5$

5) $\dfrac{(-9)\times(-4)\times5}{3\times(-2)} = \dfrac{36\times5}{-6}$

$$= \dfrac{180}{-6} = -30$$

Exercise 66 — *Questions 1–9 type A, remainder B*

1) $6\div(-2)$

2) $(-6)\div2$

3) $(-6)\div(-2)$

4) $6\div2$

5) $(-10)\div5$

6) $1\div(-1)$

7) $(-4)\div(-2)$

8) $(-3)\div3$

9) $8\div(-4)$

10) $\dfrac{(-6)\times4}{(-2)}$

11) $\dfrac{(-8)}{(-4)\times(-2)}$

12) $\dfrac{(-3)\times(-4)\times(-2)}{3\times4}$

13) $\dfrac{4\times(-6)\times(-8)}{(-3)\times(-2)\times(-4)}$

14) $\dfrac{5\times(-3)\times6}{10\times3}$

Types of Numbers

The whole numbers 1, 2, 3, . . . , 17, 18, 19, . . . etc. are called *positive numbers*.

Because they were originally used for counting only they are also called *counting numbers*.

Integers are also whole numbers but zero and negative numbers are included. Thus, -5, -2, 0, 11 and 15 are all integers.

A number with a sign in front of it is called a *directed number* as stated earlier in this chapter. -75 is a negative integer and $-\frac{2}{3}$ is a negative fraction. Both are examples of negative numbers.

Rational numbers are numbers which can be expressed as a vulgar fraction. Thus 0.625 is a rational number because it can be written $\frac{5}{8}$. All recurring decimals are rational numbers. For example,

$$0.\dot{1} = \frac{1}{9},$$

$$0.\dot{6}\dot{3} = \frac{63}{99} = \frac{7}{11}$$

$$\text{and } 0.\dot{7}2\dot{5} = \frac{725}{999}.$$

Irrational numbers cannot be expressed as a fraction. Consider $\sqrt{2}$. Since $1 \times 1 = 1$ and $2 \times 2 = 4$ the value of $\sqrt{2}$ lies between 1 and 2. Some fractions are very close to the exact value of $\sqrt{2}$, for instance:

$$\frac{7}{5} \times \frac{7}{5} = \frac{49}{25} = 1.96$$

$$\frac{71}{50} \times \frac{71}{50} = \frac{5041}{2500} = 2.0164$$

$$\frac{707}{500} \times \frac{707}{500} = \frac{499\,849}{250\,000} = 1.999\,396$$

However, it is impossible to find a fraction, which when multiplied by itself gives exactly 2. Hence $\sqrt{2}$ is an irrational number. Similarly $\sqrt{3}$, $\sqrt{5}$ and $\sqrt{7}$ are all irrational numbers. Not all square roots are irrational numbers. For instance $\sqrt{9}$ is not irrational because it equals 3. $\sqrt{2.25} = 1.5$ and hence $\sqrt{2.25}$ is rational because $1.5 = \frac{3}{2}$.

Imaginary numbers. Numbers like $\sqrt{-1}$, $\sqrt{-4}$, $\sqrt{-11}$, etc. have no real meaning. $1 \times 1 = 1$ and $(-1) \times (-1) = 1$ and hence it is impossible to find the value of $\sqrt{-1}$. Similarly, it is not possible to find $\sqrt{-4}$ or the square root of any negative number. The square root of a negative number is said to be an *imaginary number*. Numbers which are not imaginary are said to be *real*. Thus $\sqrt{16} = 4$ and $\sqrt{1.8496} = 1.36$ are real rational numbers. A number like $\sqrt{13}$ is called a *real irrational number*.

Exercise 67 — *All type A*

1) Which of the following are positive integers?

5, -8, $\frac{2}{3}$, $1\frac{1}{2}$, 2.75 and 198.

2) Which of the following are negative integers?

$8\frac{1}{2}$, -9, 7, $-\frac{1}{3}$ and $-4\frac{3}{4}$.

3) Which of the following are rational and which are irrational?

1.57, $\frac{1}{4}$, -5.625, $\sqrt{9}$, $\sqrt{15}$, 6.76 and $-3\frac{1}{2}$.

4) Which of the following are real numbers?

9.5782, -7.38, $\sqrt{8}$, $\sqrt{-4}$, $7\frac{2}{3}$ and $\sqrt{-5}$.

Sequences of Numbers

A set of numbers connected by some definite law is called a sequence or a series. Some examples are:

3, 1, -1, -3 (each number is 2 less than the preceding number)

1, 4, 9, 16 (squares of successive integers: $1^2 = 1$, $2^2 = 4$, etc.)

2, 1, $\frac{1}{2}$, $\frac{1}{4}$ (each number is $\frac{1}{2}$ of the preceding number).

Exercise 68 — *All type A*

Write down the next two terms of each of the following sequences:

1) 1, 4, 7, 10 . . .

2) 5, 11, 17, 23, . . .

3) 2, 0, −2, −4, . . .

4) −5, −3, −1, 1, . . .

5) $\frac{3}{4}, \frac{1}{4}, \frac{1}{12}, \frac{1}{36}, \ldots$

6) 16, 25, 36, 49, . . .

7) 2, −2, 2, −2, . . .

8) 1.2, 1.44, 1.728, . . .

9) 3, −1.5, 0.75, −0.375, . . .

10) 1.1, −1.21, 1.331, . . .

Exercise 69 — *Questions 1–7 type A, remainder B*

All the questions in this exercise have been taken from past C.S.E. examination papers.

1) (−4)×(−3) is equal to

   a −7   **b** 7   **c** −12
   d −1   **e** 12   (*W.M.*)

2) The value of −6−(−6) is

   a −12   **b** 0   **c** 12
   d 36   **e** none of
                 these   (*W.Y.*)

3) Find the value of $(-3)^2$.   (*S*)

4) Find the value of $\dfrac{2}{-10}$ in decimals.   (*Y.R.*)

5) Write down the next two numbers of the sequence:

1, 4, 9, 16, 25, . . .   (*Y.R.*)

6) (−2)×(−3) is equal to

   a −6   **b** 6   **c** −5
   d 5   **e** −1   (*W.M.*)

7) The value of (+4)(−2)−(−2) is

   a −6   **b** −4   **c** +4
   d +6   **e** +10   (*S.E.*)

8) Write down the next term in the pattern of numbers:

$3, -1, \frac{1}{3}, -\frac{1}{9}, \ldots$ (*A.L.*)

9) Write down the mean (average) of:
−3, −7, 2 and 0.   (*W.M.*)

10) Which of the following is a rational number?

   a $\sqrt{6}$ **b** $\sqrt{3}$ **c** $\sqrt{2}$
   d $\sqrt{4}$ **e** $\sqrt{5}$ (*N.W.*)

11) Write down the next three terms of the sequence

$1, -\frac{1}{2}, \frac{1}{4}, \ldots$ (*Y.R.*)

12) Fill in the gaps in the following sequences:

(a) $2, 1\frac{1}{3}, \frac{2}{3}, \ldots, -\frac{2}{3}, \ldots$

(b) 2, 6, 18, 54, . . ., . . .   (*Y.R.*)

Chapter 10 **Basic Algebra**

Introduction

The methods of algebra are an extension of those used in arithmetic. In algebra we use letters and symbols as well as numbers to represent quantities. When we write that a sum of money is £50 we are making a particular statement but if we write that a sum of money is £P we are making a general statement. This general statement will cover any number we care to substitute for P.

Use of Symbols

The following examples will show how verbal statements can be translated into algebraic symbols. Notice that we can choose any symbols we like to represent the quantities concerned.

1) The sum of two numbers.

Let the two numbers be x and y.
Sum of the two numbers $= x + y$

2) Three times a number.

Let the number be N.
Three times the number $= 3 \times N$

3) One number divided by another number.

Let one number be a and the other number be b.
One number divided by another number $= \dfrac{a}{b}$

4) Five times the product of two numbers.

Let the two numbers be m and n.
5 times the product of the two numbers $= 5 \times m \times n$

Exercise 70 — *All type A*

Translate the following into algebraic symbols:

1) Seven times a number, x.

2) Four times a number x minus three.

3) Five times a number x plus a second number, y.

4) The sum of two numbers x and y divided by a third number, z.

5) Half of a number, x.

6) Eight times the product of three numbers, x, y and z.

7) Product of two numbers x and y divided by a third number, z.

8) Three times a number, x, minus four times a second number, y.

Substitution

The process of finding the numerical value of an algebraic expression for given values of the symbols that appear in it is called *substitution*.

Example 1

If $x = 3$, $y = 4$ and $z = 5$ find the values of:

(a) $2y + 4$ (b) $3y + 5z$ (c) $8 - x$

(d) $\dfrac{y}{x}$ (e) $\dfrac{3y+2z}{x+z}$

Note that multiplication signs are often missed out when writing algebraic expressions so that, for instance, $2y$ means $2\times y$. These missed multiplication signs must reappear when the numbers are substituted for the symbols.

(a) $2y+4 = 2\times4+4 = 8+4 = 12$

(b) $3y+5z = 3\times4+5\times5$
$= 12+25 = 37$

(c) $8-x = 8-3 = 5$

(d) $\dfrac{y}{x} = \dfrac{4}{3} = 1\dfrac{1}{3}$

(e) $\dfrac{3y+2z}{x+z} = \dfrac{3\times4+2\times5}{3+5}$

$= \dfrac{12+10}{8} = \dfrac{22}{8} = 2\dfrac{3}{4}$

Exercise 71 — *All type A*

If $a = 2$, $b = 3$ and $c = 5$ find the values of the following:

1) $a+7$
2) $c-2$
3) $6-b$
4) $6b$
5) $9c$
6) ab
7) $3bc$
8) abc
9) $5c-2$
10) $4a+6b$

11) $8c-7$
12) $a+2b+5c$
13) $8c-4b$
14) $\frac{1}{2}a$
15) $\dfrac{ab}{8}$
16) $\dfrac{abc}{6}$
17) $\dfrac{2c}{a}$
18) $\dfrac{5a+9b+8c}{a+b+c}$

Powers

The quantity $a\times a\times a$ or aaa is usually written as a^3. a^3 is called the

third power of a. The number 3 which indicates the number of threes to be multiplied together is called the *index* (plural: *indices*).

$$2^4 = 2\times2\times2\times2 = 16$$
$$y^5 = y\times y\times y\times y\times y$$

Example 2

Find the value of b^3 when $b = 5$.

$$b^3 = 5^3 = 5\times5\times5 = 125$$

When dealing with expressions like $8mn^4$ note that it is only the symbol n which is raised to the fourth power. Thus:

$$8mn^4 = 8\times m\times n\times n\times n\times n$$

Example 3

Find the value of $7p^2q^3$ when $p = 5$ and $q = 4$.

$$7p^2q^3 = 7\times5^2\times4^3 = 7\times25\times64$$
$$= 11\,200$$

Exercise 72 — *All type A*

If $a = 2$, $b = 3$ and $c = 4$ find the values of the following:

1) a^2
2) b^4
3) ab^3
4) $2a^2c$
5) ab^2c^3
6) $5a^2+6b^2$

7) a^2+c^2
8) $7b^3c^2$
9) $\dfrac{3a^4}{c^2}$
10) $\dfrac{c^5}{ab^3}$

Laws of Indices

The laws of indices are needed when dealing with logarithms (see Chapter 12). The laws are discussed below.

64

Multiplication

Let us see what happens when we multiply powers of the same number together.

$$5^2 \times 5^4 = (5 \times 5) \times (5 \times 5 \times 5 \times 5) = 5^6$$

We see that we could have obtained the same result by adding the indices together. Hence the law is:

When multiplying powers of the same quantity together *add* the indices.

$$x^6 \times x^7 = x^{6+7} = x^{13}$$

$$y^2 \times y^3 \times y^4 \times y^5 = y^{2+3+4+5} = y^{14}$$

Division

Now let us see what happens when we divide powers of the same number.

$$\frac{3^5}{3^2} = \frac{3 \times 3 \times 3 \times 3 \times 3}{3 \times 3} = 3 \times 3 \times 3 = 3^3$$

we see that the result could have been obtained by subtracting the indices. Thus:

$$\frac{3^5}{3^2} = 3^{5-2} = 3^3$$

Hence the law is:

When dividing powers of the same quantity *subtract* the index of the denominator (bottom part) from the index of the numerator (top part).

$$\frac{x^5}{x^2} = x^{5-2} = x^3$$

$$\frac{a^3 \times a^4 \times a^8}{a^5 \times a^7} = \frac{a^{3+4+8}}{a^{5+7}}$$

$$= \frac{a^{15}}{a^{12}} = a^{15-12} = a^3$$

$$\frac{3y^2 \times 2y^5 \times 5y^4}{6y^3 \times 4y^4} = \frac{30y^{2+5+4}}{24y^{3+4}}$$

$$= \frac{30y^{11}}{24y^7} = \frac{5y^{11-7}}{4} = \frac{5y^4}{4}$$

Powers

What is the value of $(5^3)^2$? One way of solving the problem is to proceed as follows:

$$(5^3)^2 = 5^3 \times 5^3 = 5^{3+3} = 5^6$$

We could have obtained the same result by multiplying the indices together. Hence the law is:

When raising the power of a quantity to a power *multiply* the indices together.

$$(3x)^3 = 3^{1 \times 3} \times x^{1 \times 3} = 3^3 x^3 = 27x^3$$

$$(a^2 b^3 c^4)^2 = a^{2 \times 2} b^{3 \times 2} c^{4 \times 2} = a^4 b^6 c^8$$

$$\left(\frac{3m^3}{5n^2}\right)^2 = \frac{3^2 m^{3 \times 2}}{5^2 n^{2 \times 2}} = \frac{9m^6}{25n^4}$$

Negative Indices

Let us attempt to simplify $\frac{2^3}{2^6}$

$$\frac{2^3}{2^6} = \frac{2 \times 2 \times 2}{2 \times 2 \times 2 \times 2 \times 2 \times 2} = \frac{1}{2 \times 2 \times 2} = \frac{1}{2^3}$$

But by the rule for division:

$$\frac{2^3}{2^6} = 2^{3-6} = 2^{-3}$$

Hence $\qquad 2^{-3} = \frac{1}{2^3}$

A negative index therefore indicates the reciprocal of the quantity.

$$a^{-1} = \frac{1}{a}$$

$$5x^{-3} = \frac{5}{x^3}$$

$$a^2 b^{-2} c^{-3} = \frac{a^2}{b^2 c^3}$$

Fractional Indices

To find a meaning for $5^{1/3}$

$$\sqrt[3]{5} \times \sqrt[3]{5} \times \sqrt[3]{5} = 5$$

$$5^{1/3} \times 5^{1/3} \times 5^{1/3} = 5^{1/3+1/3+1/3} = 5^1 = 5$$

($\sqrt[3]{5}$ is said to be the cube root of five. Similarly $\sqrt[7]{9}$ is described as being the seventh root of nine.) Therefore a fractional index represents the root of a quantity.

The numerator of a fractional index indicates the power to which the quantity must be raised; the denominator indicates the root which is to be taken.

$$x^{2/3} = \sqrt[3]{x^2}$$

$$ab^{3/4} = a \times \sqrt[4]{b^3}$$

$$a^{1/2} = \sqrt{a}$$

(Note that for square roots the number indicating the root is usually omitted.)

$$\sqrt{64a^6} = (64a^6)^{1/2} = (8^2a^6)^{1/2}$$
$$= 8^{2 \times 1/2}a^{6 \times 1/2} = 8a^3$$

Zero Index

$$\frac{2^5}{2^5} = 2^{5-5} = 2^0$$

But $\qquad 2^5 \div 2^5 = 1$

Hence $\qquad 2^0 = 1$.

By doing several examples like this we would discover that:

Any quantity raised the power of zero is equal to 1.

$$a^0 = 1$$

$$\left(\frac{x}{y}\right)^0 = 1$$

Exercise 73 — *Questions 1–24 type A, remainder B*

Simplify the following:

1) $a^5 \times a^6$

2) $z^4 \times z^7$

3) $y^3 \times y^4 \times y^5$

4) $2^3 \times 2^5$

5) $3 \times 3^2 \times 3^5$

6) $\frac{1}{2}a \times \frac{1}{4}a^2 \times \frac{3}{4}a^3$

7) $a^5 \div a^2$

8) $m^{12} \div m^5$

9) $2^8 \div 2^4$

10) $x^{20} \div x^5$

11) $a^5 \times a^3 \div a^4$

12) $q^7 \times q^6 \div q^5$

13) $\frac{m^5}{m^3} \times \frac{m}{m^2}$

14) $\frac{l^5 \times l^6}{l^2 \times l^7}$

15) $\frac{aL^4}{aL^2}$

16) $(x^3)^4$

17) $(a^5)^3$

18) $(3x^4)^2$

19) $(2^3)^2$

20) $(10^3)^2$

21) $(ab^2)^3$

22) $(ab^2c^3)^4$

23) $(2x^2y^3z)^5$

24) $\left(\frac{3m^2}{4n^3}\right)^5$

25) Find the values of
10^{-1}, 2^{-2}, 3^{-4}, 5^{-2}.

26) Find the values of
$2^4 \times 2$, $5^2 \times 5^{1/2} \times 3^{3/2}$, $8^{1/3}$, $27^{1/3}$.

27) Express as powers of 3:
9^3, 27^5, 81^3, $9^4 \times 27^3$

28) Express as powers of a:
$\sqrt[5]{a}$, $\sqrt[3]{a^2}$, $\sqrt[7]{a^4}$, $\sqrt{a^6}$

Addition of Algebraic Terms

Like terms are numerical multiples of the same algebraic quantity. Thus,

$$7x, 5x \quad \text{and} \quad -3x$$

are three like terms.

An expression consisting of like terms can be reduced to a single term by adding the numerical coefficients together. Thus

$$7x - 5x + 3x = (7 - 5 + 3)x = 5x$$

$$3b^2 + 7b^2 = (3 + 7)b^2 = 10b^2$$

$$-3y - 5y = (-3 - 5)y = -8y$$

$$q - 3q = (1 - 3)q = -2q$$

Only like terms can be added or subtracted. Thus $7a+3b-2c$ is an expression containing three unlike terms and it cannot be simplified any further. Similarly with

$$8a^2b+7ab^3-6a^2b^2$$

which are all unlike terms.

It is possible to have several sets of like terms in an expression and each set can then be simplified:

$$8x+3y-4z-5x+7z-2y+2z$$

$$=(8-5)x+(3-2)y+(-4+7+2)z$$

$$=3x+y+5z$$

The order in which the symbols in a term are written is unimportant. Thus $abc = bca$. However, it is usual to write the symbols in alphabetical order. Thus pqr is preferred to rqp.

Multiplication and Division of Algebraic Quantities

The rules are exactly the same as those used with directed numbers:

$$(+x)(+y) = +(xy) = +xy = xy$$

$$5x \times 3y = 5 \times 3 \times x \times y = 15xy$$

$$(x)(-y) = -(xy) = -xy$$

$$(2x)(-3y) = -(2x)(3y) = -6xy$$

$$(-4x)(2y) = -(4x)(2y) = -8xy$$

$$(-3x)(-2y) = +(3x)(2y) = 6xy$$

$$\frac{+x}{+y} = +\frac{x}{y} = \frac{x}{y}$$

$$\frac{-3x}{2y} = -\frac{3x}{2y}$$

$$\frac{-5x}{-6y} = +\frac{5x}{6y} = \frac{5x}{6y}$$

$$\frac{4x}{-3y} = -\frac{4x}{3y}$$

When *multiplying* expressions containing the same symbols, indices are used:

$$m \times m = m^2$$

$$3m \times 5m = 3 \times m \times 5 \times m = 15m^2$$

$$(-m) \times m^2 = (-m) \times m \times m = -m^3$$

$$5m^2n \times 3mn^3$$

$$= 5 \times m \times m \times n \times 3 \times n \times n \times n \times n$$

$$= 15m^3n^4$$

$$3mn \times (-2n^2)$$

$$= 3 \times m \times n \times (-2) \times n \times n = -6mn^3$$

When *dividing* algebraic expressions, cancellation between numerator and denominator is often possible. Cancelling is equivalent to dividing both numerator and denominator by the same quantity:

$$\frac{pq}{p} = \frac{\not{p} \times q}{\not{p}} = q$$

$$\frac{3p^2q}{6pq^2} = \frac{3 \times \not{p} \times p \times \not{q}}{6 \times \not{p} \times \not{q} \times q} = \frac{3p}{6q} = \frac{p}{2q}$$

$$\frac{18x^2y^2z}{6xyz} = \frac{18 \times \not{x} \times x \times \not{y} \times y \times \not{z}}{6 \times \not{x} \times \not{y} \times \not{z}} = 3xy$$

Exercise 74 — *All type A*

Simplify the following:

1) $7x+11x$

2) $7x-5x$

3) $3x-6x$

4) $-2x-4x$

5) $-8x+3x$

6) $-2x+7x$

7) $8a-6a+7a$

8) $5m+13m-6m$

9) $6b^2-4b^2+3b^2$

10) $6ab-3ab-2ab$

11) $14xy+5xy-7xy+2xy$

12) $-5x+7x-3x-2x$

13) $-4x^2-3x^2+2x^2-x^2$

14) $3x-2y+4z-2x-3y+5z$
$$+6x+2y-3z$$

15) $3a^2b+2ab^3+4a^2b^2-5ab^3$
$$+11b^4+6a^2b$$

16) $1.2x^3 - 3.4x^2 + 2.6x + 3.7x^2$
$$+ 3.6x - 2.8$$

17) $pq + 2.1qr - 2.2rq + 8qp$

18) $2.6a^2b^2 - 3.4b^3 - 2.7a^3$
$$- 3a^2b^2 - 2.1b^3 + 1.5a^3$$

19) $2x \times 5y$ **23)** $x \times (-y)$

20) $3a \times 4b$ **24)** $(-3a) \times (-2b)$

21) $3 \times 4m$ **25)** $8m \times (-3n)$

22) $\frac{1}{4}q \times 16p$ **26)** $(-4a) \times 3b$

27) $8p \times (-q) \times (-3r)$

28) $3a \times (-4b) \times (-c) \times 5d$

29) $12x \div 6$ **38)** $7a^2b^2 \div 3ab$

30) $4a \div (-7b)$ **39)** $a \times a$

31) $(-5a) \div 8b$ **40)** $b \times (-b)$

32) $(-3a) \div (-3b)$ **41)** $(-m) \times m$

33) $4a \div 2b$ **42)** $(-p) \times (-p)$

34) $4ab \div 2a$ **43)** $3a \times 2a$

35) $12x^2yz^2 \div 4xz^2$ **44)** $5X \times X$

36) $(-12a^2b) \div 6a$ **45)** $5q \times (-3q)$

37) $8a^2bc^2 \div 4ac^2$ **46)** $3m \times (-3m)$

47) $(-3pq) \times (-3q)$

48) $8mn \times (-3m^2n^3)$

49) $7ab \times (-3a^2)$

50) $2q^3r^4 \times 5qr^2$

51) $(-3m) \times 2n \times (-5p)$

52) $5a^2 \times (-3b) \times 5ab$

53) $m^2n \times (-mn) \times 5m^2n^2$

Brackets

Brackets are used for convenience in grouping terms together. When removing brackets *each term* within the

bracket is multiplied by the quantity outside the bracket:

$$3(x+y) = 3x + 3y$$

$$5(2x+3y) = 5 \times 2x + 5 \times 3y = 10x + 15y$$

$$4(a-2b) = 4 \times a - 4 \times 2b = 4a - 8b$$

$$m(a+b) = ma + mb$$

$$3x(2p+3q) = 3x \times 2p + 3x \times 3q = 6px + 9qx$$

$$4a(2a+b) = 4a \times 2a + 4a \times b = 8a^2 + 4ab$$

When a bracket has a minus sign in front of it, the signs of all the terms inside the bracket are changed when the bracket is removed. The reason for this rule may be seen from the following examples:

$$-3(2x-5y) = (-3) \times 2x + (-3) \times (-5y)$$
$$= -6x + 15y$$

$$-(m+n) = -m - n$$

$$-(p-q) = -p + q$$

$$-2(p+3q) = -2p - 6q$$

When simplifying expressions containing brackets first remove the brackets and then add the like terms together:

$$(3x+7y) - (4x+3y) = 3x + 7y - 4x - 3y$$
$$= -x + 4y$$

$$3(2x+3y) - (x+5y) = 6x + 9y - x - 5y$$
$$= 5x + 4y$$

$$x(a+b) - x(a+3b) = ax + bx - ax - 3bx$$
$$= -2bx$$

$$2(5a+3b) + 3(a-2b) = 10a + 6b + 3a - 6b$$
$$= 13a$$

Exercise 75 — *Questions 1–20 type A, 21–30 type B*

Remove the brackets in the following:

1) $3(x+4)$ **3)** $3(3x+2y)$

2) $2(u+b)$ **4)** $\frac{1}{2}(x-1)$

5) $5(2p-3q)$ **11)** $-4(x+3)$

6) $7(a-3m)$ **12)** $-2(2x-5)$

7) $-(a+b)$ **13)** $-5(4-3x)$

8) $-(a-2b)$ **14)** $2k(k-5)$

9) $-(3p-3q)$ **15)** $-3y(3x+4)$

10) $-(7m-6)$ **16)** $a(p-q-r)$

17) $4xy(ab-ac+d)$

18) $3x^2(x^2-2xy+y^2)$

19) $-7P(2P^2-P+1)$

20) $-2m(-1+3m-2n)$

Remove the brackets and simplify:

21) $3(x+1)+2(x+4)$

22) $5(2a+4)-3(4a+2)$

23) $3(x+4)-(2x+5)$

24) $4(1-2x)-3(3x-4)$

25) $5(2x-y)-3(x+2y)$

26) $\frac{1}{2}(y-1)+\frac{1}{3}(2y-3)$

27) $-(4a+5b-3c)-2(2a+3b-4c)$

28) $2x(x-5)-x(x-2)-3x(x-5)$

29) $3(a-b)-2(2a-3b)+4(a-3b)$

30) $3x(x^2+7x-1)-2x(2x^2+3)$
$$-3(x^2+5)$$

Factorising

A factor is a common part of two or more terms which make up an algebraic expression. Thus the expression $3x+3y$ has two terms which have the number 3 common to both of them. Thus $3x+3y = 3(x+y)$. We say that 3 and $(x+y)$ are the factors of $3x+3y$.

Example 4

Find the factors of $ax+bx$.
ax and bx have the quantity x common to both of them.

$$\therefore \qquad ax+bx = x(a+b)$$

Note that to find the terms inside the bracket divide each of the terms making up the original expression by the quantity outside the bracket. Thus in Example 4:

$$\frac{ax}{x} = a \quad \text{and} \quad \frac{bx}{x} = b$$

Example 5

Factorise $5m-10m^2$

The given expression has the quantity $5m$ common to both terms.

$$\therefore \qquad 5m-10m^2 = 5m(1-2m)$$

$$\left(\text{since} \quad \frac{5m}{5m} = 1 \quad \text{and} \quad \frac{10m^2}{5m} = 2m.\right)$$

Exercise 76 — *All type B*

Factorise the following:

1) $2x+6$ **8)** $5a-10b+15c$

2) $4x-4y$ **9)** ax^2+ax

3) $5x-5$ **10)** $2\pi r^2+\pi rh$

4) $4x-8xy$ **11)** $3y-9y^2$

5) $mx-my$ **12)** ab^3-a^2b

6) $ax+bx+cx$

7) $\dfrac{x}{2} - \dfrac{y}{8}$

The Product of Two Binomial Expressions

A binomial expression consists of two terms. Thus $3x+5, a+b, 2x+3y$ and $4p-q$ are all binomial expressions.

To find the product of $(a+b)(c+d)$ consider the diagram (Fig. 10.1).

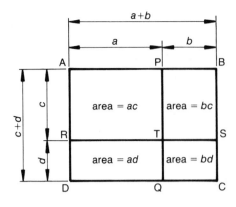

Fig. 10.1

In Fig. 10.1 the rectangular area ABCD is made up as follows:

$$ABCD = APTR + TQDR + PBST + STQC$$

i.e. $(a+b)(c+d) = ac + ad + bc + bd$

It will be noticed that the expression on the right hand side is obtained by multiplying each term in the one bracket by each term in the other bracket. The process is illustrated below where each pair of terms connected by a line are multiplied together.

$$(a+b)(c+d) = ac + ad + bc + bd$$

Example 6

1) $(3x+2)(4x+5)$

$$= 3x \times 4x + 3x \times 5 + 2 \times 4x + 2 \times 5$$
$$= 12x^2 + 15x + 8x + 10$$
$$= 12x^2 + 23x + 10$$

2) $(2p-3)(4p+7)$

$$= 2p \times 4p + 2p \times 7 - 3 \times 4p - 3 \times 7$$
$$= 8p^2 + 14p - 12p - 21$$
$$= 8p^2 + 2p - 21$$

3) $(z-5)(3z-2)$

$$= z \times 3z + z \times (-2)$$
$$\qquad\qquad -5 \times 3z - 5 \times (-2)$$
$$= 3z^2 - 2z - 15z + 10$$
$$= 3z^2 - 17z + 10$$

4) $(2x+3y)(3x-2y)$

$$= 2x \times 3x + 2x \times (-2y)$$
$$\qquad\qquad + 3y \times 3x + 3y \times (-2y)$$
$$= 6x^2 - 4xy + 9xy - 6y^2$$
$$= 6x^2 + 5xy - 6y^2$$

The Square of a Binomial Expression

$$(a+b)^2 = (a+b)(a+b) = a^2 + ab + ba + b^2$$
$$= a^2 + 2ab + b^2$$
$$(a-b)^2 = (a-b)(a-b) = a^2 - ab - ba + b^2$$
$$= a^2 - 2ab + b^2$$

The square of a binomial expression is the sum of the squares of the two terms and twice their product.

Example 7

1) $(2x+5)^2 = (2x)^2 + 2 \times 2x \times 5 + 5^2$
$$= 4x^2 + 20x + 25$$

2) $(3x-2)^2 = (3x)^2 + 2 \times 3x \times (-2)$
$$+ (-2)^2$$
$$= 9x^2 - 12x + 4$$

3) $(2x+3y)^2 = (2x)^2 + 2 \times 2x \times 3y + (3y)^2$
$$= 4x^2 + 12xy + 9y^2$$

The Sum and Difference of Two Terms

$$(a+b)(a-b) = a^2 - ab + ba - b^2 = a^2 - b^2$$

This result is the difference of the squares of the two terms.

Example 8

1) $(8x+3)(8x-3) = (8x)^2 - 3^2$
$$= 64x^2 - 9$$

2) $(2x+5y)(2x-5y) = (2x)^2 - (5y)^2$
$$= 4x^2 - 25y^2$$

Exercise 77 — *All type A*

Find the products of the following:

1) $(x+1)(x+2)$

2) $(x+3)(x+1)$

3) $(x+4)(x+5)$

4) $(2x+5)(x+3)$

5) $(3x+7)(x+6)$

6) $(5x+1)(x+4)$

7) $(2x+4)(3x+2)$

8) $(5x+1)(2x+3)$

9) $(7x+2)(3x+5)$

10) $(x-1)(x-3)$

11) $(x-4)(x-2)$

12) $(x-6)(x-3)$

13) $(2x-1)(x-4)$

14) $(x-2)(3x-5)$

15) $(x-8)(4x-1)$

16) $(2x-4)(3x-2)$

17) $(3x-1)(2x-5)$

18) $(7x-5)(3x-2)$

19) $(x+3)(x-1)$

20) $(x-2)(x+7)$

21) $(x-5)(x+3)$

22) $(2x+5)(x-2)$

23) $(3x-5)(x+6)$

24) $(3x+5)(x+6)$

25) $(3x+5)(2x-3)$

26) $(6x-7)(2x+3)$

27) $(3x-5)(2x+3)$

28) $(3x+2y)(x+y)$

29) $(2p-q)(p-3q)$

30) $(3v+2u)(2v-3u)$

31) $(2a+b)(3a-b)$

32) $(5a-7)(a-6)$

33) $(3x+4y)(2x-3y)$

34) $(x+1)^2$

35) $(2x+3)^2$

36) $(3x+7)^2$

37) $(x-1)^2$

38) $(3x-5)^2$

39) $(2x-3)^2$

40) $(2a+3b)^2$

41) $(x+y)^2$

42) $(P+3Q)^2$

43) $(a-b)^2$

44) $(3x-4y)^2$

45) $(M-2N)^2$

46) $(x-1)(x+1)$

47) $(x-3)(x+3)$

48) $(x+7)(x-7)$

49) $(2x+5)(2x-5)$

50) $(3x-7)(3x+7)$

51) $(2x-1)(2x+1)$

52) $(a+b)(a-b)$

53) $(3x-2y)(3x+2y)$

54) $(5a+2b)(5a-2b)$

Factors of Quadratic Expressions

A quadratic expression is one in which the highest power of the symbol used is the square. For instance, x^2-5x+3 and $3x^2-9$ are both quadratic expressions.

Case 1. Where the coefficient of the squared term is unity

$$(x+4)(x+3) = x^2+7x+12$$

Note that in the quadratic expression $x^2+7x+12$ the last term 12 has the factors 4×3. Also the coefficient of x is 7 which is the sum of the factors 4 and 3. This example gives the clue whereby quadratic expressions may be factorised.

Example 9

1) Factorise x^2+6x+5

We note
that $5 = 5\times1$ and $5+1 = 6$

$\therefore$ $x^2+6x+5 = (x+5)(x+1)$

2) Factorise $x^2+10x+16$

Now $16 = 16\times1$ or 8×2 or 4×4

But the sum of the factors must be 10. The only factors which add up to 10 are 8 and 2.

$\therefore$ $x^2+10x+16 = (x+8)(x+2)$

3) Factorise x^2+4x-5

Now $-5 = (-5)\times1$ or $5\times(-1)$

But the sum of the factors must be 4.
Since $5+(-1)=4$ then

$$x^2+4x-5 = (x+5)(x-1)$$

4) Factorise $x^2+3x-10$

Now $-10 = (-10)\times 1$ or $10\times(-1)$ or $(-5)\times 2$ or $5\times(-2)$.

Since the sum of the factors must be 3, the only pair that meets this requirement is 5 and -2. Hence:

$$x^2+3x-10 = (x+5)(x-2)$$

5) Factorise $x^2-8x+15$

Now $15 = 15\times 1$ or 5×3 or $(-5)\times(-3)$ or $(-1)\times(-15)$. But the sum of the factors must be -8. Since $-5+(-3) = -8$ then,

$$x^2-8x+15 = (x-5)(x-3)$$

Case 2. Where the coefficient of the squared term is not unity

In this case we find all the possible factors of the first and last terms of the quadratic expression. Then, by trying the various combinations the combination which gives the correct middle term may be found.

Example 10

1) Factorise $2x^2+5x-3$

Factors of $2x^2$		Factors of -3	
$2x$	x	-3	$+1$
		$+3$	-1

The combinations of these factors are:

$$(2x-3)(x+1) = 2x^2-x\times 3$$
which is incorrect

$$(2x+1)(x-3) = 2x^2-5x-3$$
which is incorrect

$$(2x+3)(x-1) = 2x^2+x-3$$
which is incorrect

$$(2x-1)(x+3) = 2x^2+5x-3$$
which is correct

Hence $2x^2+5x-3 = (2x-1)(x+3)$

2) Factorise $12x^2-35x+8$

Factors of $12x^2$		Factors of 8	
$12x$	x	1	8
$6x$	$2x$	-1	-8
$4x$	$3x$	2	4
		-2	-4

By trying each combination in turn, it is found that the only one that will produce the correct middle term of $-35x$ is $(3x-8)(4x-1)$.

Hence $12x^2-35x+8 = (3x-8)(4x-1)$

Case 3. Where the factors form a perfect square.

It has been shown that:

$$(a+b)^2 = a^2+2ab+b^2$$

and $\quad (a-b)^2 = a^2-2ab+b^2$

The square of a binomial expression therefore consists of: (square of 1st term)+(twice the product of the two terms)+(square of 2nd term).

Thus, to factorise $9a^2+12ab+4b^2$ we note that:

$$9a^2 = (3a)^2 \quad \text{and} \quad 4b^2 = (2b)^2$$

also $\quad 12ab = 2\times 3a\times 2b$.

Hence $\quad 9a^2+12ab+4b^2 = (3a+2b)^2$

Example 11

1) Factorise $16x^2-40x+25$

$16x^2 = (4x)^2;\ 25 = 5^2,\ 40x = 2\times 4x\times 5.$

$\therefore \qquad 16x^2-40x+25 = (4x-5)^2$

2) Factorise $25x^2+20x+4$

$25x^2 = (5x)^2;\ 4 = 2^2;\ 20x = 2\times 5x\times 2$

$\therefore \qquad 25x^2+20x+4 = (5x+2)^2$

Case 4. The factors of the difference of two squares.

It has been previously shown that:

$$(a+b)(a-b) = a^2 - b^2$$

The factors of the difference of two squares are therefore the sum and difference of the square roots of each of the given terms.

Example 12

1) Factorise $9m^2 - 4n^2$

Now $9m^2 = (3m)^2$ and $4n^2 = (2n)^2$

$\therefore$ $9m^2 - 4n^2 = (3m+2n)(3m-2n)$

2) Factorise $4x^2 - 9$

Now $4x^2 = (2x)^2$ and $9 = 3^2$

$\therefore$ $4x^2 - 9 = (2x+3)(2x-3)$

Exercise 78 — *Questions 1–27 type B, remainder C*

Factorise the following:

1) $x^2 + 4x + 3$

2) $x^2 + 6x + 8$

3) $x^2 + 9x + 20$

4) $x^2 - 3x + 2$

5) $x^2 - 6x + 8$

6) $x^2 - 7x + 12$

7) $x^2 + 2x - 15$

8) $x^2 + 3x - 28$

9) $x^2 + 6x - 7$

10) $x^2 - x - 12$

11) $x^2 - 5x - 14$

12) $x^2 - 2xy + y^2$

13) $x^2 - 6x + 9$

14) $x^2 + 10x + 25$

15) $9x^2 - 12x + 4$

16) $x^2 - 9$

17) $m^2 - 25$

18) $4x^2 - 25$

19) $x^2 - y^2$

20) $4a^2 - 9b^2$

In questions 21 to 27 complete the bracket which has been left blank.

21) $x^2 - x - 6 = (x+2)(\qquad)$

22) $x^2 - 12x + 35 = (x-5)(\qquad)$

23) $6x^2 + 31x + 40 = (3x+8)(\qquad)$

24) $10x^2 - 31x + 15 = (2x-5)(\qquad)$

25) $x^2 + 2x + 1 = (\qquad)^2$

26) $x^2 - 2x + 1 = (\qquad)^2$

27) $9p^2 - 25 = (3p+5)(\qquad)$

Factorise in questions 28 to 35.

28) $2x^2 + 13x + 15$

29) $3m^2 - 5m - 28$

30) $4x^2 - 10x - 6$

31) $10a^2 + 19a - 15$

32) $21x^2 + 37x + 10$

33) $26p^2 + 33p - 9$

34) $4x^2 + 12x + 9$

35) $9x^2 + 6x + 1$

Multiplication and Division of Fractions

As with ordinary arithmetic fractions, numerators can be multiplied together as can denominators, in order to form a single fraction. Thus,

$$\frac{a}{b} \times \frac{c}{d} = \frac{a \times c}{b \times d} = \frac{ac}{bd}$$

and

$$\frac{3x}{2y} \times \frac{p}{4q} \times \frac{r^2}{s} = \frac{3x \times p \times r^2}{2y \times 4q \times s} = \frac{3xpr^2}{8yqs}$$

Factors which are common to both numerator and denominator may be cancelled. It is important to realise that this cancelling means dividing the numerator and denominator by the same quantity. For instance,

$$\frac{8ab}{3mn} \times \frac{9n^2m}{4ab^2}$$

$$= \frac{\overset{2}{\cancel{8}} \times \cancel{a} \times \cancel{b} \times \overset{3}{\cancel{9}} \times \cancel{m} \times n \times \cancel{m}}{\cancel{3} \times \cancel{m} \times \cancel{n} \times \cancel{4} \times \cancel{a} \times \cancel{b} \times b} = \frac{6n}{b}$$

73

and

$$\frac{7ab}{8mn^2} \times \frac{3m^2n^3}{2ab^3} \times \frac{16an}{63bm}$$

$$= \frac{\cancel{7} \times \cancel{a} \times \cancel{b} \times \cancel{3} \times \cancel{m} \times m \times \cancel{n} \times n \times \cancel{16} \times a \times n}{\cancel{8} \times \cancel{m} \times n \times \cancel{n} \times \cancel{2} \times \cancel{a} \times b \times b \times b \times \underset{3}{\cancel{63}} \times \cancel{b} \times \cancel{m}}$$

$$= \frac{an^2}{3b^3}$$

To divide by a fraction invert it and then multiply:

Example 13

1) Simplify $\dfrac{ax^2}{by} \div \dfrac{a^2}{b^2y^2}$

$$\frac{ax^2}{by} \div \frac{a^2}{b^2y^2} = \frac{ax^2}{by} \times \frac{b^2y^2}{a^2} = \frac{bx^2y}{a}$$

Exercise 79 — *All type B*

Simplify the following:

1) $\dfrac{a}{bc^2} \times \dfrac{b^2c}{a}$ **4)** $\dfrac{3pq}{5rs} \div \dfrac{p^2}{15s^2}$

2) $\dfrac{3pq}{r} \times \dfrac{qs}{2t} \times \dfrac{3rs}{pq^2}$ **5)** $\dfrac{6ab}{5cd} \div \dfrac{4a^2}{7bd}$

3) $\dfrac{2z^2y}{3ac^2} \times \dfrac{6a^2}{5zy^2} \times \dfrac{10c^3}{3y^2}$

Addition and Subtraction of Fractions

The method for algebraic fractions is the same as for arithmetical fractions, that is:

1) Find the L.C.M. of the denominators.

2) Express each fraction with the common denominator.

3) Add or subtract the fractions.

74

Example 14

1) Simplify $\dfrac{a}{2} + \dfrac{b}{3} - \dfrac{c}{4}$

The L.C.M. of 2, 3, and 4 is 12

$$\frac{a}{2} + \frac{b}{3} - \frac{c}{4} = \frac{6a}{12} + \frac{4b}{12} - \frac{3c}{12}$$

$$= \frac{6a + 4b - 3c}{12}$$

2) Simplify $\dfrac{2}{x} + \dfrac{3}{2x} + \dfrac{4}{3x}$

The L.C.M. of x, $2x$ and $3x$ is $6x$.

$$\frac{2}{x} + \frac{3}{2x} + \frac{4}{3x} = \frac{12 + 9 + 8}{6x} = \frac{29}{6x}$$

The sign in front of a fraction applies to the fraction as a whole. The line which separates the numerator and denominator acts as a bracket.

Example 15

Simplify $\dfrac{m}{12} + \dfrac{2m+n}{4} - \dfrac{m-2n}{3}$

The L.C.M. of 12, 4 and 3 is 12.

$$\therefore \qquad \frac{m}{12} + \frac{2m+n}{4} - \frac{m-2n}{3}$$

$$= \frac{m + 3(2m+n) - 4(m-2n)}{12}$$

$$= \frac{m + 6m + 3n - 4m + 8n}{12}$$

$$= \frac{3m + 11n}{12}$$

Exercise 80 — *All type B*

Simplify the following:

1) $\dfrac{x}{3} + \dfrac{x}{4} + \dfrac{x}{5}$ **4)** $\dfrac{3}{y} - \dfrac{5}{3y} + \dfrac{4}{5y}$

2) $\dfrac{5a}{12} - \dfrac{7a}{18}$ **5)** $\dfrac{3}{5p} - \dfrac{2}{3q}$

3) $\dfrac{2}{q} - \dfrac{3}{2q}$ **6)** $\dfrac{3x}{2y} - \dfrac{5y}{6x}$

7) $3x - \dfrac{4y}{5z}$

9) $3m - \dfrac{2m+n}{7}$

8) $1 - \dfrac{2x}{5} + \dfrac{x}{8}$

10) $\dfrac{3a+5b}{4} - \dfrac{a-3b}{2}$

11) $\dfrac{3m-5n}{6} - \dfrac{3m-7n}{2}$

12) $\dfrac{x-2}{4} + \dfrac{2}{5}$

14) $\dfrac{3x-5}{10} + \dfrac{2x-3}{15}$

13) $\dfrac{x-5}{3} - \dfrac{x-2}{4}$

Operations on Numbers

Given any two numbers, there are various ways of operating on them apart from the familiar operations of adding, subtracting, dividing and multiplying. The method is shown in Examples 16 and 17.

Example 16

If $a*b$ means $\sqrt{ab}$ find the value of $4*9$.

Here we have $a = 4$ and $b = 9$.

Hence $4*9 = \sqrt{4 \times 9} = 6$.

Example 17

If $a*b$ means $\frac{1}{2}(2a-b)$ find the value of $5*2$.

Here $a = 5$ and $b = 2$.

Hence $5*2 = \frac{1}{2}(2 \times 5 - 2)$
$= \frac{1}{2}(10-2) = \frac{1}{2} \times 8 = 4$

Exercise 81 — *All type B*

1) If $a*b$ means $2a+b$ find the value of $3*1$.

2) If $x*y$ means $3x-2y$ find the value of $2*5$.

3) If $a*b$ means $\frac{1}{4}(a-b)$ find the value of $5*3$.

4) If $a*b$ means $(a+b)^2$ find the value of $2*3$.

5) If $x*y$ means $\sqrt{xy}$ find the value of $9*16$.

6) If $a*b$ means $\sqrt{a^2-b^2}$ find the value of $5*3$.

7) If $p*q$ means $\frac{1}{2}(p^2+q^3)$ find the value of $4*2$.

8) If $a*b$ means $(a-b^2)^2$ find the value of $3*(-2)$.

9) If $a*b$ means $(a^3+b)^2$ find the value of $(-5)*3$.

10) If $m*n$ means $m^2-2mn+n^3$ find the value of $2*3$.

Exercise 82 — *Questions 1–15 type A, 16–31 type B, 32–35 type C*

All the questions in this exercise have been taken from past C.S.E. examination papers.

1) Given $p = 1$, $q = -1$ and $r = 0$

(a) The value of $p+q+r$ is:

   a -2 **b** -1 **c** 0
   d 2 **e** 1

(b) The value of pq is:

   a 1 **b** 2 **c** 0
   d -2 **e** -1

(c) The value of $p(q+r)$ is

   a -1 **b** 0 **c** 1
   d 2 **e** -2 *(N.W.)*

2) $(2x+y)+(x-2y)$ is:

   a $3x+y$ **b** $x-y$ **c** $x-3y$
   d $x+3y$ **e** $3x-y$ *(N.W.)*

3) $\dfrac{2^3 \times 2^4}{2^2}$ is equal to:

   a 2^4 **b** 2^3 **c** 2^2
   d 2^6 **e** 2^5 *(N.W.)*

75

4) $(2x+y)-(x-2y)$ is equal to:

   a $3x-y$ **b** $x+3y$ **c** $x-3y$

   d $3x+y$ **e** $x-y$ (N.W.)

5) $(2x+y)(x-2y)$ is equal to:

   a $2x^2-2y^2$

   b $2x^2+2y^2$

   c $2x^2+3xy+2y^2$

   d $2x^2+3xy-2y^2$

   e $2x^2-3xy-2y^2$ (N.W.)

6) If $x=2$ the value of $2x^2+3$ is:

   a 11   **b** 19   **c** 14

   d 24   **e** 50   (W.M.)

7) $(2x-1)(x+2)$ is equal to:

   a $2x^2-2$ **b** $2x^2+3x-2$

   c $2x^2-3x-2$ **d** $3x+1$

   e $2x^2+4x-2$ (W.M.)

8) Which one of the following is *not* equal to $\frac{1}{2}pq$?

   a $\dfrac{pq}{2}$ **b** $p\times\dfrac{q}{2}$ **c** $\dfrac{1}{2}qp$

   d $\dfrac{1}{2p}\times q$ **e** $q\times\dfrac{p}{2}$ (S.E.)

9) $(3a^2)^3$ is equal to:

   a $3a^6$ **b** $9a^6$ **c** $18a$

   d $27a^2$ **e** $27a^6$ (S.E.)

10) The value of $(2^3)^2$ is:

   a 16   **b** 32   **c** 36

   d 48   **e** 64   (S.E.)

11) The value of 2^2+3^3 is:

   a 13   **b** 25   **c** 31

   d 36   **e** 81   (S.E.)

12) If $x=3$ and $y=5$ find the value of

 (a) $x+2y$ (b) $2xy$

 (c) $x+y^2$ (d) $\sqrt{2(x+y)}$

                            (E.M.)

13) If $a=1$, $b=-2$ and $c=3$, what is the value of

$$\frac{ab-c}{c+ab}\ ?\qquad\qquad (S)$$

14) If $x=3$ and $y=-2$, calculate the value of $2x^2-y^2$.   (W.M.)

15) Simplify the expression $2a-4b+3c+3a+3b-5c-a-b$.

                            (W.M.)

16) The value of $64^{1/3}$ is:

       a 2   **b** 8   **c** 16

       d 4   **e** $21\frac{1}{3}$ (N.W.)

17) $4\times10^2\times2\times10^{-4}$ is equal to:

   a 8×10^6 **b** 8×10^{-2}

   c 8×10^{-8} **d** 6×10^6

   e 6×10^{-2} (S.E.)

18) Find the values of:

 (a) 1^0 (b) 2^6 (c) $(-2)^3$

 (d) 5^{-1} (M)

19) Factorise:

 (a) $24+6y$ (b) y^2-100

 (c) $x^2+7x+12$ (M)

20) $3(x-y)-2(x+y)$ when simplified is:

   a $x-y$ **b** $x-5y$

   c $x-2y$ **d** x

   e $(x-y)(x+y)$ (W.M.)

21) $(x-2)$ and $(x+3)$ are the factors of:

   a $2x+1$ **b** x^2-9

   c x^2-6 **d** x^2-x-6

   e x^2+x-6 (W.M.)

22) Expand $(2x-3y)^2$.   (W.M.)

23) Calculate the value of 48×4^{-2}.

                            (W.M.)

24) Write down 10^{-3} as:

 (a) a vulgar fraction,

 (b) a decimal fraction.   (Y.R.)

25) If $a*b$ means $\frac{1}{4}(a+b)$ calculate:

 (a) $(4*12)*20$

 (b) $4*(12*20)$ (Y.R.)

26) Simplify:

$(n+1)(n+1)-n(n+2)$ (Y.R.)

27) Simplify:

(a) $6x + 3x$ (b) $-6x + 3x$

(c) $6x \div 3x$ (d) $-6x \times (-3x)$

                                          (W)

28) Factorise completely:

(a) $2abc - 6abd$

(b) $4(a-b) - c(a-b)$ *(W)*

29) If $a*b$ means $(a+b)^2$ find the value of $(2*1)*3$.   *(N.W.)*

30) Factorise $x^2 - 5x + 4$.   *(Y.R.)*

31) Simplify $\dfrac{1}{x} + \dfrac{1}{3x}$ *(Y.R.)*

32) If $y = x^2 - 10x - 24$ find the value of y when:

(a) $x = 0$ (b) $x = 13$

(c) $x = -2$ *(Y.R.)*

33) Factorise completely $3a^2 - 3b^2$.   *(W.M.)*

34) Factorise $10 - 15x^2$ *(E.A.)*

35) Factorise:

(a) $9x^2 - 16$ (b) $9x^2 - 16x$

(c) $x^2 - 9x - 22$ *(S)*

Chapter 11 Equations

Introduction

Fig. 11.1 shows a pair of scales which are in balance. That is each scale pan contains exactly the same number of grams. Therefore

$$x + 2 = 7$$

This is an example of an equation. To solve the equation we have to find a value for x such that the scales remain in balance. Now the only way to keep the scales in balance is to add or subtract the same amount from each pan. If we take 2 kilogrammes from the left hand pan then we are left with x kilogrammes in this pan, but we must also take 2 kilogrammes from the right hand pan to maintain balance. That is,

$$x + 2 - 2 = 7 - 2$$
$$x = 5$$

Therefore x is 5 kilogrammes.

We now take a second example as shown in Fig. 11.2. In the left hand pan we have three packets exactly the same, whilst in the right hand pan there is 6 kg. How many kilogrammes are there in each packet?

If we let there be x kilogrammes in each packet then there are $3x$ kilogrammes in the three packets. Therefore we have the equation:

$$3x = 6$$

We can maintain the balance of the scales if we multiply or divide the quantities in each scale by the same amount. In our equation if we divide

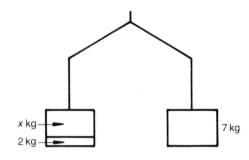

Fig. 11.1

each side by three we have

$$\frac{3x}{3} = \frac{6}{3}$$

Cancelling the threes on the left hand side we have

$$x = 2$$

and hence each packet contains 2 kilogrammes.

From these two examples we can say:

1) An equation expresses balance between two sets of quantities.

2) We can add or subtract the same amount from each side of the equation without destroying the balance.

3) We can multiply or divide each side of the equation by the same amount without destroying the balance.

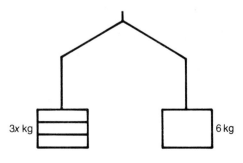

Fig. 11.2

Simple Equations

Simple equations contain only the first power of the unknown quantity. Thus

$$7t - 5 = 4t + 7$$

$$\frac{5x}{3} = \frac{2x + 5}{2}$$

are both examples of simple equations. After an equation is solved, the solution should be checked by substituting the result in each side of the equation separately. If each side of the equation then has the same value the solution is correct.

Solving Simple Equations

Equations requiring multiplication and division.

Example 1

1) Solve the equation $\frac{x}{6} = 3$

Multiplying each side by 6, we get

$$\frac{x}{6} \times 6 = 3 \times 6$$

$$x = 18$$

Check: when $x = 18$, L.H.S. $= \frac{18}{6} = 3$

R.H.S. $= 3$

Hence the solution is correct.

2) Solve the equation $5x = 10$

Dividing each side by 5, we get

$$\frac{5x}{5} = \frac{10}{5}$$

$$x = 2$$

Check:

when $x = 2$, L.H.S. $= 5 \times 2 = 10$

R.H.S. $= 10$

Hence the solution is correct.

Equations requiring addition and subtraction.

Example 2

1) Solve $x - 4 = 8$

If we add 4 to each side, we get

$$x - 4 + 4 = 8 + 4$$

$$x = 12$$

The operation of adding 4 to each side is the same as transferring -4 to the R.H.S. but in so doing the sign is changed from a minus to a plus. Thus,

$$x - 4 = 8$$

$$x = 8 + 4$$

$$x = 12$$

Check:

when $x = 12$, L.H.S. $= 12 - 4 = 8$

R.H.S. $= 8$

Hence the solution is correct.

2) Solve $x + 5 = 20$

If we subtract 5 from each side, we get

$$x + 5 - 5 = 20 - 5$$

$$x = 15$$

Alternatively moving $+5$ to the R.H.S.

$$x = 20 - 5$$

$$x = 15$$

Check:

when $x = 15$, L.H.S. $= 15 + 5 = 20$

R.H.S. $= 20$

$\therefore$ The solution is correct.

Equations containing the unknown quantity on both sides.

In equations of this kind group all the terms containing the unknown quantity on one side of the equation and the remaining terms on the other side.

Example 3

1) Solve $7x + 3 = 5x + 17$

Transferring $5x$ to the L.H.S. and $+3$ to the R.H.S.

$$7x - 5x = 17 - 3$$
$$2x = 14$$
$$x = \frac{14}{2}$$
$$x = 7$$

Check:

when $x = 7$, L.H.S. $= 7 \times 7 + 3 = 52$

R.H.S. $= 5 \times 7 + 17 = 52$

Hence the solution is correct.

2) Solve $3x - 2 = 5x + 6$

$$3x - 5x = 6 + 2$$
$$-2x = 8$$
$$x = \frac{8}{-2}$$
$$x = -4$$

Check: when $x = -4$,

L.H.S. $= 3 \times (-4) - 2 = -14$

R.H.S. $= 5 \times (-4) + 6 = -14$

Hence the solution is correct.

Equations containing brackets.

When an equation contains brackets remove these first and then solve as shown previously.

Example 4

1) Solve $2(3x + 7) = 16$

Removing the bracket,

$$6x + 14 = 16$$
$$6x = 16 - 14$$
$$6x = 2$$

$$x = \frac{2}{6}$$
$$x = \frac{1}{3}$$

Check: when $x = \frac{1}{3}$,

L.H.S. $= 2 \times \left(3 \times \frac{1}{3} + 7\right) = 2 \times (1 + 7)$

$$= 2 \times 8 = 16$$

R.H.S. $= 16$

Hence the solution is correct.

2) Solve $3(x + 4) - 5(x - 1) = 19$

Removing the brackets

$$3x + 12 - 5x + 5 = 19$$
$$-2x + 17 = 19$$
$$-2x = 19 - 17$$
$$-2x = 2$$
$$x = \frac{2}{-2}$$
$$x = -1$$

Check: when $x = -1$,

L.H.S. $= 3 \times (-1 + 4) - 5 \times (-1 - 1)$

$$= 3 \times 3 - 5 \times (-2)$$
$$= 9 + 10 = 19$$

R.H.S. $= 19$

Hence the solution is correct.

Equations containing fractions.

When an equation contains fractions, *multiply each term of the equation* by the L.C.M. of the denominators.

Example 5

1) Solve $\frac{x}{4} + \frac{3}{5} = \frac{3x}{2} - 2$

The L.C.M. of the denominators 2, 4 and 5 is 20.

Multiplying each term by 20 gives,

$$\frac{x}{4} \times 20 + \frac{3}{5} \times 20 = \frac{3x}{2} \times 20 - 2 \times 20$$

$$5x + 12 = 30x - 40$$

$$5x - 30x = -40 - 12$$

$$-25x = -52$$

$$x = \frac{-52}{-25}$$

$$\therefore \qquad x = \frac{52}{25}$$

The solution may be verified by the check method shown in the previous examples.

2) Solve the equation

$$\frac{x-4}{3} - \frac{2x-1}{2} = 4$$

In solving equations of this type remember that the line separating the numerator and denominator acts as a bracket. The L.C.M. of the denominators 3 and 2 is 6. Multiplying *each term* of the equation by 6,

$$\frac{x-4}{3} \times 6 - \frac{2x-1}{2} \times 6 = 4 \times 6$$

$$2(x-4) - 3(2x-1) = 24$$

$$2x - 8 - 6x + 3 = 24$$

$$-4x - 5 = 24$$

$$-4x = 24 + 5$$

$$-4x = 29$$

$$x = \frac{29}{-4}$$

$$x = -\frac{29}{4}$$

Exercise 83 — *Questions 1–19 type A, remainder B*

Solve the equations

1) $x + 2 = 7$

2) $t - 4 = 3$

3) $2q = 4$

4) $x - 8 = 12$

5) $q + 5 = 2$

6) $3x = 9$

7) $\frac{y}{2} = 3$

8) $\frac{m}{3} = 4$

9) $2x + 5 = 9$

10) $5x - 3 = 12$

11) $6p - 7 = 17$

12) $3x + 4 = -2$

13) $7x + 12 = 5$

14) $6x - 3x + 2x = 20$

15) $14 - 3x = 8$

16) $5x - 10 = 3x + 2$

17) $6m + 11 = 25 - m$

18) $3x - 22 = 8x + 18$

19) $0.3d = 1.8$

20) $1.2x - 0.8 = 0.8x + 1.2$

21) $2(x + 1) = 8$

22) $5(m - 2) = 15$

23) $3(x - 1) - 4(2x + 3) = 14$

24) $5(x + 2) - 3(x - 5) = 29$

25) $3x = 5(9 - x)$

26) $4(x - 5) = 7 - 5(3 - 2x)$

27) $\frac{x}{5} - \frac{x}{3} = 2$

28) $\frac{x}{3} + \frac{x}{4} + \frac{x}{5} = \frac{5}{6}$

29) $\frac{m}{2} + \frac{m}{3} + 3 = 2 + \frac{m}{6}$

30) $3x + \frac{3}{4} = 2 + \frac{2x}{3}$

31) $\frac{3}{m} = 3$

32) $\frac{5}{x} = 2$

33) $\frac{4}{t} = \frac{2}{3}$

34) $\frac{7}{x} = \frac{5}{3}$

35) $\frac{4}{7}y - \frac{3}{5}y = 2$

36) $\frac{1}{3x} + \frac{1}{4x} = \frac{7}{20}$

37) $\frac{x+3}{4} - \frac{x-3}{5} = 2$

38) $\frac{2x}{15} - \frac{x-6}{12} - \frac{3x}{20} = \frac{3}{2}$

39) $\frac{2m-3}{4} = \frac{4-5m}{3}$

40) $\frac{3-y}{4} = \frac{y}{3}$

Chapter 12 Logarithms

Numbers in Standard Form

Any number can be expressed as a value between 1 and 10 multiplied by a power of 10. A number expressed in this way is said to be in standard form. The repeating of zeros in very large and very small numbers often leads to errors. Stating the number in standard form helps to avoid these errors.

Example 1

1) $49.4 = 4.94 \times 10$

2) $385.3 = 3.853 \times 100$
$= 3.853 \times 10^2$

3) $20\,000\,000 = 2 \times 10\,000\,000$
$= 2 \times 10^7$

4) $0.596 = \dfrac{5.96}{10} = 5.96 \times 10^{-1}$

5) $0.000\,478 = \dfrac{4.78}{10\,000} = \dfrac{4.78}{10^4}$
$= 4.78 \times 10^{-4}$

Exercise 84 — *All type A*

1) Write the following in standard form:

(a) 19.6   (e) 0.013
(b) 385   (f) 0.003 85
(c) 59 876   (g) 0.000 698
(d) 1 500 000   (h) 0.023 85

2) Write down the values of the following:

(a) 1.5×10^2 (e) 2.5×10^{-1}
(b) 4.7×10^4 (f) 4.0×10^{-3}
(c) 3.6×10^6 (g) 8.0×10^{-5}
(d) 9.45×10^3 (h) 4.0×10^{-2}

3) State which of the following pairs of numbers is the larger:

(a) 5.8×10^2 and 2.1×10^3
(b) 9.4×10^3 and 9.95×10^3
(c) 8.58×10^4 and 9.87×10^3

4) State which of the following pairs of numbers is the smaller:

(a) 2.1×10^{-2} and 3.8×10^{-2}
(b) 8.72×10^{-3} and 9.7×10^{-2}
(c) 3.83×10^{-2} and 2.11×10^{-4}

Logarithms

Any positive number can be expressed as a power of 10. For example $100 = 10^2$ and $86 = 10^{1.9345}$. These powers of 10 are called logarithms to the base 10. That is,

$$\text{number} = 10^{\text{power}} = 10^{\text{logarithm}}$$

We have seen that $86 = 10^{1.9345}$ and we write

$$\log_{10} 86 = 1.9345$$

The base 10 is indicated as shown above, but it is frequently omitted and we write,

$$\log 86 = 1.9345$$

The logarithm tables give the logarithms of numbers between 1 and 10; they are shown on pages 83 and 84. The figures in the first column of the complete table are the numbers from 10 to 99. The corresponding figures in the column headed 0 are the logarithms of these numbers. Thus

$$\log 2.1 = 0.3222$$

If the number has a third significant figure the logarithm is found in the appropriate column of the next 9 columns. Thus

$$\log 2.13 = 0.3284$$

When the number has a fourth significant figure we use the last 9 columns which give us, for every fourth significant figure, a number which must be added to the logarithm already found for the first three significant figures. Thus to find log 2.134 we find log 2.13 = 0.3284. Using the last 9 columns we find in the column headed 4, the number 8. This is added to 3284 to give 3292.

$$\log 2.134 = 0.3292$$

Exercise 85 — *All type A*

Write down the logarithms of the following numbers:

1) 3.6   3) 3.42   5) 9.17

2) 4.8   4) 8.39   6) 4.186

Logarithms

	0	1	2	3	4	5	6	7	8	9	1	2	3	4	5	6	7	8	9
10	0000	0043	0086	0128	0170						4	8	13	17	21	25	30	34	38
						0212	0253	0294	0334	0374	4	8	12	16	20	24	28	32	36
11	0414	0453	0492	0531	0569						4	8	12	15	19	23	27	31	35
						0607	0645	0682	0719	0755	4	7	11	15	18	22	26	30	33
12	0792	0828	0864	0899	0934						4	7	11	14	18	21	25	28	32
						0969	1004	1038	1072	1106	3	7	10	14	17	20	24	27	31
13	1139	1173	1206	1239	1271						3	7	10	13	16	20	23	26	30
						1303	1335	1367	1399	1430	3	6	9	13	16	19	22	25	28
14	1461	1492	1523	1553	1584						3	6	9	12	15	18	21	24	27
						1614	1644	1673	1703	1732	3	6	9	12	15	18	21	24	27
15	1761	1790	1818	1847	1875						3	6	9	11	14	17	20	23	26
						1903	1931	1959	1987	2014	3	6	8	11	14	17	19	22	25
16	2041	2068	2095	2122	2148						3	5	8	11	13	16	19	21	24
						2175	2201	2227	2253	2279	3	5	8	10	13	16	18	21	23
17	2304	2330	2355	2380	2405						3	5	8	10	13	15	18	20	23
						2430	2455	2480	2504	2529	2	5	7	10	12	15	17	20	22
18	2553	2577	2601	2625	2648						2	5	7	10	12	14	17	19	21
						2672	2695	2718	2742	2765	2	5	7	9	12	14	16	19	21
19	2788	2810	2833	2856	2878						2	5	7	9	11	14	16	18	20
						2900	2923	2945	2967	2989	2	4	7	9	11	13	15	18	20
20	3010	3032	3054	3075	3096	3118	3139	3160	3181	3201	2	4	6	8	11	13	15	17	19
21	3222	3243	3263	3284	3304	3324	3345	3365	3385	3404	2	4	6	8	10	12	14	16	18
22	3424	3444	3464	3483	3502	3522	3541	3560	3579	3598	2	4	6	8	10	12	14	15	17
23	3617	3636	3655	3674	3692	3711	3729	3747	3766	3784	2	4	6	7	9	11	13	15	17
24	3802	3820	3838	3856	3874	3892	3909	3927	3945	3962	2	4	5	7	9	11	12	14	16
25	3979	3997	4014	4031	4048	4065	4082	4099	4116	4133	2	3	5	7	9	10	12	14	15
26	4150	4166	4183	4200	4216	4232	4249	4265	4281	4298	2	3	5	7	8	10	11	13	15
27	4314	4330	4346	4362	4378	4393	4409	4425	4440	4456	2	3	5	6	8	9	11	13	14
28	4472	4487	4502	4518	4533	4548	4564	4579	4594	4609	2	3	5	6	8	9	11	12	14
29	4624	4639	4654	4669	4683	4698	4713	4728	4742	4757	1	3	4	6	7	9	10	12	13
30	4771	4786	4800	4814	4829	4843	4857	4871	4886	4900	1	3	4	6	7	9	10	11	13
31	4914	4928	4942	4955	4969	4983	4997	5011	5024	5038	1	3	4	6	7	8	10	11	12
32	5051	5065	5079	5092	5105	5119	5132	5145	5159	5172	1	3	4	5	7	8	9	11	12
33	5185	5198	5211	5224	5237	5250	5263	5276	5289	5302	1	3	4	5	6	8	9	10	12
34	5315	5328	5340	5353	5366	5378	5391	5403	5416	5428	1	3	4	5	6	8	9	10	11
35	5441	5453	5465	5478	5490	5502	5514	5527	5539	5551	1	2	4	5	6	7	9	10	11
36	5563	5575	5587	5599	5611	5623	5635	5647	5658	5670	1	2	4	5	6	7	8	10	11
37	5682	5694	5705	5717	5729	5740	5752	5763	5775	5786	1	2	3	5	6	7	8	9	10
38	5798	5809	5821	5832	5843	5855	5866	5877	5888	5899	1	2	3	5	6	7	8	9	10
39	5911	5922	5933	5944	5955	5966	5977	5988	5999	6010	1	2	3	4	5	7	8	9	10
40	6021	6031	6042	6053	6064	6075	6085	6096	6107	6117	1	2	3	4	5	6	8	9	10
41	6128	6138	6149	6160	6170	6180	6191	6201	6212	6222	1	2	3	4	5	6	7	8	9
42	6232	6243	6253	6263	6274	6284	6294	6304	6314	6325	1	2	3	4	5	6	7	8	9
43	6335	6345	6355	6365	6375	6385	6395	6405	6415	6425	1	2	3	4	5	6	7	8	9
44	6435	6444	6454	6464	6474	6484	6493	6503	6513	6522	1	2	3	4	5	6	7	8	9
45	6532	6542	6551	6561	6571	6580	6590	6599	6609	6618	1	2	3	4	5	6	7	8	9
46	6628	6637	6646	6656	6665	6675	6684	6693	6702	6712	1	2	3	4	5	6	7	7	8
47	6721	6730	6739	6749	6758	6767	6776	6785	6794	6803	1	2	3	4	5	5	6	7	8
48	6812	6821	6830	6839	6848	6857	6866	6875	6884	6893	1	2	3	4	4	5	6	7	8
49	6902	6911	6920	6928	6937	6946	6955	6964	6972	6981	1	2	3	4	4	5	6	7	8

7) 8.305   **9)** 2.876

8) 6.117   **10)** 5.698

To find the logarithms of numbers outside the range of 1 to 10, we make use of numbers in standard form. Then, by using the multiplication law of indices and the log tables we find the complete logarithm. For example

To find log 249.3

$$249.3 = 2.493 \times 10^2$$

From the log tables:

$$\log 2.493 = 0.3967$$

$$249.3 = 10^{0.3967} \times 10^2 = 10^{2.3967}$$

$$\log 249.3 = 2.3967$$

A logarithm therefore consists of two parts:

  (i) a whole number part called the *characteristic*.

  (ii) a decimal part called the *mantissa*.

Logarithms

	0	1	2	3	4	5	6	7	8	9	1	2	3	4	5	6	7	8	9
50	6990	6998	7007	7016	7024	7033	7042	7050	7059	7067	1	2	3	3	4	5	6	7	8
51	7076	7084	7093	7101	7110	7118	7126	7135	7143	7152	1	2	3	3	4	5	6	7	8
52	7160	7168	7177	7185	7193	7202	7210	7218	7226	7235	1	2	2	3	4	5	6	7	7
53	7243	7251	7259	7267	7275	7284	7292	7300	7308	7316	1	2	2	3	4	5	6	6	7
54	7324	7332	7340	7348	7356	7364	7372	7380	7388	7396	1	2	2	3	4	5	6	6	7
55	7404	7412	7419	7427	7435	7443	7451	7459	7466	7474	1	2	2	3	4	5	5	6	7
56	7482	7490	7497	7505	7513	7520	7528	7536	7543	7551	1	2	2	3	4	5	5	6	7
57	7559	7566	7574	7582	7589	7597	7604	7612	7619	7627	1	2	2	3	4	5	5	6	7
58	7634	7642	7649	7657	7664	7672	7679	7686	7694	7701	1	1	2	3	4	4	5	6	7
59	7709	7716	7723	7731	7738	7745	7752	7760	7767	7774	1	1	2	3	4	4	5	6	7
60	7782	7789	7796	7803	7810	7818	7825	7832	7839	7846	1	1	2	3	4	4	5	6	6
61	7853	7860	7868	7875	7882	7889	7896	7903	7910	7917	1	1	2	3	4	4	5	6	6
62	7924	7931	7938	7945	7952	7959	7966	7973	7980	7987	1	1	2	3	3	4	5	6	6
63	7993	8000	8007	8014	8021	8028	8035	8041	8048	8055	1	1	2	3	3	4	5	5	6
64	8062	8069	8075	8082	8089	8096	8102	8109	8116	8122	1	1	2	3	3	4	5	5	6
65	8129	8136	8142	8149	8156	8162	8169	8176	8182	8189	1	1	2	3	3	4	5	5	6
66	8195	8202	8209	8215	8222	8228	8235	8241	8248	8254	1	1	2	3	3	4	5	5	6
67	8261	8267	8274	8280	8287	8293	8299	8306	8312	8319	1	1	2	3	3	4	5	5	6
68	8325	8331	8338	8344	8351	8357	8363	8370	8376	8382	1	1	2	3	3	4	4	5	6
69	8388	8395	8401	8407	8414	8420	8426	8432	8439	8445	1	1	2	2	3	4	4	5	6
70	8451	8457	8463	8470	8476	8482	8488	8494	8500	8506	1	1	2	2	3	4	4	5	6
71	8513	8519	8525	8531	8537	8543	8549	8555	8561	8567	1	1	2	2	3	4	4	5	5
72	8573	8579	8585	8591	8597	8603	8609	8615	8621	8627	1	1	2	2	3	4	4	5	5
73	8633	8639	8645	8651	8657	8663	8669	8675	8681	8686	1	1	2	2	3	4	4	5	5
74	8692	8698	8704	8710	8716	8722	8727	8733	8739	8745	1	1	2	2	3	3	4	5	5
75	8751	8756	8762	8768	8774	8779	8785	8791	8797	8802	1	1	2	2	3	3	4	5	5
76	8808	8814	8820	8825	8831	8837	8842	8848	8854	8859	1	1	2	2	3	3	4	5	5
77	8865	8871	8876	8882	8887	8893	8899	8904	8910	8915	1	1	2	2	3	3	4	4	5
78	8921	8927	8932	8938	8943	8949	8954	8960	8965	8971	1	1	2	2	3	3	4	4	5
79	8976	8982	8987	8993	8998	9004	9009	9015	9020	9025	1	1	2	2	3	3	4	4	5
80	9031	9036	9042	9047	9053	9058	9063	9069	9074	9079	1	1	2	2	3	3	4	4	5
81	9085	9090	9096	9101	9106	9112	9117	9122	9128	9133	1	1	2	2	3	3	4	4	5
82	9138	9143	9149	9154	9159	9165	9170	9175	9180	9186	1	1	2	2	3	3	4	4	5
83	9191	9196	9201	9206	9212	9217	9222	9227	9232	9238	1	1	2	2	3	3	4	4	5
84	9243	9248	9253	9258	9263	9269	9274	9279	9284	9289	1	1	2	2	3	3	4	4	5
85	9294	9299	9304	9309	9315	9320	9325	9330	9335	9340	1	1	2	2	3	3	4	4	5
86	9345	9350	9355	9360	9365	9370	9375	9380	9385	9390	1	1	2	2	3	3	4	4	5
87	9395	9400	9405	9410	9415	9420	9425	9430	9435	9440	0	1	1	2	2	3	3	4	4
88	9445	9450	9455	9460	9465	9469	9474	9479	9484	9489	0	1	1	2	2	3	3	4	4
89	9494	9499	9504	9509	9513	9518	9523	9528	9533	9538	0	1	1	2	2	3	3	4	4
90	9542	9547	9552	9557	9562	9566	9571	9576	9581	9586	0	1	1	2	2	3	3	4	4
91	9590	9595	9600	9605	9609	9614	9619	9624	9628	9633	0	1	1	2	2	3	3	4	4
92	9638	9643	9647	9652	9657	9661	9666	9671	9675	9680	0	1	1	2	2	3	3	4	4
93	9685	9689	9694	9699	9703	9708	9713	9717	9722	9727	0	1	1	2	2	3	3	4	4
94	9731	9736	9741	9745	9750	9754	9759	9763	9768	9773	0	1	1	2	2	3	3	4	4
95	9777	9782	9786	9791	9795	9800	9805	9809	9814	9818	0	1	1	2	2	3	3	4	4
96	9823	9827	9832	9836	9841	9845	9850	9854	9859	9863	0	1	1	2	2	3	3	4	4
97	9868	9872	9877	9881	9886	9890	9894	9899	9903	9908	0	1	1	2	2	3	3	4	4
98	9912	9917	9921	9926	9930	9934	9939	9943	9948	9952	0	1	1	2	2	3	3	4	4
99	9956	9961	9965	9969	9974	9978	9983	9987	9991	9996	0	1	1	2	2	3	3	3	4

As can be seen from the above example the characteristic depends upon the size of the number. It is found by subtracting 1 from the number of figures which occur to the left of the decimal point in the given number. The mantissa is found directly from the log tables.

Example 2

1) In log 8293 the characteristic is 3 and hence   log 8293 = 3.9188

2) In log 829.3 the characteristic is 2 and hence   log 829.3 = 2.9188

3) In log 82.93 the characteristic is 1 and hence   log 82.93 = 1.9188

4) In log 8.293 the characteristic is 0 and hence   log 8.293 = 0.9188

Numbers which have the same set of significant figures have the same mantissa in their logarithms.

Exercise 86 — *All type A*

1) Write down the characteristics for the following:

(a)	23	(e)	950 000	(h)	333.4
(b)	23 000	(f)	55.27	(i)	2893
(c)	17 970	(g)	1.794	(j)	390.1
(d)	983				

2) Write down the logarithms of the following numbers:

(a)   7, 70, 700, 7000, 70 000
(b)   3.1, 31, 310, 3100, 3 100 000
(c)   48.3, 483 000, 4.83, 483
(d)   7895, 7.895, 78.95, 78 950
(e)   1.003, 10.03, 1003, 100.3

Anti-Logarithms

The table of anti-logarithms contains the numbers which correspond to the given logarithm. The table (shown on pages 86 and 87) is used in a similar

way to the log tables but it must be remembered that:

(i) The mantissa (or decimal part) of the logarithm only is used in the table.

(ii) The number of figures to the left of the decimal point is found by *adding 1* to the characteristic of the logarithm.

Example 3

To find the number whose logarithm is 2.1825.

Using the mantissa .1825 we find from the anti-log tables that the number corresponding is 1523. Since the characteristic is 2, the number must have three figures to the left of the decimal point. The number is therefore 152.3.

Note that
$$\log 152.3 = 2.1825.$$

Exercise 87 — *Questions 1–4 type A, remainder B*

Write down the anti-logs of the following:

1)   0.32, 2.32, 4.32, 1.32

2)   3.275, 0.275, 4.275, 6.275

3)   0.5987, 1.5987, 4.5987, 2.5987

4)   3.8949, 0.8949, 2.8949, 4.8949

Find the values of the following:

5) $10^{0.38}$ **7)** $10^{3.1683}$

6) $10^{1.263}$ **8)** $10^{2.563}$

Rules for the Use of Logarithms

It has been shown that logarithms are indices and hence when using logarithms the rules of indices must be observed.

(i) *Multiplication*

To find 39.27×6.127

$$\log 39.27 = 1.5941$$
and $\log 6.127 = 0.7873$

$$39.27 \times 6.127 = 10^{1.5941} \times 10^{0.7873}$$
$$= 10^{1.5941+0.7873}$$
$$= 10^{2.3814}$$

By finding the anti-log of 2.3814 we find that

$$39.27 \times 6.127 = 240.6$$

From this example we see that the rule for multiplication using logs is:

Find the logs of the numbers to be multiplied and add them together. The required product is found by taking the anti-log of the sum.

The method shown above is not very convenient and it is better to use the tabular method shown across the page.

Antilogarithms

	0	1	2	3	4	5	6	7	8	9	1	2	3	4	5	6	7	8	9
0.00	1000	1002	1005	1007	1009	1012	1014	1016	1019	1021	0	0	1	1	1	1	2	2	2
0.01	1023	1026	1028	1030	1033	1035	1038	1040	1042	1045	0	0	1	1	1	1	2	2	2
0.02	1047	1050	1052	1054	1057	1059	1062	1064	1067	1069	0	0	1	1	1	1	2	2	2
0.03	1072	1074	1076	1079	1081	1084	1086	1089	1091	1094	0	0	1	1	1	1	2	2	2
0.04	1096	1099	1102	1104	1107	1109	1112	1114	1117	1119	0	1	1	1	1	2	2	2	2
0.05	1122	1125	1127	1130	1132	1135	1138	1140	1143	1146	0	1	1	1	1	2	2	2	2
0.06	1148	1151	1153	1156	1159	1161	1164	1167	1169	1172	0	1	1	1	1	2	2	2	2
0.07	1175	1178	1180	1183	1186	1189	1191	1194	1197	1199	0	1	1	1	1	2	2	2	2
0.08	1202	1205	1208	1211	1213	1216	1219	1222	1225	1227	0	1	1	1	1	2	2	2	3
0.09	1230	1233	1236	1239	1242	1245	1247	1250	1253	1256	0	1	1	1	1	2	2	2	3
0.10	1259	1262	1265	1268	1271	1274	1276	1279	1282	1285	0	1	1	1	1	2	2	2	3
0.11	1288	1291	1294	1297	1300	1303	1306	1309	1312	1315	0	1	1	1	2	2	2	2	3
0.12	1318	1321	1324	1327	1330	1334	1337	1340	1343	1346	0	1	1	1	2	2	2	3	3
0.13	1349	1352	1355	1358	1361	1365	1368	1371	1374	1377	0	1	1	1	2	2	2	3	3
0.14	1380	1384	1387	1390	1393	1396	1400	1403	1406	1409	0	1	1	1	2	2	2	3	3
0.15	1413	1416	1419	1422	1426	1429	1432	1435	1439	1442	0	1	1	1	2	2	2	3	3
0.16	1445	1449	1452	1455	1459	1462	1466	1469	1472	1476	0	1	1	1	2	2	2	3	3
0.17	1479	1483	1486	1489	1493	1496	1500	1503	1507	1510	0	1	1	1	2	2	2	3	3
0.18	1514	1517	1521	1524	1528	1531	1535	1538	1542	1545	0	1	1	1	2	2	2	3	3
0.19	1549	1552	1556	1560	1563	1567	1570	1574	1578	1581	0	1	1	1	2	2	3	3	3
0.20	1585	1589	1592	1596	1600	1603	1607	1611	1614	1618	0	1	1	1	2	2	3	3	3
0.21	1622	1626	1629	1633	1637	1641	1644	1648	1652	1656	0	1	1	2	2	2	3	3	3
0.22	1660	1663	1667	1671	1675	1679	1683	1687	1690	1694	0	1	1	2	2	2	3	3	3
0.23	1698	1702	1706	1710	1714	1718	1722	1726	1730	1734	0	1	1	2	2	2	3	3	4
0.24	1738	1742	1746	1750	1754	1758	1762	1766	1770	1774	0	1	1	2	2	2	3	3	4
0.25	1778	1782	1786	1791	1795	1799	1803	1807	1811	1816	0	1	1	2	2	2	3	3	4
0.26	1820	1824	1828	1832	1837	1841	1845	1849	1854	1858	0	1	1	2	2	3	3	3	4
0.27	1862	1866	1871	1875	1879	1884	1888	1892	1897	1901	0	1	1	2	2	3	3	4	4
0.28	1905	1910	1914	1919	1923	1928	1932	1936	1941	1945	0	1	1	2	2	3	3	4	4
0.29	1950	1954	1959	1963	1968	1972	1977	1982	1986	1991	0	1	1	2	2	3	3	4	4
0.30	1995	2000	2004	2009	2014	2018	2023	2028	2032	2037	0	1	1	2	2	3	3	4	4
0.31	2042	2046	2051	2056	2061	2065	2070	2075	2080	2084	0	1	1	2	2	3	3	4	4
0.32	2089	2094	2099	2104	2109	2113	2118	2123	2128	2133	0	1	1	2	2	3	3	4	4
0.33	2138	2143	2148	2153	2158	2163	2168	2173	2178	2183	0	1	1	2	2	3	3	4	4
0.34	2188	2193	2198	2203	2208	2213	2218	2223	2228	2234	1	1	2	2	3	3	4	4	5
0.35	2239	2244	2249	2254	2259	2265	2270	2275	2280	2286	1	1	2	2	3	3	4	4	5
0.36	2291	2296	2301	2307	2312	2317	2323	2328	2333	2339	1	1	2	2	3	3	4	4	5
0.37	2344	2350	2355	2360	2366	2371	2377	2382	2388	2393	1	1	2	2	3	3	4	4	5
0.38	2399	2404	2410	2415	2421	2427	2432	2438	2443	2449	1	1	2	2	3	3	4	4	5
0.39	2455	2460	2466	2472	2477	2483	2489	2495	2500	2506	1	1	2	2	3	3	4	5	5
0.40	2512	2518	2523	2529	2535	2541	2547	2553	2559	2564	1	1	2	2	3	4	4	5	5
0.41	2570	2576	2582	2588	2594	2600	2606	2612	2618	2624	1	1	2	3	3	4	5	5	5
0.42	2630	2636	2642	2649	2655	2661	2667	2673	2679	2685	1	1	2	3	3	4	4	5	6
0.43	2692	2698	2704	2710	2716	2723	2729	2735	2742	2748	1	1	2	3	3	4	4	5	6
0.44	2754	2761	2767	2773	2780	2786	2793	2799	2805	2812	1	1	2	3	3	4	4	5	6
0.45	2818	2825	2831	2838	2844	2851	2858	2864	2871	2877	1	1	2	3	3	4	5	5	6
0.46	2884	2891	2897	2904	2911	2917	2924	2931	2938	2944	1	1	2	3	3	4	5	5	6
0.47	2951	2958	2965	2972	2979	2985	2992	2999	3006	3013	1	1	2	3	3	4	5	5	6
0.48	3020	3027	3034	3041	3048	3055	3062	3069	3076	3083	1	1	2	3	4	4	5	6	6
0.49	3090	3097	3105	3112	3119	3126	3133	3141	3148	3155	1	1	2	3	4	4	5	6	6

number	log
39.27	1.5941
6.127	0.7873
Answer = 240.6	**2.3814**

(ii) *Division*

To find $\dfrac{293.6}{18.78}$

$$\log 293.6 = 2.4678$$

and $\log 18.78 = 1.2737$

$$\frac{293.6}{18.78} = \frac{10^{2.4678}}{10^{1.2737}} = 10^{2.4678-1.2737}$$

$$= 10^{1.1941}$$

By finding the antilog of 1.1941 we see that

$$\frac{293.6}{18.78} = 15.63$$

From this example we see that the

Antilogarithms

	0	1	2	3	4	5	6	7	8	9	1	2	3	4	5	6	7	8	9
0.50	3162	3170	3177	3184	3192	3199	3206	3214	3221	3228	1	1	2	3	4	4	5	6	7
0.51	3236	3243	3251	3258	3266	3273	3281	3289	3296	3304	1	2	2	3	4	5	5	6	7
0.52	3311	3319	3327	3334	3342	3350	3357	3365	3373	3381	1	2	2	3	4	5	5	6	7
0.53	3388	3396	3404	3412	3420	3428	3436	3443	3451	3459	1	2	2	3	4	5	6	6	7
0.54	3467	3475	3483	3491	3499	3508	3516	3524	3532	3540	1	2	2	3	4	5	6	6	7
0.55	3548	3556	3565	3573	3581	3589	3597	3606	3614	3622	1	2	2	3	4	5	6	7	7
0.56	3631	3639	3648	3656	3664	3673	3681	3690	3698	3707	1	2	3	3	4	5	6	7	8
0.57	3715	3724	3733	3741	3750	3758	3767	3776	3784	3793	1	2	3	3	4	5	6	7	8
0.58	3802	3811	3819	3828	3837	3846	3855	3864	3873	3882	1	2	3	4	4	5	6	7	8
0.59	3890	3899	3908	3917	3926	3936	3945	3954	3963	3972	1	2	3	4	5	5	6	7	8
0.60	3981	3990	3999	4009	4018	4027	4036	4046	4055	4064	1	2	3	4	5	6	6	7	8
0.61	4074	4083	4093	4102	4111	4121	4130	4140	4150	4159	1	2	3	4	5	6	7	8	9
0.62	4169	4178	4188	4198	4207	4217	4227	4236	4246	4256	1	2	3	4	5	6	7	8	9
0.63	4266	4276	4285	4295	4305	4315	4325	4335	4345	4355	1	2	3	4	5	6	7	8	9
0.64	4365	4375	4385	4395	4406	4416	4426	4436	4446	4457	1	2	3	4	5	6	7	8	9
0.65	4467	4477	4487	4498	4508	4519	4529	4539	4550	4560	1	2	3	4	5	6	7	8	9
0.66	4571	4581	4592	4603	4613	4624	4634	4645	4656	4667	1	2	3	4	5	6	7	9	10
0.67	4677	4688	4699	4710	4721	4732	4742	4753	4764	4775	1	2	3	4	5	7	8	9	10
0.68	4786	4797	4808	4819	4831	4842	4853	4864	4875	4887	1	2	3	4	6	7	8	9	10
0.69	4893	4909	4920	4932	4943	4955	4966	4977	4989	5000	1	2	3	5	6	7	8	9	10
0.70	5012	5023	5035	5047	5058	5070	5082	5093	5105	5117	1	2	4	5	6	7	8	9	11
0.71	5129	5140	5152	5164	5176	5188	5200	5212	5224	5236	1	2	4	5	6	7	8	10	11
0.72	5248	5260	5272	5284	5297	5309	5321	5333	5336	5358	1	2	4	5	6	7	9	10	11
0.73	5370	5383	5395	5408	5420	5433	5445	5458	5470	5483	1	3	4	5	6	8	9	10	11
0.74	5495	5508	5521	5534	5546	5559	5572	5585	5598	5610	1	3	4	5	6	8	9	10	12
0.75	5623	5636	5649	5662	5675	5689	5702	5715	5728	5741	1	3	4	5	7	8	9	10	12
0.76	5754	5768	5781	5794	5808	5821	5834	5848	5861	5875	1	3	4	5	7	8	9	11	12
0.77	5888	5902	5916	5929	5943	5957	5970	5984	5998	6012	1	3	4	5	7	8	10	11	12
0.78	6026	6039	6053	6067	6081	6095	6109	6124	6138	6152	1	3	4	6	7	8	10	11	13
0.79	6166	6180	6194	6209	6223	6237	6252	6266	6281	6295	1	3	4	6	7	9	10	11	13
0.80	6310	6324	6339	6353	6368	6383	6397	6412	6427	6442	1	3	4	6	7	9	10	12	13
0.81	6457	6471	6486	6501	6516	6531	6546	6561	6577	6592	2	3	5	6	8	9	11	12	14
0.82	6607	6622	6637	6653	6668	6683	6699	6714	6730	6745	2	3	5	6	8	9	11	12	14
0.83	6761	6776	6792	6808	6823	6839	6855	6871	6887	6902	2	3	5	6	8	9	11	13	14
0.84	6918	6934	6950	6966	6982	6998	7015	7031	7047	7063	2	3	5	6	8	10	11	13	15
0.85	7079	7096	7112	7129	7145	7161	7178	7194	7211	7228	2	3	5	7	8	10	12	13	15
0.86	7244	7261	7278	7295	7311	7328	7345	7362	7379	7396	2	3	5	7	8	10	12	13	15
0.87	7413	7430	7447	7464	7482	7499	7516	7534	7551	7568	2	3	5	7	9	10	12	14	16
0.88	7586	7603	7621	7638	7656	7674	7691	7709	7727	7745	2	4	5	7	9	11	12	14	16
0.89	7762	7780	7798	7816	7834	7852	7870	7889	7907	7925	2	4	5	7	9	11	13	14	16
0.90	7943	7962	7980	7998	8017	8035	8054	8072	8091	8110	2	4	6	7	9	11	13	15	17
0.91	8128	8147	8166	8185	8204	8222	8241	8260	8279	8299	2	4	6	8	9	11	13	15	17
0.92	8318	8337	8356	8375	8395	8414	8433	8453	8472	8492	2	4	6	8	10	12	14	15	17
0.93	8511	8531	8551	8570	8590	8610	8630	8650	8670	8690	2	4	6	8	10	12	14	16	18
0.94	8710	8730	8750	8770	8790	8810	8831	8851	8872	8892	2	4	6	8	10	12	14	16	18
0.95	8913	8933	8954	8974	8995	9016	9036	9057	9078	9099	2	4	6	8	10	12	15	17	19
0.96	9120	9141	9162	9183	9204	9226	9247	9268	9290	9311	2	4	6	8	11	13	15	17	19
0.97	9333	9354	9376	9397	9419	9441	9462	9484	9506	9528	2	4	7	9	11	13	15	17	20
0.98	9550	9572	9594	9616	9638	9661	9683	9705	9727	9750	2	4	7	9	11	13	16	18	20
0.99	9772	9795	9817	9840	9863	9886	9908	9931	9954	9977	2	5	7	9	11	14	16	18	20

rule for division using logarithms is:

Find the logarithm of each number. Subtract the log of the denominator from the log of the numerator. The quotient is found by taking the antilog of the difference.

A better way of performing the process is the tabular method shown below.

number	log
293.6	2.4678
18.78	1.2737
Answer = 15.63	1.1941

Example 4

Find the value of $\dfrac{783.9 \times 2.023}{2.168 \times 39.47}$

number	log	number	log
783.9	2.8943	2.168	0.3361
2.023	0.3060	39.47	1.5963
numerator	3.2003	denominator	1.9324
denominator	1.9324		
Answer = 18.53	1.2679		

Exercise 88 — *Questions 1–8 type A, remainder B*

Use logs to find the values of the following:

1) 17.63×20.54

2) 328.4×54.7

3) $6819 \times 1.285 \times 17$

4) $305.2 \times 1.003 \times 12.36$

5) $25.14 \div 12.95$

6) $8.165 \div 3.142$

7) $128.3 \div 12.95$

8) $1.975 : 1.261$

9) $\dfrac{95.83 \times 6.138}{8.179}$

10) $\dfrac{9.125 \times 123}{120.2}$

11) $\dfrac{42.7 \times 16.15 \times 3.298}{11.69 \times 7.58}$

12) $\dfrac{16.13 \times 270.5 \times 1.297}{15.38 \times 139.6 \times 1.389}$

(iii) *Powers*

To find $(3.968)^3$

$\log 3.968 = 0.5986$ and therefore $3.968 = 10^{0.5986}$

$(3.968)^3 = (10^{0.5986})^3 = 10^{0.5986 \times 3}$
$\qquad = 10^{1.7958}$

By finding the antilog of 1.7958,

$\qquad (3.968)^3 = 62.48$

From this example we see that the rule for finding powers of numbers is:

Find the log of the number and multiply it by the index denoting the power. The value of the number raised to the given power is found by taking the antilog of the product.

Example 5

Find the value of $(11.63 \times 2.87)^4$

number	log
11.63	1.0656
2.87	0.4579
11.63×2.87	1.5235
	$\times 4$
Answer = 1 242 000	6.0940

(iv) *Roots*

To find $\sqrt[4]{70.35}$

$\log 70.35 = 1.8473$ and therefore
$\qquad\qquad 70.35 = 10^{1.8473}$

$\sqrt[4]{70.35} = (70.35)^{\frac{1}{4}} = (10^{1.8473})^{\frac{1}{4}}$
$\qquad = 10^{1.8473 \times \frac{1}{4}}$
$\qquad = 10^{1.8473 \div 4} = 10^{0.4618}$

By finding the antilog of 0.4618,

$$\sqrt[4]{70.35} = 2.896$$

From this example we see that the rule for finding the root of a number is:

Find the log of the number and divide it by the number denoting the root. The result obtained by this division is the log of the required root and its antilog is the required root.

Example 6

Find the value of $\sqrt[3]{(1.832)^2 \times 6.327}$

number	log
1.832	0.2630
	×2
$(1.832)^2$	0.5260
6.327	0.8012
$(1.832)^2 \times 6.327$	1.3272
	÷3
Answer = 2.770	0.4424

Exercise 89 — *Questions 1–3 type A, remainder B*

Use logs to find the values of the following:

1) $(7.326)^3$

2) $(29.38)^2$

3) $(1.098)^5$

4) $(2.998)^2 \times 11.35$

5) $(16.29)^3 \div 86.76$

6) $73.25 \div (3.924)^3$

7) $\dfrac{(7.36)^2 \times (1.088)^3}{42.35}$

8) $\dfrac{45\,827}{(56.3)^2 \times (1.82)^3}$

9) $\sqrt[3]{15.38}$

10) $\sqrt[3]{(2.593)^2}$

11) $\sqrt{1.637} \times 11.87$

12) $\sqrt{61.5} \times (19.27)^3$

Logarithms of Numbers between 0 and 1

$$0.1 = \frac{1}{10} = 10^{-1}$$

Hence $\log 0.1 = -1$.

$$0.01 = \frac{1}{100} = \frac{1}{10^2} = 10^{-2}$$

Hence $\log 0.1 = -2$.

$$0.001 = \frac{1}{1000} = \frac{1}{10^3} = 10^{-3}$$

Hence $\log 0.001 = -3$.

From these results we may deduce that:

The logarithms of numbers between 0 and 1 are negative.

Example 7

To find the logarithm of 0.3783

$$0.3783 = \frac{3.783}{10} = 3.783 \times 10^{-1}$$
$$= 10^{0.5778} \times 10^{-1}$$
$$= 10^{-1+0.5778}$$

$$\log 0.3783 = -1 + 0.5778$$

The characteristic is therefore -1 and the mantissa is 0.5778. In the case of numbers greater than 1, the mantissa remains the same when the numbers are multiplied or divided by powers of 10. That is, with the same set of significant figures we have the same mantissa. It would be advantageous if we could do the same thing for the logs of numbers between 0 and 1. This can be done if we retain the negative characteristic as shown above. However to write $\log 0.3783$ as $-1+0.5778$ would be awkward so we adopt the notation $\bar{1}.5778$. The minus sign is written above the characteristic but it must be clearly understood that

$$\bar{1}.5778 = -1+0.5778$$

$$\bar{2}.6093 = -2+0.6093$$

We refer to $\bar{1}.5778$ as 'bar 1 point 5778' and $\bar{2}.6093$ as 'bar 2 point 6093'.

Using the bar notation:

$$\log 0.4623 \quad = \bar{1}.6649$$

$$\log 0.046\,23 \ = \bar{2}.6649$$

$$\log 0.004\,623 = \bar{3}.6649$$

The negative characteristic is numerically one more than the number of zeros which follow the decimal point in the given number.

The Anti-Logs for Logs with Negative Characteristics

When using the anti-log tables only the mantissa is used. The number of zeros following the decimal point is 1 less than the numerical value of the negative characteristic.

Example 8

To find the number whose log is $\bar{2}.5231$.

Using the mantissa .5231 we find, in the antilog tables, that the corresponding number is 3335. Since the characteristic is $\bar{2}$, the number must have one zero following the decimal point. Hence the number is 0.033 35. (Note that $\log 0.033\,35 = \bar{2}.5231$.)

Exercise 90 — *All type A*

Write down the logs of the following numbers:

1) 2.817, 0.2817, 0.028 17, 0.002 817

2) 4.597, 0.4597, 0.004 597, 0.000 045 97

3) 0.097 68, 0.000 976 8, 0.9768

4) 0.000 058 75, 0.058 75, 0.000 587 5

Find the numbers whose logs are:

5) $\bar{1}.4337$ 8) $\bar{2}.4871$

6) $\bar{3}.8199$ 9) $\bar{8}.5319$

7) $\bar{4}.5486$ 10) $\bar{1}.0218$

Adding and Subtracting Negative Characteristics

The rules are the same as when adding or subtracting directed numbers.

Example 9

1) Add $\bar{2}$ and $\bar{3}$.
$$\bar{2}+\bar{3} = -2+(-3) = -2-3$$
$$= -5 = \bar{5}$$

2) Add $\bar{3}$, $\bar{2}$ and $\bar{1}$.
$$\bar{3}+\bar{2}+\bar{1} = -3+(-2)+(-1)$$
$$= -3-2-1 = -6 = \bar{6}$$

3) Find $\bar{3}-\bar{2}$.
$$\bar{3}-\bar{2} = -3-(-2) = -3+2$$
$$= -1 = \bar{1}$$

4) Find $2-\bar{3}$.
$$2-\bar{3} = 2-(-3) = 2+3 = 5$$

Exercise 91 — *All type A*

Add the following:

1) $1+\bar{1}$ 2) $3+\bar{2}$ 3) $\bar{1}+\bar{3}$

4) $\bar{2}+\bar{2}$ **7)** $\bar{3}+0$ **10)** $2+\bar{4}$

5) $3+\bar{2}$ **8)** $\bar{5}+\bar{4}$

6) $0+\bar{2}$ **9)** $\bar{6}+3$

Subtract the following:

11) $2-3$ **15)** $1-\bar{2}$ **18)** $\bar{1}-\bar{4}$

12) $2-5$ **16)** $3-\bar{2}$ **19)** $\bar{4}-\bar{1}$

13) $0-3$ **17)** $\bar{2}-\bar{2}$ **20)** $0-\bar{3}$

14) $\bar{2}-1$

Example 10

Add together the following logarithms:

$\bar{1}.7318$	Adding the decimal
$\bar{1}.8042$	parts together we get.
$\bar{2}.7658$	2.3018. The characteristic
———	then becomes
$\bar{2}.3018$	$2+(-2)+(-1)+(-1)$
	$=-2=\bar{2}.$

Example 11

Subtract the following logarithms:

$\bar{3}.5903$	The characteristic of the
$\bar{2}.4061$	answer becomes (since
———	there is no carry over)
$\bar{1}.1842$	$-3-(-2)=-3+2$
	$=-1=\bar{1}.$

Example 12

Subtract the following logarithms:

$\bar{3}.2584$	We cannot take 0.5789
1.5789	from 0.2584 so we borrow
———	1 from $\bar{3}$ thereby making
$\bar{5}.6795$	it $\bar{4}$. We now take 0.5789
	from 1.2584. The charac-

teristic becomes $(-4)-1=-5=\bar{5}.$

Exercise 92 — *All type B*

Add the following:

1) $\bar{2}.7+1.4$ **3)** $0.6+\bar{2}.3$

2) $\bar{1}.2+3.1$ **4)** $2.7+\bar{3}.4$

5) $2.1+\bar{1}.0$ **10)** $1.2+\bar{1}.9$

6) $\bar{1}.3+\bar{1}.4$ **11)** $\bar{3}.7+1.5$

7) $\bar{2}.0+\bar{2}.1$ **12)** $\bar{2}.8+\bar{3}.7$

8) $\bar{2}.4+\bar{1}.6$ **13)** $\bar{1}.9+4.5$

9) $\bar{2}.4+\bar{1}.8$ **14)** $\bar{2}.6+3.7$

15) $1.5176+1.8973+\bar{5}.4398+0.0625$

16) $\bar{3}.3785+2.2778+1.6879+\bar{2}.8898$

17) $3.1189+\bar{2}.7615+\bar{5}.2319+\bar{6}.0527$

Subtract the following:

18) $3.8-\bar{2}.7$ **25)** $2.5-3.6$

19) $\bar{2}.6-1.4$ **26)** $1.3-1.8$

20) $\bar{1}.7-\bar{1}.3$ **27)** $\bar{2}.3-1.8$

21) $\bar{1}.8-\bar{3}.5$ **28)** $\bar{2}.3-\bar{1}.8$

22) $1.7-3.2$ **29)** $\bar{1}.5-\bar{1}.7$

23) $2.8-\bar{2}.6$ **30)** $\bar{1}.3-\bar{3}.5$

24) $\bar{3}.5-\bar{1}.4$

31) $3.2973-\bar{4}.3879$

32) $0.4973-0.8769$

33) $\bar{2}.5321-1.9897$

34) $\bar{3}.0036-\bar{6}.8798$

Multiplying and Dividing Negative Characteristics

Again the rules are exactly the same as those used with directed numbers.

Example 13

Multiply $\bar{2}.6192$ by 4.

$\bar{2}.6192$	$0.6192\times4=2.4768.$
$\times4$	Carrying the 2 we have
———	the characteristic
$\bar{6}.4768$	$=4\times(-2)+2=-8+2$
	$=-6=\bar{6}.$

Example 14

Divide $\bar{5}.8293$ by 3.

We must make the negative characteristic exactly divisible by 3, so we write

$$\bar{5}.8293 \div 3 = (\bar{6} + 1.8293) \div 3$$
$$= \bar{2}.6098$$

The work is best set out as follows:

$$\frac{3)\bar{6} + 1.8293}{\bar{2} + 0.6098} = \bar{2}.6098$$

Example 15

Find the value of $\sqrt[5]{0.0139}$.

To find the root of a number we find the log of the number and divide it by the number denoting the root. Thus,

$$\log 0.0139 = \bar{2}.1430$$

$$\frac{5)\bar{5} + 3.1430}{\bar{1} + 0.6286} = \bar{1}.6286$$

By finding the antilog of $\bar{1}.6286$,

$$\sqrt[5]{0.0139} = 0.4252$$

(Note that:

$$\bar{5} + 3.1430 = -5 + 3 + 0.1430$$
$$= -2 + 0.1430 = \bar{2}.1430)$$

Exercise 93 — *All type B*

Simplify the following:

1) $\bar{1}.4 \times 2$ 10) $\bar{4}.1 \div 3$

2) $\bar{3}.1 \times 3$ 11) $(0.3614)^3$

3) $\bar{1}.7 \times 2$ 12) $(0.7856)^5$

4) $\bar{2}.8 \times 3$ 13) $(0.001\,347)^2$

5) $\bar{1}.8 \times 5$ 14) $\sqrt{0.2569}$

6) $\bar{2}.6 \div 2$ 15) $\sqrt[3]{0.069\,87}$

7) $\bar{3}.9 \div 3$ 16) $\sqrt[3]{0.000\,781\,6}$

8) $\bar{1}.2 \div 2$ 17) $\sqrt[5]{0.6978}$

9) $\bar{3}.5 \div 5$

Find the value of the following:

18) $\dfrac{0.3786 \times 0.039\,72}{31.67}$

19) $\dfrac{97.61 \times 0.000\,46}{0.091\,74}$

20) $\dfrac{0.0146 \times 0.798 \times 643}{33\,000 \times 11.8}$

Exercise 94 — *Questions 1–13 type A, remainder B*

All the questions in this exercise have been taken from past C.S.E. examination papers.

1) Use appropriate tables to find:
(a) the logarithm of 74.6
(b) the antilogarithm of 0.746
(c) $(74.6)^2$
(d) $\sqrt{74.6}$ (*W.Y.*)

2) 120 000 written in standard form is

   a 1.2×10 **b** 1.2×10^2

   c 1.2×10^3 **d** 1.2×10^4

   e 1.2×10^5 (*W.Y.*)

3) 4.5×10^3 is a number in standard form. The number is:

   a 0.0045   **b** 0.045

   c 450   **d** 4500

   e 45 000   (*S.E.*)

4) Use logarithms to find the value of $\dfrac{18.46}{8.765}$ (*W.M.*)

5) Use logarithms to find the value of $\dfrac{175.2 \times 47.7}{11.9}$.   (*M*)

6) Use logarithms to calculate:
(a) 15.8×80.7
(b) $(14.7)^3$
(c) $\sqrt{44.5}$
(d) $498 \div 3.14$ (*S*)

7) If $\log 5 = 0.6990$, then $\log 0.05$ is

    a $\bar{2}.6990$ **b** $\bar{1}.6990$

    c 0.6990 **d** 1.6990

    e 2.6990 (*S.E.*)

8) If the logarithm of 5.444 is 0.7359, the logarithm of 544 400 is:

    a 3.7359 **b** 4.7359

    c 5.7359 **d** 6.7359

    e 7.7359 (*S.E.*)

9) If $\log x = 2.8765$, then the value of x is

    a greater than 100

    b between 10 and 100

    c less than 10

    d negative

    e between 0 and 1   (*W.M.*)

10) The number 36 700 written in standard form is

    a 36.7×10^3 **b** 3.67×10^5

    c 3.67×10^4 **d** 3.6700

    e 367×10^2 (*N.W.*)

11) The surface area of the earth is five hundred and ten million, one hundred thousand square kilometres.

(a) Write this as a number.
(b) Now write the answer to (a) in standard form.   (*Y.R.*)

12) Find the value of n when 7 million is written in the form 7×10^n.
                (*S.W.*)

13) If $\log a = 2.1271$, $\log b = 1.8965$ and $c = 0.4652$ use tables to find:

(a) a (c) $\log c^3$

(b) abc (d) $\sqrt{b}$

                (*Y.R.*)

14) If a log of $\bar{1}.3600$ is divided by 4 the answer is:

    a $\bar{1}.0900$ **b** $\bar{1}.3400$

    c $\bar{1}.8400$ **d** $\bar{1}.5900$

    e $\bar{1}.6800$ (*Y.R.*)

15)

(a) If $a = 30.2$, find $\log a$
(b) If $\log b = 0.5441$, find b
(c) Calculate $a \times b$
(d) Solve the following equation

$$10^{1.4800} \times 10^{1.5441} = 10^x$$

Find the number, the logarithm of which is equal to x.   (*Y.R.*)

Chapter 13   Simple Interest

Simple Interest

Interest is the profit return on investment. If money is invested then interest is paid to the investor. If money is borrowed then the person who borrows the money will have to pay interest to the lender. The money which is invested or lent is called the *principal*. The percentage return is called the *rate per cent*. Thus interest at a rate of 12% means that the interest on a principal of £100 will be £12 per annum. The total formed by adding the principal and the interest is called the *amount*. The amount is therefore the total sum of money which remains invested after a period of time.

With simple interest the principal always stays the same no matter how many years the investment (or the loan) lasts.

Example 1

How much interest does a man pay if he borrows £400 for one year at an interest rate of 12%?

$$\text{Interest} = 12\% \text{ of } £400$$
$$= \frac{12}{100} \times £400 = £48$$

If money is borrowed for two years the amount of interest payable will be doubled; for three years three times as much interest is payable; and so on.

The interest payable (or earned) depends upon:

  (i) The amount borrowed or lent, i.e. the *principal*.

  (ii) The rate of interest charged, i.e. the *rate %*.

  (iii) The period of the loan, i.e. the *time* (in years).

To calculate the *simple interest* use the formula below:

$$I = \frac{PRT}{100}$$

where P stands for the principal
           R stands for the rate per cent
           T stands for the time in years

Example 2

Find the simple interest on £500 borrowed for 4 years at 11%.

Here we have $P = £500$, $R = 11\%$ and $T = 4$ years. Substituting these values in the simple interest formula gives:

$$I = \frac{500 \times 11 \times 4}{100} = 220$$

Thus the simple interest is £220.

Example 3

£700 is invested at 4% per annum. How long will it take for the amount to reach £784?

The interest = £784 − £700 = £84.

We therefore have $I = 84$, $R = 4$ and $P = 700$ and we have to find T. Substituting these values in the simple interest formula gives:

$$84 = \frac{700 \times 4 \times T}{100}$$

$$84 \times 100 = 700 \times 4 \times T$$

$$T = \frac{84 \times 100}{700 \times 4} = 3$$

Hence the time taken is 3 years.

Simple interest tables (see below) are sometimes used to find the amount of interest due at the end of a given period of time. The table shows the appreciation (the increase in value) of £1. For instance:

£1 invested for 8 years at 11% per annum will become £1.88.

£1 invested for 15 years at 8% per annum will become £2.20.

Example 4

Using the simple interest tables calculate the simple interest earned by £850 invested for 9 years at 10% per annum.

From the simple interest table, in 9 years at 10% p.a. £1 becomes £1.90. To find the amount accruing from £850 multiply 1.90 by £850.

Amount accruing
$$= 1.90 \times £850 = £1615$$

Interest earned
$$= £1615 - £850 = £765.$$

Exercise 95 — *Questions 1–8 type A, remainder B*

1) Find the simple interest on £700 invested for 3 years at 6% per annum.

2) Find the simple interest on £500 invested for 6 months at 8% per annum.

3) In what length of time will £500 be the interest on £2500 which is invested at 5% per annum?

4) In what length of time will £16 be the simple interest on £480 invested at 8% per annum?

Table of Simple Interest

Appreciation of £1 for periods from 1 year to 25 years

Year	5%	6%	7%	8%	9%	10%	11%	12%	13%	14%
1	1·050	1·060	1·070	1·080	1·090	1·100	1·110	1·120	1·130	1·140
2	1·100	1·120	1·140	1·160	1·180	1·200	1·220	1·240	1·260	1·280
3	1·150	1·180	1·210	1·240	1·270	1·300	1·330	1·360	1·390	1·420
4	1·200	1·240	1·280	1·320	1·360	1·400	1·440	1·480	1·520	1·560
5	1·250	1·300	1·350	1·400	1·450	1·500	1·550	1·600	1·650	1·700
6	1·300	1·360	1·420	1·480	1·540	1·600	1·660	1·720	1·780	1·840
7	1·350	1·420	1·490	1·560	1·630	1·700	1·770	1·840	1·910	1·980
8	1·400	1·480	1·560	1·640	1·720	1·800	1·880	1·960	2·040	2·120
9	1·450	1·540	1·630	1·720	1·810	1·900	1·990	2·080	2·170	2·260
10	1·500	1·600	1·700	1·800	1·900	2·000	2·100	2·200	2·300	2·400
11	1·550	1·660	1·770	1·880	1·990	2·100	2·210	2·320	2·430	2·540
12	1·600	1·720	1·840	1·960	2·080	2·200	2·320	2·440	2·560	2·680
13	1·650	1·780	1·910	2·040	2·170	2·300	2·430	2·560	2·690	2·820
14	1·700	1·840	1·980	2·120	2·260	2·400	2·540	2·680	2·820	2·960
15	1·750	1·900	2·050	2·200	2·350	2·500	2·650	2·800	2·950	3·100
16	1·800	1·960	2·120	2·280	2·440	2·600	2·760	2·920	3·080	3·240
17	1·850	2·020	2·190	2·360	2·530	2·700	2·870	3·040	3·210	3·380
18	1·900	2·080	2·260	2·440	2·620	2·800	2·980	3·160	3·340	3·520
19	1·950	2·140	2·330	2·520	2·710	2·900	3·090	3·280	3·470	3·660
20	2·000	2·200	2·400	2·600	2·800	3·000	3·200	3·400	3·600	3·800
21	2·050	2·260	2·470	2·680	2·890	3·100	3·310	3·520	3·730	3·940
22	2·100	2·320	2·540	2·760	2·980	3·200	3·420	3·640	3·860	4·080
23	2·150	2·380	2·610	2·840	3·070	3·300	3·530	3·760	3·990	4·220
24	2·200	2·440	2·680	2·920	3·160	3·400	3·640	3·880	4·120	4·360
25	2·250	2·500	2·750	3·000	3·250	3·500	3·750	4·000	4·250	4·500

5) In what length of time will £75 be the simple interest on £500 invested at 6% per annum?

6) The interest on £600 invested for 5 years is £210. What is the rate per cent?

7) The interest on £200 invested for 4 months is £6. What is the rate per cent?

8) What principal is needed so that the interest will be £48 if it is invested at 3% per annum for 5 years?

9) Which receives the more interest per annum:

£150 invested at 4% or £180 invested at $3\frac{1}{2}$%?

What is the annual difference?

10) A man invests £700 at 6% per annum and £300 at 8% per annum.

What is his total annual interest on these investments?

11) A man deposited £350 in a bank and £14 interest was added at the end of the first year. The whole amount was left in the bank for a second year at the same rate of interest. Find the amount of interest on the £364 paid in the second year.

12) Using the simple interest table calculate the simple interest earned in each of the following cases:

(a) £350 invested at 6% p.a. for 9 years.

(b) £500 invested at 11% p.a. for 5 years.

(c) £2500 invested at 8% p.a. for 16 years.

(d) £7000 invested at 13% p.a. for 11 years.

(e) £900 invested at 9% p.a. for 21 years.

Chapter 14 The Metric System

The Metric System of Length

The metric system is essentially a decimal system. The standard unit of length is the metre but for some purposes the metre is too large a unit and it is therefore split up into smaller units as follows:

1 metre (m) = 10 decimetres (dm)

= 100 centimetres (cm)

= 1000 millimetres (mm)

When dealing with large distances the metre is too small a unit and large distances are measured in kilometres.

1 kilometre (km) = 1000 metres

Since the metric system is essentially a decimal system we can easily convert from one unit to another by simply moving the decimal point the required number of places.

Example 1

Convert 3.792 m into centimetres.

$$1 \text{ m} = 100 \text{ cm}$$

$$3.792 \text{ m} = 100 \times 3.792 \text{ cm}$$

$$= 379.2 \text{ cm}$$

Example 2

Convert 98 375 mm into metres.

$$1000 \text{ mm} = 1 \text{ m}$$

$$1 \text{ mm} = \frac{1}{1000} \text{ m}$$

$$98\,375 \text{ mm} = \frac{98\,375}{1000} \text{ m} = 98.375 \text{ m}$$

Sometimes you may have difficulty in deciding whether to multiply or divide when converting from one unit to another. If you remember that when converting to a smaller unit you multiply and when converting to a larger unit you divide, this difficulty will disappear.

The Metric System for Mass

The standard unit of mass is the kilogramme which is suitable for most purposes connected with weights and measures. However for some purposes the kilogramme is too large a unit and the gramme is then used. For very small masses the milligramme is used.

1 kilogramme (kg) = 1000 grammes (g)

1 gramme = 1000 milligrammes (mg)

For very large masses the tonne is used, such that

1 tonne = 1000 kg

Example 3

Convert 5397 mg into grammes

$$1000 \text{ mg} = 1 \text{ g}$$

$$1 \text{ mg} = \frac{1}{1000} \text{ g}$$

$$5397 \text{ mg} = \frac{5397}{1000} \text{ g} = 5.397 \text{ g}$$

Example 4

Convert 2.56 kg into grammes.

$$1 \text{ kg} = 1000 \text{ g}$$

$$2.56 \text{ kg} = 1000 \times 2.56 \text{ g} = 2560 \text{ g}$$

Example 5

Convert 5.4 tonnes into kilogrammes.

$$5.4 \text{ tonnes} = 5.4 \times 1000 \text{ kg}$$
$$= 5400 \text{ kg}$$

Exercise 96 — *All type A*

1) Convert to metres:

(a) 5.63 km   (f) 6895 mm
(b) 0.68 km   (g) 73 mm
(c) 17.698 km   (h) 4597 cm
(d) 592 cm   (i) 798 mm
(e) 68 cm   (j) 5 mm

2) Convert to kilometres:

(a) 9753 m   (d) 2985 cm
(b) 259 m   (e) 790 685 mm
(c) 58 m

3) Convert to centimetres:

(a) 4.68 m   (d) 3897 mm
(b) 0.782 m   (e) 88 mm
(c) 5.16 km

4) Convert to millimetres:

(a) 1.234 m   (d) 389 cm
(b) 0.58 km   (e) 0.052 m
(c) 25.8 cm

5) Convert to kilogrammes:

(a) 530 g   (c) 2473 mg
(b) 35 000 g   (d) 597 600 mg

6) Convert into grammes:

(a) 56 000 mg   (d) 0.081 kg
(b) 96 mg   (e) 584 mg
(c) 8.63 kg

7) Convert 18 200 kg into tonnes.

8) Convert 19.4 tonnes into kilo-grammes.

The Addition and Subtraction of Metric Quantities

When adding or subtracting lengths or masses it is important that all the quantities be converted to a common unit.

Example 6

Add together 36.1 m, 39.2 cm and 532 mm and express the answer in metres.

$$39.2 \text{ cm} = \frac{39.2}{100} \text{ m} = 0.392 \text{ m}$$

$$532 \text{ mm} = \frac{532}{1000} \text{ m} = 0.532 \text{ m}$$

We now have to add the lengths 36.1 m, 0.392 m and 0.532 m. We write the numbers down in the same way as when adding decimal numbers, that is, with the decimal points directly underneath each other. Thus

```
  36.1
   0.392
   0.532
  ──────
  37.024
```

The answer is therefore, 37.024 m.

Example 7

From a length of cloth 120 m long, the following lengths are cut: $3\frac{1}{2}$ m, $30\frac{1}{4}$ m, 18 m 36 cm and 8 m 27 cm. What length of cloth remains?

Converting all the lengths to metres and decimals of a metre we have:

Lengths cut off = 3.5 m, 30.25 m, 18.36 m and 8.27 m

Adding these lengths together

$$3.5$$
$$30.25$$
$$18.36$$
$$8.27$$
$$\overline{60.38}$$

Hence the total length cut off the cloth is 60.38 m. To find the length remaining we have to subtract 60.38 m from 120 m. Thus

$$120.00$$
$$60.38$$
$$\overline{59.62}$$

Hence 59.62 m of cloth remains.

Exercise 97 — *All type A*

1) Add together 39 cm, 3.62 m and 497 mm and express the answer in millimetres.

2) Add together 26.3 cm, 347 mm and 0.783 m and express the answer in metres.

3) A piece of cord 1.3 m long has the following lengths cut from it: 26 cm, $\frac{1}{2}$ m, 358 mm and 12 cm. How much cord remains?

4) Add together the following masses and express the answer in kilogrammes: 583 g, 19.164 kg and 20 500 mg.

5) A housewife buys the following items of food: 500 g tomatoes, 3 kg potatoes, 250 g butter and $\frac{1}{2}$ kg of sugar. What is the total mass of her purchases?

6) A greengrocer starts the day with 85 kg of apples. He sells $2\frac{1}{2}$ kg, 500 g, 2500 g, $3\frac{1}{4}$ kg and 2 kg 250 g. What mass of apples has he left?

7) A motorist drives 5.8 km to work, but on the way he has to make a detour of 750 m. He drives to an hotel for lunch which is a distance of 830 m from his office. He drives home without having to make a detour. How far, in kilometres, has he driven during the day?

8) Calculate the amount of ribbon left on a reel containing 50 m when the following lengths are cut: 50 cm, $\frac{1}{2}$ m, 2 m 30 cm and $4\frac{1}{4}$ m.

Multiplying and Dividing Metric Quantities

Multiplying and dividing metric quantities are done in the same way as the multiplication and division of decimal numbers.

Example 8

28 lengths of cloth each 3.8 m long are required for the manufacture of dresses. What total length of cloth is required?

Length required $= 28 \times 3.8$ m

$$28$$
$$38$$
$$\overline{}$$
$$840$$
$$224$$
$$\overline{1064}$$

Placing the decimal point, we see that total length of cloth required = 106.4 m.

Alternatively we can perform the multiplication by using logs.

number	log
28	1.4472
3.8	0.5798
Answer = 106.4	2.0270

Hence, as before, the total length of cloth required = 106.4 m.

Example 9

How many lengths of string each 79 cm long can be cut from a ball containing 54 m and what length remains?

To do this problem we can either bring 79 cm to metres or we can convert 54 m into centimetres. Adopting the latter course we have

$$54 \text{ m} = 54 \times 100 \text{ cm} = 5400 \text{ cm}$$

We now have to divide 5400 by 79. This is best done by taking logs. Thus

number	log
5400	3.7324
79	1.8976
Answer = 68.36	1.8348

Hence we can cut 68 lengths of string and a piece 0.36 of a length remains.

$$\text{Length remaining} = 0.36 \times 79 \text{ cm}$$
$$= 28.4 \text{ cm}$$

Therefore we can cut 68 lengths of string and a piece 28.4 cm long remains.

Exercise 98

1) 47 pieces of wood each 85 cm long are required. What total length of wood, in metres, is needed?

2) 158 lengths of cloth each 3.2 m long are required. Find the total length of cloth needed.

3) 27 lengths of cloth each 2 m 26 cm are to be cut from a roll containing 80 m. What length of cloth remains?

4) How many lengths of string each 58 cm long can be cut from a ball containing 30 m and how much string remains?

5) How many lengths of wood 18 cm long can be cut from a plank $6\frac{1}{2}$ m long?

6) Frozen peas are packed in boxes which contain 450 g. What mass of peas are needed to fill 2340 boxes?

7) Calculate the number of pieces of wallpaper each 2.7 m long that can be cut from a roll 17 m long.

8) 6 curtains are required each 2 m long. Allowing 5 cm for turnover at the top and 5 cm at the bottom of each curtain, how much material is needed?

Exercise 99 — *All type A*

All the questions in this exercise have been taken from past C.S.E. examination papers.

1) How many centimetres are there in 1.72 m? *(S)*

2) Express 7500 grammes in kilogrammes. *(S)*

3) How many 25 ml doses can be obtained from a bottle containing 1 litre of medicine? *(S)*

4) Write 15 m 48 mm in metres. *(S)*

5) One length of plain wallpaper on a wall measures 2.1 m. How many lengths can be cut from a roll 10.5 m long if there is no waste? *(S)*

6) Express each of the following in metres:
(a) 2 km
(b) 2 km 56 m
(c) 672 cm   *(W)*

7) How many:
(a) milligrammes in 3 g
(b) centimetres in 9 m
(c) litres in 3500 ml?   *(W.Y.)*

8) My metre rule was broken into 4 equal pieces. The length of each piece is:

a 25 cm   **b** 15 cm
c 10 cm   **d** 50 cm
e 20 cm   *(N.W.)*

9) How many lengths of tape, each 75 cm long, can be cut from a reel of tape 10 m long and how long will be the piece left over?   *(Y.R.)*

10) Express 45 cm as a fraction of 1 m. Simplify your answer as far as possible.   *(W.M.)*

11) How many metres are there in 0.25 km?   *(S.W.)*

12) Express 3.56 m in centimetres.   *(N.W.)*

13) A piece of material is 2 m 40 cm long. A length of 95 cm is cut off one end. What length is left?   *(A.L.)*

14) A lorry which weighs 3.6 tonnes unladen, is loaded with 10.5 tonnes of soil. What is the total weight of the lorry?   *(E.A.)*

15) Which is the heaviest: 80 g, 0.8 kg, 8000 mg, 0.88 g?   *(E.A.)*

16) 42 600 m expressed in kilometres is:

a 0.426   **b** 4.26
c 42.6   **d** 426
e 4260   *(S.E.)*

17) 650 mm written in metres is

a 6500   **b** 65
c 6.5   **d** 0.065
e 0.65   *(W.M.)*

18) Four packets have weights marked: 2 kg, 250 g, 500 g, $3\frac{1}{2}$ kg. Their total weight in kilogrammes is

a 5.25   **b** 6
c 6.25   **d** 13
e 75.55   *(S.E.)*

Chapter 15   Areas

Unit of Length

In Chapter 14 we saw that the standard unit of length is the metre (abbreviation: m) and that it is split up into smaller units as follows:

1 metre (m) = 10 decimetres (dm)

= 100 centimetres (cm)

= 1000 millimetres (mm)

Units of Area

The area of a plane figure is measured by seeing how many square units it contains. 1 square metre is the area contained inside a square which has a side of 1 metre (Fig. 15.1). Similarly 1 square centimetre is the area inside a square whose side is 1 cm and 1 square millimetre is the area inside a square whose side is 1 mm.

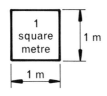

Fig. 15.1

The standard abbreviations for units of area are:

square metre $= m^2$

square centimetre $= cm^2$

square millimetre $= mm^2$

Area of a Rectangle

The rectangle (Fig. 15.2) has been divided into 4 rows of 2 squares, each square having an area of 1 cm². The rectangle, therefore, has an area of 4×2 cm² = 8 cm².   All that we have done to find the area is to multiply the length by the breadth. The same rule will apply to any rectangle. Hence:

Area of rectangle = length × breadth

If we let A = the area of the rectangle

   l = the length of the rectangle

and b = the breadth of the rectangle

$$A = lb$$

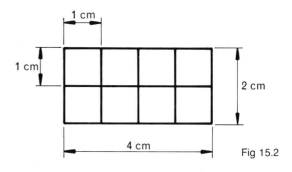

Fig 15.2

In using this formula the units of l and b must be the same, that is they both must be in metres, centimetres or millimetres.

Example 1

A carpet measures 5.2 m by 6.3 m. What is its area?

102

We are given that $l = 5.2$ m and $b = 6.3$ m. Hence the area is:

$$A = 5.2 \times 6.3 = 32.76 \text{ m}^2$$

Example 2

Find the area of a piece of sheet metal measuring 184 cm by 73 cm. Express the answer in square metres.

In problems of this type it is best to express each of the dimensions in metres before attempting to find the area. Thus:

$$184 \text{ cm} = 1.84 \text{ m}$$

and

$$73 \text{ cm} = 0.73 \text{ m}$$

The area of sheet metal is then

$$A = 1.84 \times 0.73 = 1.343 \text{ m}^2$$

Example 3

A room 9.3 m long and 7.6 m wide is to be carpeted so as to leave a surround 50 cm wide as shown in Fig. 15.3. Find the area of the surround.

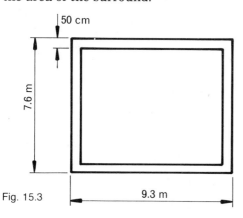

Fig. 15.3

The easiest way of solving this problem is to find the area of the room and subtract from it the area of the carpet.

$$\text{Area of room} = 9.3 \times 7.6$$
$$= 70.68 \text{ m}^2$$
$$\text{Area of carpet} = 8.3 \times 6.6$$
$$= 54.78 \text{ m}^2$$

$$\text{Area of surround} = 70.68 - 54.78$$
$$= 15.90 \text{ m}^2$$

The areas of many shapes can be found by splitting the shape up into rectangles and finding the area of each rectangle separately. The area of the shape is then found by adding the areas of the separate rectangles together.

Example 4

Find the area of the shape shown in Fig. 15.4.

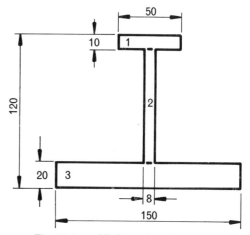

Fig. 15.4   All dimensions in millimetres

The shape can be divided up into three rectangles as shown in the diagram.

Area of shape
$$= \text{area of } 1 + \text{area of } 2 + \text{area of } 3$$
$$= (50 \times 10) \text{ mm}^2 + (90 \times 8) \text{ mm}^2$$
$$+ (150 \times 20) \text{ mm}^2$$
$$= 500 \text{ mm}^2 + 720 \text{ mm}^2$$
$$+ 3000 \text{ mm}^2 = 4220 \text{ mm}^2$$

Exercise 100 — *All type A*

1) Find the areas of the following rectangles:

(a) 7 cm by 8 cm
(b) 20 mm by 11 mm
(c) 18 m by 35 m.

2) A piece of wood is 3.7 m long and 28 cm wide. What is its area in square metres?

3) A rectangular piece of metal is 198 cm long and 88 cm wide. What is its area in square metres?

4) A room 5.8 m long and 4.9 m wide is to be covered with vinyl. What area of vinyl is needed?

5) What is the total area of the walls of a room which is 6.7 m long, 5.7 m wide and 2.5 m high?

6) A rectangular lawn is 32 m long and 23 m wide. A path 1.5 m wide is made around the lawn. What is the area of the path?

7) A room 8.5 m long and 6.3 m wide is to be carpeted to leave a surround 60 cm wide around the carpet. What is:

(a) the area of the room?
(b) the area of the carpet?
(c) the area of the surround?

8) Find the areas of the shapes shown in Fig. 15.5.

(a)

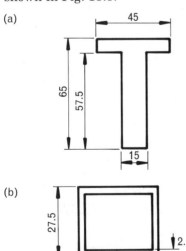

(b)

(c)

(d)

(e)

(f)

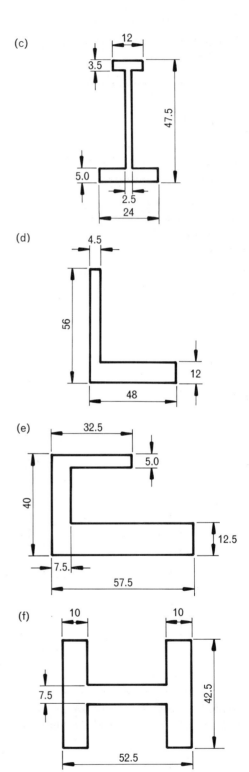

Fig. 15.5 (all dimensions in mm)

We can find the length of a rectangle given its area and its breadth by solving an equation as shown in Chapter 11.

Example 5

A rectangle has an area of 60 cm² and its breadth is 12 cm. What is its length?

We are given that $A = 60$ and $b = 12$. Hence:

$$60 = 12 \times l$$

$$l = \frac{60}{12} = 5$$

Therefore the length of the rectangle is 5 cm.

Example 6

A piece of wood has an area of 1.8 m² and a width of 30 cm. What is its length?

We must first convert 30 cm into metres, that is 30 cm = 0.3 m. We now have that $A = 1.8$ and $b = 0.3$. Substituting these values in the formula for the area of a rectangle we have:

$$1.8 = 0.3 \times l$$

$$l = \frac{1.8}{0.3} = 6$$

Hence the length of the piece of wood is 6 m.

The Square

A square is a rectangle with all its sides equal in length. Hence:

area of square = side × side = side²

We can express this as a formula by letting A represent the area of the square and l the length of the side. Thus:

$$A = l^2$$

Example 7

A square has an area of 20.25 cm².

What is the length of its side?

Length of side = $\sqrt{\text{area}} = \sqrt{20.25}$
   = 4.5 cm

Exercise 101 — *All type B*

1) The area of a rectangle is 72 m². If its length is 12 m find its width.

2) The area of a room is 44.82 m². It is 5.4 m wide. How long is it?

3) A carpet measuring 6 m by 7 m is laid in a room measuring 6.5 m by 8 m. Calculate the area not covered by the carpet.

4) A carpet has an area of $30\frac{1}{4}$ m². If it is square calculate the length.

5) A piece of vinyl has an area of 12.3 m². If its length is $20\frac{1}{2}$ m, what is its width in centimetres?

6) A room is 5.4 m long and 4.2 m wide. It takes 1575 square tiles to cover the floor. Calculate the area of each tile and state its dimensions.

7) How many square tiles each 15 cm square are needed to cover a floor 4.5 m long by 12 m wide?

8) A householder makes a square lawn in his garden which has a side of 12 m. If the plot of ground is 15 m by 14 m, what area is left?

The Parallelogram

A parallelogram is a plane figure bounded by four straight lines whose opposite sides are parallel (Fig. 15.6).

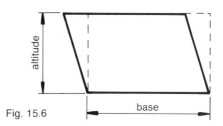

Fig. 15.6

A parallelogram is, in effect, a rectangle pushed out of square as shown in Fig. 15.6 where the equivalent rectangle is shown dotted. Hence:

area of parallelogram

= length of base×vertical height

$$A = bh$$

where A = area, b = length of base and h = vertical height (or altitude).

Example 8

Find the area of a parallelogram whose base is 15 cm long and whose altitude is 8 cm.

$$\text{Area} = 15×8 = 120 \text{ cm}^2$$

Example 9

A parallelogram has an area of 36 cm². If its base is 9 cm find its altitude.

We are given that $A = 36$ and that $b = 9$. Hence:

$$36 = 9×h \quad \text{or} \quad h = \frac{36}{9} = 4$$

Hence the altitude is 4 cm.

Exercise 102 — *All type B*

1) Find the area of a parallelogram whose base is 7 cm long and whose vertical height is 8 cm.

2) What is the area of a parallelogram whose base is 7 cm long and whose altitude is 65 cm? Give the answer in square metres.

3) The area of a parallelogram is 64 m². Its base is 16 m long. Calculate its altitude.

4) A parallelogram has an area of 25.92 cm². Its altitude is 3.6 cm. Find its length of base.

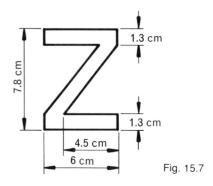

Fig. 15.7

5) Fig. 15.7 shows a steel section. Find its area in square centimetres.

Area of a Triangle

The diagonal of the parallelogram shown in Fig. 15.8 splits the parallelogram into two equal triangles. Hence:

area of triangle

= ½×base×vertical height

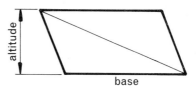

Fig. 15.8

Sometimes the vertical height is called the altitude and:

area of triangle = ½×base×altitude

As a formula the statement becomes:

$$A = \tfrac{1}{2}bh$$

where:

b = the base and h = the altitude.

Example 10

A triangle has a base 5 cm long and a vertical height of 12 cm. Calculate its area.

$$\text{Area of triangle} = \tfrac{1}{2}×\text{base}×\text{height}$$
$$= \tfrac{1}{2}×5×12 = 30 \text{ cm}^2$$

When we are given the lengths of three sides of a triangle we can find its area by using the formula given below:

$$A = \sqrt{s \times (s-a) \times (s-b) \times (s-c)}$$

where s stands for half of the perimeter of the triangle and a, b and c are the lengths of the sides of the triangle.

Example 11

The sides of a triangle are 13 cm, 8 cm and 7 cm long. Calculate the area of the triangle.

$$s = \tfrac{1}{2}\text{ perimeter} = \tfrac{1}{2} \times (13+8+7)$$
$$= \tfrac{1}{2} \times 28 = 14 \text{ cm}$$

$a = 13\,\text{cm}$, $b = 8\,\text{cm}$ and $c = 7\,\text{cm}$.

Area of triangle
$$= \sqrt{14 \times (14-13) \times (14-8) \times (14-7)}$$
$$= \sqrt{14 \times 1 \times 6 \times 7} = \sqrt{588} = 24.25 \text{ cm}^2$$

Exercise 103 — *Questions 1–2 type A, remainder B*

1) Find the area of a triangle whose base is 18 cm and whose altitude is 12 cm.

2) Find the area of a triangle whose base is 7.5 cm and whose altitude is 5.9 cm.

3) A triangle has sides 4 cm, 7 cm and 9 cm. What is its area?

4) A triangle has sides 37 mm, 52 mm and 63 mm long. What is its area in square centimetres?

5) A triangle has an area of 60 cm² and a base 12 cm long. What is its altitude?

Area of a Trapezium

A trapezium is a plane figure bounded by four straight lines which has one pair of parallel sides (Fig. 15.9).

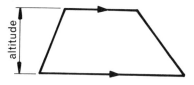

Fig. 15.9

Area of trapezium
= ½ the sum of the lengths of the parallel sides × the distance between them

Example 12

The parallel sides of a trapezium are 12 cm and 16 cm long. The distance between the parallel sides is 9 cm. What is the area of the trapezium?

Area of trapezium $= \tfrac{1}{2} \times (12+16) \times 9$
$$= \tfrac{1}{2} \times 28 \times 9$$
$$= 126 \text{ cm}^2$$

Example 13

The area of a trapezium is 220 cm² and the parallel sides are 26 cm and 14 cm long. Find the distance between the parallel sides.

$\tfrac{1}{2}$ the sum of the parallel sides
$$= \tfrac{1}{2} \times (26+14) = \tfrac{1}{2} \times 40 = 20$$

distance between the parallel sides
$$= 220 \div 20 = 11 \text{ cm}$$

Exercise 104 — *All type B*

1) Find the area of a trapezium whose parallel sides are 7 cm and 9 cm long and whose altitude is 5 cm.

2) The parallel sides of a trapezium are 15 cm and 9.8 cm long. If the distance between the parallel sides is 7.6 cm, what is the area of the trapezium?

3) The area of a trapezium is 500 cm² and its parallel sides are 35 cm and 65 cm long. Find the altitude of the trapezium.

4) Find the area of a trapezium whose parallel sides are 75 mm and 82 mm and whose vertical height is 39 mm. Give the answer in square centimetres.

5) Find the area of the trapezium shown in Fig. 15.10.

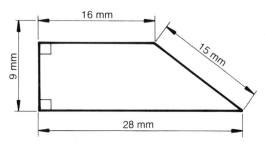

Fig. 15.10

Mensuration of the Circle

The names of the main parts of a circle are shown in Fig. 15.11. The value

$$\frac{\text{circumference}}{\text{diameter}} = 3.14159\ldots\ldots\ldots$$

The exact value has never been worked out but for most problems a value of 3.142 is sufficiently accurate when working in decimals. When working in fractions a value of $\frac{22}{7}$ can be taken.

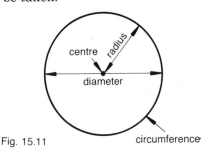

Fig. 15.11

The value $\dfrac{\text{circumference}}{\text{diameter}}$ is so important that it has been given the

special symbol π (the Greek letter pi). We take π as being 3.142 or $\frac{22}{7}$.

$$\text{Since} \quad \frac{\text{circumference}}{\text{diameter}} = \pi$$

$$\textbf{circumference} = \pi \times \textbf{diameter}$$

or $\quad$ **circumference** $= 2 \times \pi \times$ **radius**

or $\qquad\qquad C = 2\pi r = \pi d$

Example 14

The diameter of a circle is 300 mm. What is its circumference?

Circumference $= \pi \times 300$

$$= 3.142 \times 300$$

$$= 942.6 \text{ mm}$$

Example 15

The radius of a circle is 14 cm. What is its circumference?

Circumference $= 2 \times \pi \times$ radius

$$= 2 \times \tfrac{22}{7} \times 14 = 88 \text{ cm}$$

Example 16

A wheel 700 mm diameter makes 30 revolutions. How far does a point on the rim travel?

Distance travelled in 1 revolution

$$= \pi \times \text{diameter} = \tfrac{22}{7} \times 700$$

$$= 2200 \text{ mm}$$

Distance travelled in 30 revolutions

$$= 30 \times 2200 = 66\,000 \text{ mm} = 66 \text{ m}$$

Example 17

Find the radius of a circle whose circumference is 93.8 cm.

$$\text{Radius} = \frac{\text{circumference}}{2 \times \pi}$$

$$= \frac{93.8}{2 \times 3.142} = \frac{93.8}{6.284}$$

The best way of calculating the answer is to use logs:

number	log
93.8	1.9722
6.284	0.7983
14.92	1.1739

Hence the radius of the circle is 14.92 cm.

Exercise 105 — *Questions 1–8 type A, remainder B*

Find the circumference of the following circles:

1) Radius 21 cm

2) Radius 350 mm

3) Radius 43 m

4) Radius 3.16 cm

5) Diameter 28 cm

6) Diameter 85 mm

7) Diameter 8.423 m

8) Diameter 1400 mm

9) A wheel has a diameter of 560 mm. How far, in metres, will a point on the rim travel in 50 revolutions?

10) A circular flower bed has a circumference of 64 m. What is its radius?

11) 8 circular cushion covers, each with a radius of 60 cm, are to be decorated with braiding around their circumference. How many metres of braiding is needed?

12) A pond which is circular has a circumference of 12.62 m. What is its radius?

13) Find the diameter of a circle whose circumference is 110 cm.

14) Find the diameter of a circle whose circumference is 956 mm.

The Area of a Circle

It can be shown that:

Area of circle $= \pi \times \text{radius}^2 = \pi r^2$

Example 18

Find the area of a circle whose radius is 30 cm.

Area of circle
$$= \pi \times 30^2 = 3.142 \times 900$$
$$= 2827.8 \text{ cm}^2$$

Example 19

Find the area of a circle whose diameter is 28 cm.

Since diameter $= 28$ cm,
$$\text{radius} = 14 \text{ cm}$$

Area of circle $= \pi \times \text{radius}^2$
$$= \tfrac{22}{7} \times 14^2 = 616 \text{ cm}^2$$

Example 20

Find the area of the annulus shown in Fig. 15.12.

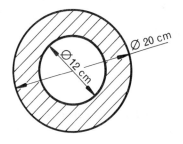

Fig. 15.12

Outer radius $= 10$ cm;

inner radius $= 6$ cm

Area of outer circle

$= \pi \times 10^2 = 314.2$ cm²

Area of inner circle

$= \pi \times 6^2 = 113.1$ cm²

Area of annulus

$= 314.2 - 113.1 = 201.1$ cm²

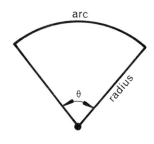

Fig. 15.13

Exercise 106 — *All type A*

Find the areas of the following circles:

1) 14 cm radius

2) 350 mm radius

3) 2.82 m radius

4) 42 cm diameter

5) 7.78 m diameter

6) 197.6 mm diameter

7) An annulus has an inside radius of 6 cm and an outside radius of 9 cm. Calculate its area.

8) A copper pipe has a bore of 32 mm and an outside diameter of 42 mm. Find the area of its cross section.

9) A pond having a diameter of 36 m has to have a path 1 m wide laid around its circumference. What is the area of the path?

10) A circular flower bed is to have a path laid around its circumference. If the flower bed has a diameter of 60 m and the path is to be $1\frac{1}{2}$ m wide, find the area of the path.

Sector of a Circle

The area and the arc of a sector of a circle (Fig. 15.13) depend upon the angle that the sector subtends at the centre of the circle of which the sector is part.

Referring to the diagram (Fig. 15.13).

Arc of the sector

$$= 2 \times \pi \times \text{radius} \times \frac{\theta}{360}$$

or

$$C = 2\pi r \times \frac{\theta}{360}$$

Area of the sector

$$= \pi \times \text{radius}^2 \times \frac{\theta}{360}$$

or

$$A = \pi r^2 \times \frac{\theta}{360}$$

Example 21

Find the length of arc and the area of a sector of a circle which subtends an angle of 108° at the centre, if its radius is 8 cm.

$$\text{Length of arc} = 2 \times \pi \times 8 \times \frac{108}{360}$$

$$= \frac{24 \times \pi}{5} = 15.08 \text{ cm}$$

$$\text{Area of sector} = \pi \times 8^2 \times \frac{108}{360}$$

$$= \frac{96 \times \pi}{5} = 60.33 \text{ cm}^2$$

Exercise 107 — *All type B*

Find the length of arc and the area of the following sectors of a circle:

1) Radius 4 cm; sector angle 45°.

2) Radius 10 cm; sector angle 90°.

110

3) Radius 3 cm; sector angle 60°.

4) Radius 2.7 m; sector angle 84°.

5) Radius 78 mm; sector angle 175°.

6) Calculate the shaded area shown in Fig. 15.14.

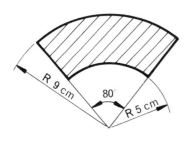

Fig. 15.14

Areas of Composite Figures

Many shapes are composed of straight lines and arcs of circles. The areas of such shapes are found by splitting up the shape into figures such as rectangles, triangles, etc. and sectors of circles.

Example 22

A table top is the shape shown in Fig. 15.15. Find its area.

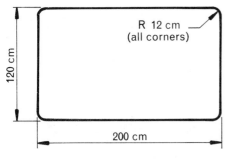

Fig. 15.15

The table top can be split up into 4 quarter circles and 5 rectangles as shown in Fig. 15.16.

Fig. 15.16

Area of 4 quarter circles

$$= 4 \times \tfrac{1}{4} \times \pi \times 12^2 = \pi \times 12^2 = 452 \text{ cm}^2$$

Area of 5 rectangles

$$= 2 \times 12 \times 96 + 2 \times 12 \times 176 + 96 \times 176$$

$$= 2304 + 4224 + 16\,896 = 23\,424 \text{ cm}^2$$

Area of table top

$$= 452 + 23\,424 = 23\,876 \text{ cm}^2$$

Exercise 108 — *All type B*

Find the areas of the shaded portions of the figures shown in Fig. 15.17.

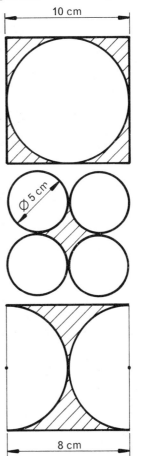

111

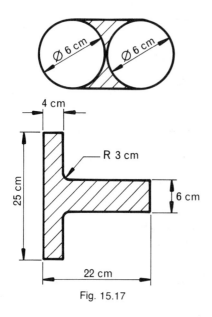

Fig. 15.17

Algebraic Problems with Areas

Many problems dealing with areas and perimeters can be solved by forming equations and solving them.

Example 23

A rectangle has adjacent sides equal to x and $(x+2)$ cm as shown in Fig. 15.18. If its perimeter is 56 cm find the dimensions of the rectangle.

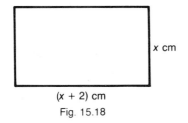

$(x + 2)$ cm

Fig. 15.18

Perimeter $= x+x+x+2+x+2 = 4x+4$.

But the perimeter is given as 56 cm. Hence:

$$4x+4 = 56$$

$$4x = 52$$

$$x = \frac{52}{4} = 13$$

Hence the dimensions of the rectangle are

$$x = 13 \, \text{cm}$$

and

$$x+2 = 15 \, \text{cm}$$

Exercise 109 — *All type B*

1) A triangle has a base x cm long and an altitude of 8 cm. If its area is 20 cm^2, find the value of x.

2) The circumference of a circle is 440 cm. Its diameter is x cm. Find x.

3) A rectangle has adjacent sides equal to x and $(x+4)$ cm. Its perimeter is 20 cm.

(a) Obtain an expression, in terms of x, for the perimeter of the rectangle.

(b) Write down an equation from which x may be found.

(c) Solve this equation.

4) A room is 3 m longer than it is wide. If its perimeter is 126 m, find the dimensions of the room.

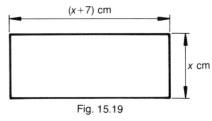

$(x+7)$ cm

x cm

Fig. 15.19

5) Fig. 15.19 shows a rectangle.

(a) Write an expression for its perimeter.

(b) Write an expression for its area.

(c) If the area of the rectangle is 18 cm^2, write down an equation from which x may be found.

6) The rectangle shown in Fig. 15.20 is made up of four smaller rectangles. Write down an expression for the area of the large rectangle ABCD.

112

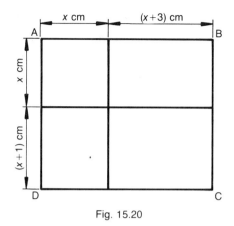

Fig. 15.20

Exercise 110 — *Questions 1–5 type A, remainder B*

All the questions in this exercise have been taken from past C.S.E. examination papers.

1) Calculate the area of the shape shown in Fig. 15.21 *(Y.R.)*

Fig. 15.21

2) Calculate the area of the shape shown in Fig. 15.22. *(Y.R.)*

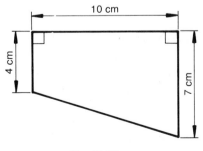

Fig. 15.22

3) How many square centimetres are there in a square metre?

    a 100   **b** 1000   **c** 10 000
    d 100 000 **e** 1 000 000   *(S.E.)*

4) Calculate the length of the perimeter of the quadrant of the circle drawn in Fig. 15.23 taking $\pi = \frac{22}{7}$.
                                       (W.M.)

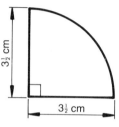

Fig. 15.23

5) The area of triangle PQR (Fig. 15.24) is

    a 7 cm²   **b** 10 cm²   **c** 12 cm²
    d 24 cm²   **e** 48 cm²   *(S.E.)*

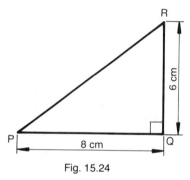

Fig. 15.24

6) The radius of a circle is 2 cm. Taking $\pi = 3.14$, calculate the circumference of the circle. *(Y.R.)*

7) Calculate the area of a triangle whose sides are 8, 15 and 17 cm.
                                       (E.M.)

8) Fig. 15.25 shows a metal framework made of thin wire. ABCD is a square and A, B, C and D are the centres of four circles which have equal radii.

(a) If the radius of each circle is 3 cm, find the following, taking $\pi = 3.14$ where necessary:

113

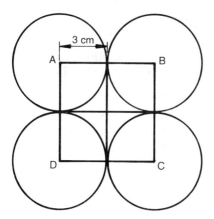

Fig. 15.25

   (i) the circumference of one of
      the circles,
   (ii) the area of one of the circles,
  (iii) the total length of the
      straight pieces of metal in
      the framework,
  (iv) the total length of metal
      used.

(b) Find the formula for the total
length of metal used if the radius
of one of the circles is x cm.
Leave your answer in terms of π.
                            (Y.R.)

9) Find the area of the shaded border
of the rectangle which is 0.3 cm wide
all the way round (Fig. 15.26).   (W.M.)

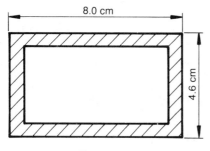

Fig. 15.26

10) The circumference of a circle is
176 cm. Calculate its radius.   (W.M.)

11) In the diagram (Fig. 15.27) the
radius of the large circle is 6 cm and

the radius of the small circle is 4 cm.
Calculate the area of the shaded part.
(Take $\pi = 3.14$).   (W.M.)

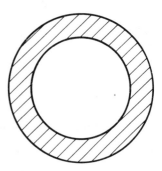

Fig. 15.27

12) If the perimeter of a square is
36 cm then the area of the square in
square centimetres is

    a 9   **b** 6   **c** 36
    d 81   **e** 36^2 (N.W.)

13) The diagram Fig. 15.28, *which is
not drawn to scale*, shows an ornamen-
tal garden; all measurements are in
metres. The garden consists of two
small rectangular flower borders and a
circular goldfish pool. The remaining
area is grass.

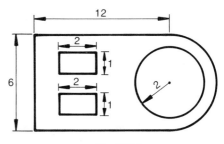

Fig. 15.28

Taking the value of π as 3.14, calculate:

(a) the area of the goldfish pool,
(b) the perimeter of the whole gar-
     den, including the flower beds
     and the goldfish pool,
(c) the area of the whole garden,
(d) the area of the grass.   (Y.R.)

Chapter 16 Solids

The Unit of Volume

Volume is measured by seeing how many cubic units a solid contains. 1 cubic centimetre (abbreviation: cm³) is the volume contained inside a cube whose edge is 1 cm (Fig. 16.1).

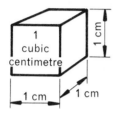

Fig. 16.1

Similarly, 1 cubic metre (abbreviation: m³) is the volume contained in a cube whose edge is 1 m.

The cuboid shown in Fig. 16.2 can be divided up into 3 layers of small cubes each having a volume of 1 cm³. There are 5×4 cubes in each layer and therefore the total number of small cubes is 5×4×3 = 60. The cuboid therefore has a volume of 60 cm³.

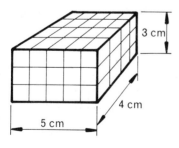

Fig. 16.2

All that we have done in order to find the volume of the cuboid is to multiply the length by the breadth by the height. This rule applies to any cuboid and hence

Volume of cuboid
= length×breadth×height

Since the area of the end of the cuboid is breadth×height we can write

Volume of cuboid
= area of end×length

This statement is true for any solid which has the same cross-section throughout its length.

Volume of solid
= area of cross-section×length

As a formula we write

$$V = Al$$

where V = volume, A = area of cross-section and l = length.

Example 1

Find the volume of a cuboid which is 32 cm long, 28 cm wide and 2 cm high.

Volume of cuboid

= length×breadth×height
= 32×28×2 = 1792 cm³

Example 2

Calculate the volume of a cuboid which is 120 cm long, 82 cm wide and 52 cm high. Give the answer in cubic metres.

In this problem it is best to express the dimensions of the cuboid in metres before attempting to find the volume. Thus:

length = 1.20 m, breadth = 0.82 m

and　　　　height = 0.52 m

Volume = length×breadth×height

$$= 1.20×0.82×0.52 = 0.512 \text{ m}^3$$

Example 3

Find the volume of the steel bar shown in Fig. 16.3.

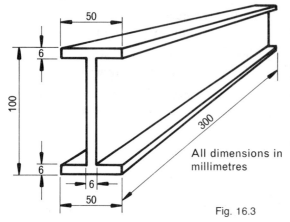

All dimensions in millimetres

Fig. 16.3

Since the bar has the same cross-section throughout its length

Volume

　　　= area of cross-section×length

Area of cross-section

$$= 50×6+50×6+88×6$$

$$= 300+300+528$$

$$= 1128 \text{ mm}^2$$

Volume

$$= 1128×300 = 338\,400 \text{ mm}^3$$

Example 4

A block of wood has the cross-section shown in Fig. 16.4. If it is 9 m long calculate its volume.

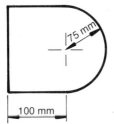

Fig. 16.4

Because the length is given in metres it will be convenient to find the volume in cubic metres.

Area of cross-section

$$= 0.100×0.150+\tfrac{1}{2}+\pi×0.075^2$$

$$= 0.015+0.0088 = 0.0238 \text{ m}^2$$

Volume

　　　= area of cross-section×length

$$= 0.0238×9 = 0.2142 \text{ m}^3$$

Volume of a Cylinder

A cylinder (Fig. 16.5) has a constant cross-section which is a circle. Hence:

Volume of cylinder
　　$= \pi×$radius$^2×$length (or height)

or　　　　$$V = \pi r^2 h$$

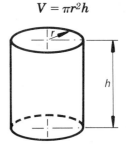

Fig. 16.5

Example 5

Find the volume of a cylinder which has a radius of 14 cm and a height of 12 cm.

Volume

$$= \tfrac{22}{7}×14^2×12 = 22×2×14×12$$

$$= 7392 \text{ cm}^3$$

Example 6

A pipe has the dimensions shown in Fig. 16.6. Calculate its volume.

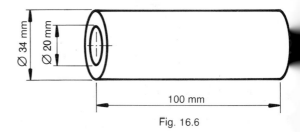

Fig. 16.6

116

Volume

$$= \text{cross-sectional area} \times \text{length}$$

Cross-sectional area

$$= \pi \times 17^2 - \pi \times 10^2 = 593.8 \text{ mm}^2$$

Volume

$$= 593.8 \times 100 = 59\,380 \text{ mm}^3$$

Exercise 111 — *All type B*

1) Find the volume of a rectangular block 8 cm long, 5 cm wide and 3.5 cm high.

2) The diagram (Fig. 16.7) shows the cross-section of a steel bar. If it is 250 mm long, calculate its volume.

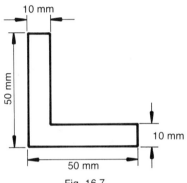

Fig. 16.7

3) Find the volume of a cylinder whose radius is 7 cm and whose height is 50 cm.

4) A hole 40 mm diameter is drilled in a plate 25 mm thick. What volume of metal is removed from the plate?

5) A block of wood has the cross-section shown in Fig. 16.8. If it is 8 cm long calculate its volume in cubic centimetres.

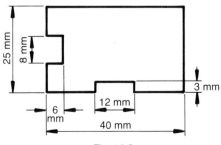

Fig. 16.8

6) Calculate the volume of a metal tube whose bore is 50 mm and whose thickness is 8 mm if it is 6 m long. Give the answer in cubic metres.

7) Fig. 16.9 shows a washer which is 0.2 cm thick. Calculate its volume.

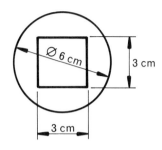

Fig. 16.9

8) Fig. 16.10 shows a triangular prism. Calculate its volume.

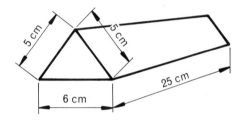

Fig. 16.10

9) A tent has a triangular cross-section whose base is 3 m and whose height is 2.2 m. If it is 7 m long, what is the volume inside the tent?

10) A pipe is 8 m long. It has a bore of 8 cm and an outside diameter of 10 cm. Calculate the volume of the pipe in cubic centimetres.

Surface Areas

We frequently need to find the surface areas of solid figures such as cylinders and rectangular blocks. The surface area is composed of the areas of the ends and the lateral surface area. The lateral surface area of a solid with a

117

constant cross-section is found by multiplying the perimeter of the cross-section by the length. That is:

Lateral surface area

= perimeter of cross-section ×

length

Example 7

Find the total surface area of a cylinder whose diamter is 28 cm and whose height is 50 cm.

The total surface area is composed of the areas of the two ends and the area of the curved surface. Thus:

Area of one end

$$= \pi \times \text{radius}^2 = \tfrac{22}{7} \times 14^2 = 616 \text{ cm}^2$$

Area of curved surface

$$= \pi \times \text{diameter} \times \text{height}$$
$$= \tfrac{22}{7} \times 28 \times 50 = 4400 \text{ cm}^2$$

Total surface area

$$= 2 \times 616 + 4400 = 5632 \text{ cm}^2$$

Example 8

Find the lateral surface area of the triangular prism shown in Fig. 16.11.

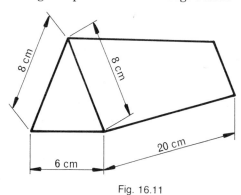

Fig. 16.11

Lateral surface area

$$= \text{perimeter of the end} \times \text{length}$$

Perimeter of end

$$= 8 + 8 + 6 = 22 \text{ cm}$$

Lateral surface area

$$= 22 \times 20 = 440 \text{ cm}^2$$

118

Exercise 112 — *All type B*

1) A room is 5 m long, 4.5 m wide and 2.5 m high. What is the surface area of the walls?

2) A rectangular block of wood is 50 cm long, 10 cm wide and 8 cm high. Find its total surface area.

3) A tent is in the shape of a triangular prism. It is 8 m long, 5 m wide and 3 m high. How much canvas was used in its construction?

4) A cylinder is 5 m long and it has a diameter of 28 cm. What is its total surface area in square metres?

5) A cylindrical tank is 1.5 m diameter and 3 m high. Its curved surface and the top are to be lagged. What area of lagging is required?

6) A closed water tank with vertical sides has a horizontal base in the shape of a rectangle with semi-circular

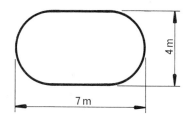

Fig. 16.12

ends as shown in Fig. 16.12. The total inside length of the tank is 7 m, its width 4 m and its height 2 m. Calculate the total surface area of the tank.

7) Find the curved surface area of a cylinder whose diameter is 3.25 m and whose height is 8.12 m.

The Cone

The volume of a cone (Fig. 16.13) is one-third of the volume of the equivalent cylinder. That is:

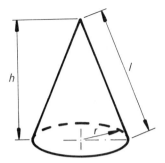

Fig. 16.13

Volume of cone
$$= \tfrac{1}{3} \times \pi \times \textbf{radius}^2 \times \textbf{vertical height}$$
or
$$V = \tfrac{1}{3}\pi r^2 h$$

The surface area of a cone depends upon the slant height and the radius.

Curved surface area of cone
$$= \pi \times \textbf{radius} \times \textbf{slant height}$$
or
$$A = \pi r l$$

Example 9

Find the volume and total surface area of a cone which has a vertical height of 8 cm and a radius of 6 cm.

Volume
$$= \tfrac{1}{3} \times \pi \times \text{radius}^2 \times \text{vertical height}$$
$$= \tfrac{1}{3} \times 3.142 \times 6^2 \times 8$$
$$= 301.6 \text{ cm}^3$$

To find the surface area we must first calculate the slant height. From Fig. 16.13:

Slant height $= \sqrt{6^2 + 8^2} = \sqrt{36 + 64}$
$$= \sqrt{100} = 10 \text{ cm}$$

Curved surface area
$$= \pi \times \text{radius} \times \text{slant height}$$
$$= 3.142 \times 6 \times 10$$
$$= 188.5 \text{ cm}^2$$

Area of base $= \pi \times \text{radius}^2$
$$= 3.142 \times 6^2 = 113.1$$

Total surface area
$$= 188.5 + 113.1$$
$$= 301.6 \text{ cm}^2$$

The Pyramid

The volume of a pyramid (Fig. 16.14) is one-third of the equivalent prism. That is:

Volume of pyramid
$$= \tfrac{1}{3} \times \textbf{area of base} \times \textbf{vertical height}$$
or
$$V = \tfrac{1}{3}Ah$$

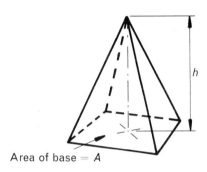

Area of base $= A$

Fig. 16.14

Example 10

Find the volume of a pyramid which has a rectangular base 8 cm long and 5 cm wide and a vertical height of 7 cm.

Volume of pyramid
$$= \tfrac{1}{3} \times \text{area of base} \times \text{vertical height}$$
$$= \tfrac{1}{3} \times 8 \times 5 \times 7 = 93.33 \text{ cm}^3$$

The Sphere

Volume of a sphere $= \tfrac{4}{3} \times \pi \times \textbf{radius}^3$
or
$$V = \tfrac{4}{3}\pi r^3$$

Surface area of a sphere
$$= 4 \times \pi \times \textbf{radius}^2$$
or
$$A = 4\pi r^2$$

Example 11

A sphere has a diameter of 12 cm. Calculate its volume and surface area.

Volume of sphere

$$= \tfrac{4}{3} \times \pi \times \text{radius}^3$$

$$= \tfrac{4}{3} \times \pi \times 6^3 = 904.9 \text{ cm}^3$$

Surface area of sphere

$$= 4 \times \pi \times \text{radius}^2$$

$$= 4 \times 3.142 \times 6^2$$

$$= 452.4 \text{ cm}^2$$

Exercise 113 — *All type B*

1) Find the volume and curved surface area of a cone with a radius of 4 cm and a vertical height of 3 cm.

2) A cone has a diameter of 12 cm and a slant height of 8 cm. Calculate its total surface area and its volume.

3) A pyramid has a base which is an equilateral triangle of side 6 cm. If its altitude is 4 cm, calculate the volume of the pyramid.

4) A pyramid has a square base of side 12 cm and an altitude of 6 cm. What is its volume?

5) A sphere has a diameter of 10 cm. Calculate its volume and surface area.

6) A hemisphere has a radius of 9 cm. What is its volume?

7) Fig. 16.15 represents a bird cage in the form of a cylinder surmounted by a cone.

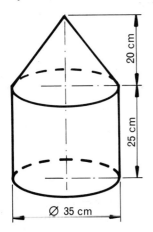

Fig. 16.15

Calculate:

(a) the total volume of the cage,

(b) the total surface area except for the base.

8) Fig. 16.16 shows a flask which may be considered to be a sphere with a cylindrical neck. Calculate the volume of the flask.

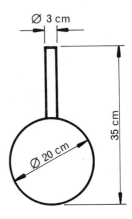

Fig. 16.16

Capacity

The capacity of a container is the volume that it will contain. It is sometimes measured in the same units as for volume, that is, in cubic metres, cubic centimetres or cubic millimetres.

However, for liquid measure the litre (abbreviation: ℓ) is frequently used, such that

$$1 \text{ litre} = 1000 \text{ cm}^3$$

Example 12

A rectangular tank has inside measurements of 3 m long, 2 m wide and 1.5 m high. How many litres of liquid will it hold?

Since 1 litre is 1000 cm³ it is best to calculate the volume (or capacity) in cubic centimetres to start with.

Thus:

Capacity

$$= 300 \times 200 \times 150 = 9\,000\,000 \text{ cm}^3$$

$$= \frac{9\,000\,000}{1000} = 9000 \text{ litres}$$

Small capacities are often measured in millilitres and:

$$1000 \text{ millilitres (m}\ell) = 1 \text{ litre}$$

Example 13

How many doses of 5 millilitres can be obtained from a cylindrical medicine bottle which is 5 cm in diameter and 12 cm high?

Volume of cylinder

$$= \pi \times \text{radius}^2 \times \text{height}$$

$$= 3.142 \times 2.5^2 \times 12$$

$$= 235.7 \text{ cm}^3$$

Since there are 1000 cm³ to 1 litre, 1 cm³ = 1 millilitre. Hence:

Number of 5 mℓ doses $= \dfrac{235.7}{5}$

$$= 47 \text{ full doses}$$

The Flow of Water

When a tank or container is being filled with water the time taken to fill the tank depends upon the quantity of water entering the tank in unit time. The rate of flow is often stated in cubic centimetres per second (cm³/s) or cubic metres per minute (m³/min). In the case of water flowing through a pipe the speed of flow, usually in metres per minute (m/min), is often given.

Example 14

A tank which contains 250 m³ of water when full is to be filled through a pipe which delivers water at a rate of 2 m³/min. How long does it take to fill the tank?

$$\text{Time taken} = \frac{\text{volume to fill tank}}{\text{rate of flow}}$$

$$= \frac{250}{2} = 125 \text{ min}$$

Example 15

Water is flowing through a pipe whose bore is 75 mm at a speed of 2 m/s. Calculate the discharge from the pipe in:

(a) cubic metres per second
(b) litres per minute

(a) Bore of pipe = 75 mm = 0.075 m

Area of pipe $= \pi \times (0.0375)^2$

$$= 0.0044 \text{ m}^2$$

Discharge from the pipe

$$= \text{speed of flow} \times \text{area of the pipe}$$

$$= 2 \times 0.0044 = 0.0088 \text{ m}^3/\text{s}$$

(b) Since   1 m = 100 cm,

$$1 \text{ m}^3 = 100^3 \text{ cm}^3$$

$$= 1\,000\,000 \text{ cm}^3$$

Discharge from pipe

$$= 0.0088 \times 1\,000\,000 \text{ cm}^3/\text{s}$$

$$= 8800 \text{ cm}^3/\text{s}$$

Since   1 litre = 1000 cm³

Discharge from the pipe

$$= \frac{8800}{1000} = 8.8 \text{ litres per second}$$

$$= 8.8 \times 60$$

$$= 528 \text{ litres per minute}$$

Exercise 114 — *Questions 1–10 type B, remainder C*

1) A rectangular tank is 2.5 m long, 1.4 m wide and 0.8 m high. How many litres of water will it hold?

121

2)   A cylindrical garden pool has a radius of 3 m. How many litres of water will it hold if it is filled to a depth of 140 cm?

3)   What is the volume of a cylindrical tank 2 m diameter and 3 m high? Give the answer in cubic metres. How many litres does the tank hold?

4)   A water pipe has a diameter of 20 mm and a length of 25 m. How many litres of water are contained in the pipe?

5)   A cylindrical tank contains 15 375 cm³ of water when full. How many litres does it contain?

6)   A rectangular medicine bottle is 8 cm wide, 4 cm long and 12 cm high. What is its capacity in millilitres? How many doses of 4 mℓ can be obtained from a full bottle?

7)   A conical wine glass is 4.5 cm diameter and 6 cm high. What is its capacity in millilitres? How many glasses could be filled from a bottle of wine containing half a litre?

8)   A petrol storage tank measures 3 m by 2 m by 1.5 m being rectangular in shape. Calculate the number of litres of petrol that it will contain when full.

9)   An ice cream carton is cylindrical in shape being 6 cm diameter and 8 cm high. How many litres of ice cream are needed to fill 50 such cartons?

10)   A container is in the form of a hemisphere with an internal diameter of 24 cm. How many litres of liquid will it hold?

11)   Water is poured into a container at a rate of 300 cm³/s. How long does it take for the container to contain 45 000 cm³?

12)   Water is flowing through a pipe whose bore is 15 cm at a speed of 3 m/s. Find the discharge from the pipe:

(a)   in cubic metres per second.

(b)   in litres per minute.

13)   Water flows along a channel at a rate of 3 m/s. Calculate the number of litres of water flowing along the channel each minute if its cross-sectional area is 10 m².

14)   A tank is in the form of a cylinder 3 m diameter and 5 m high. Calculate the volume of water it will hold when full. If water flows into the tank at a rate of 50 cm³/s find how long it will take to fill the tank.

15)   Water is poured into a cylindrical reservoir 10 m in diameter at a rate of 3000 litres per minute. At what rate does the water level rise in cm/min?

Mass and Density

The density of a substance is the mass per unit volume. Densities are usually measured in kilogrammes per cubic metre (kg/m³) or in grammes per cubic centimetre (g/cm³). The mass of an object may be found by using the formula:

Mass = density × volume of material in the object

The table on page 122 gives the densities of various common substances.

Example 16

Find the mass of a block of copper 5 cm by 6 cm by 8 cm. Take the density of copper to be 9 g/cm³.

Volume of block $= 5 \times 6 \times 8 = 240$ cm³

Mass of block $=$ volume × density

$$= 240 \times 9$$

$$= 2160 \text{ g or } 2.16 \text{ kg}$$

Densities of Various Substances			
Substance	**Density (g/cm³)**	**Substance**	**Density (g/cm³)**
Alcohol	0.79	Gravel	1.8
Aluminium	2.7	Ice	0.90
Asbestos	2.8	Iron	7.9
Brick,		Kerosene	0.80
common	1.8	Lead	11.4
Cement	3.1	Masonry	2.4
Coal,		Petroleum	
bituminous	1.3	oil	0.82
Concrete	2.2	Salt,	
Copper	8.9	common	2.1
Gasoline	0.70	Sand, dry	1.6
Glass	2.6	Silver	10.5
Gold	19.3	Water, fresh	1.0

Example 17

Fig. 16.17 shows the cross-section of a cast iron pillar. If the pillar is 3 m high, calculate its mass given that the density of cast iron is 8 g/cm³.

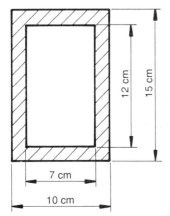

Fig. 16.17

Since the density is given in grammes per cubic centimetre it will be best to calculate the volume in cubic centimetres. Thus:

Volume of pillar

$$= (15 \times 10 - 12 \times 7) \times 300$$
$$= (150 - 84) \times 300$$
$$= 66 \times 300 = 19\,800 \text{ cm}^3$$

Mass of pillar

$$= \text{volume} \times \text{density}$$
$$= 19\,800 \times 8$$
$$= 158\,400 \text{ g or } 158.4 \text{ kg}$$

Exercise 115 — *All type B*

1) A piece of masonry has a volume of 250 cm³. If the density of masonry is 2.4 g/cm³, calculate the mass of the masonry.

2) What is the mass of 1 m³ of sand if the density of sand is 1.6 g/cm³?

3) Find the mass of a block of lead which is 25 cm long, 8 cm wide and 4 cm high. The density of lead is 11.4 g/cm³.

4) Calculate the mass of a copper rod 6 cm diameter and 4 m long. The density of copper is 8.9 g/cm³.

5) A cylindrical water tank is 3 m diameter and 2 m long. What mass of water does it contain?

6) The density of petrol is 0.70 g/cm³. What mass of petrol is there in a tank which contains 25 litres?

7) A sheet of copper is 3 m wide and 8 m long. Its thickness is 5 mm. If the density of copper is 9 g/cm³ calculate the mass of the sheet.

8) What is the mass of a steel pipe 20 cm outside diameter and 16 cm inside diameter and 5 m long? Take the density of steel to be 8 g/cm³.

9) A slab of marble is 85 cm long, 59 cm wide and 24 cm thick. If the density of marble is 2.5 g/cm³, calculate the mass of the slab.

10) A stone pillar is 30 cm diameter and 9 m long. If the density of stone is 2.5 g/cm³, calculate the mass of the pillar.

More Difficult Problems

Many problems with volumes and surface areas of solid figures can be solved by forming an equation. The method is shown in Example 18.

123

Example 18

A steel ingot whose volume is 2 m³ is rolled into plate which is 15 mm thick and 1.75 m wide. Calculate the length of the plate in metres.

Using the formula: $V = lbh$

and substituting the given values we have:

$$2 = l \times 1.75 \times 0.015$$

$$l = \frac{2}{1.75 \times 0.015} = 76.19 \text{ m}$$

Hence the length of the plate is 76.19 m

Exercise 116 — *All type C*

1)   Calculate the length of a rectangular tank whose volume is 120 cm³ if its width is 8 cm and its height is 3 cm.

2)   A cylinder has a volume of 54 m³. If its diameter is 3 m calculate its length.

3)   A sphere has a volume of 127 cm³. What is its radius?

4)   Calculate the cross-sectional area of a triangular prism whose volume is 90 cm³ and whose length is 18 cm.

5)   Find the thickness of a piece of metal if its volume is 1800 cm³ and its length and width are 90 cm and 80 cm respectively.

6)   A block of lead is hammered out to make a square sheet 10 mm thick. If the original dimensions of the block are   1.5 m×1 m×0.75 m   find the dimensions of the square.

7)   A steel ingot is in the shape of a cylinder 1.5 m diameter and 3.5 m long. How many metres of square bar of 50 mm side can be rolled from it?

8)   Calculate the diameter of a cylin-der whose volume is 220 cm³ and whose height is equal to its diameter.

9)   An ingot whose volume is 2 m³ is to be made into ball bearings whose diameters are 12 mm. Assuming that there is no wastage how many ball bearings can be made?

10)   A cylindrical can holds 18 litres of petrol. Find the depth of petrol if the can has a diameter of 60 cm.

11)   A rectangular slab of stone has a mass of 6 kg. Its length is 20 cm and its width is 15 cm. What is its thickness if the density of the stone is 2.5 g/cm³?

12)   A sheet of copper has a mass of 18 kg. If the density of copper is 9 g/cm³ and the length of the sheet is $\frac{1}{2}$ m, calculate the cross-sectional area of the sheet.

Similar Figures

Two plane figures are similar if the ratios of their corresponding sides are equal. Thus in Fig. 16.18 the two rectangles ABCD and WXYZ are similar because

$$\text{ratio of shorter sides} = \frac{6}{3} = 2$$

and $\text{ratio of longer sides} = \dfrac{8}{4} = 2$

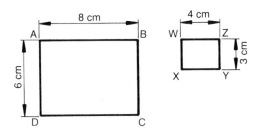

Fig. 16.18

The ratio of the areas of similar figures is equal to the ratio of the squares

on corresponding sides. Thus for the
rectangles in Fig. 16.18,

$$\frac{\text{Area ABCD}}{\text{Area WXYZ}} = \left(\frac{\text{AD}}{\text{WZ}}\right)^2 = \left(\frac{\text{AB}}{\text{WX}}\right)^2$$

Example 19

The trapeziums shown in Fig. 16.19
are similar. If the area of ABCD is
20 cm² find the area of WXYZ.

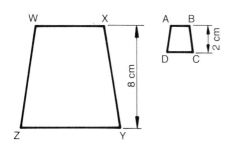

Fig. 16.19

$$\frac{\text{Area WXYZ}}{\text{Area ABCD}} = \left(\frac{8}{2}\right)^2 = 16$$

$$\frac{\text{Area WXYZ}}{20} = 16$$

Area WXYZ = 20×16 = 320 cm²

Similar Solids

Two solids are similar if the ratios of
their corresponding linear dimensions
are equal. The two cylinders shown in
Fig. 16.20 are similar because

$$\frac{\text{Height of cylinder A}}{\text{Height of cylinder B}}$$

$$= \frac{\text{diameter of cylinder A}}{\text{diameter of cylinder B}}$$

The surface areas of similar solids are
proportional to the squares of their
linear dimensions. Hence for the similar cylinders shown in Fig. 16.20,

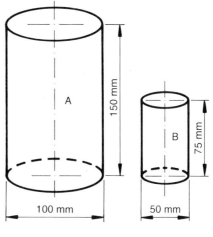

Fig. 16.20

$$\frac{\text{Surface area of cylinder A}}{\text{Surface area of cylinder B}}$$

$$= \left(\frac{\text{height of cylinder A}}{\text{height of cylinder B}}\right)^2$$

$$= \left(\frac{\text{diameter of cylinder A}}{\text{diameter of cylinder B}}\right)^2$$

Example 20

Find the surface area of a sphere
whose diameter is 120 mm. Hence find
the surface area of a sphere whose
diameter is 60 mm.

Surface area of 120 mm diameter
sphere

$$= 4\pi r^2 = 4\times3.142\times60^2$$

$$= 45\,239 \text{ mm}^2$$

Surface area of 60 mm diameter sphere / Surface area of 120 mm diameter sphere

$$\frac{\text{Surface area of 60 mm diameter sphere}}{\text{Surface area of 120 mm diameter sphere}} = \left(\frac{60}{120}\right)^2$$

Surface area of 60 mm diameter
sphere

$$= \tfrac{1}{4}\times\text{surface area of 120 mm diameter sphere}$$

$$= \tfrac{1}{4}\times45\,239 = 11\,310 \text{ mm}^2$$

125

The volumes of similar solids are proportional to the cubes of their linear dimensions. Hence for the similar cylinders shown in Fig. 16.20,

$$\frac{\text{Volume of cylinder A}}{\text{Volume of cylinder B}}$$

$$= \left(\frac{\text{height of cylinder A}}{\text{height of cylinder B}}\right)^3$$

$$= \left(\frac{\text{diameter of cylinder A}}{\text{diameter of cylinder B}}\right)^3$$

Example 21

The volume of a cone whose height is 135 mm is 1090 mm³. Find the volume of a similar cone whose height is 72 mm.

$$\frac{\text{Volume of cone whose height is 72 mm}}{\text{Volume of cone whose height is 135 mm}} = \left(\frac{72}{135}\right)^3$$

$$= 0.1517$$

Volume of cone whose height is 72 mm
$$= 0.1517 \times 1090 = 165.4 \text{ mm}^3$$

Exercise 117 — *All type B*

1) A circle of 7 cm radius has an area of 154 cm². What is the area of a circle whose radius is 3.5 cm?

2) Are the rectangles shown in Fig. 16.21 similar? Give reasons for your answer.

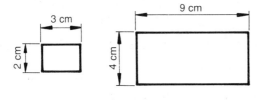

Fig. 16.21

3) Two triangles are similar. One has a base of 20 cm and an area of 400 cm². The other has a base x centimetres long and an area of 100 cm². Find x.

4) Two similar trapeziums A and B have areas of 800 cm² and 500 cm² respectively. If the altitude of B is 20 cm, find the altitude of A.

5) Two spheres have radii 3 cm and 5 cm respectively. Find their volumes.

6) A spherical cap has a height of 2 cm and a volume of 8 cm³. A similar cap has a height of 3 cm. What is its volume?

7) The volume of a cone of height 14.2 cm is 210 cm³. Find the height of a similar cone whose volume is 60 cm³.

8) Find the surface area of a metal sphere whose radius is 73 mm. What is the area of a sphere whose radius is 29 mm?

9) The curved surface of a cone has an area of 20.5 cm². What is the curved surface area of a similar cone whose height is 1.5 times as great as the first cone?

10) Find the mass of a hemispherical bowl of copper whose external and internal diameters are 24 cm and 16 cm respectively. The density of copper is 8.9 g/cm³. What is the mass of a similar bowl whose external diameter is 20 cm?

Nets

Suppose that we have to make a cube out of thin sheet metal. We need a pattern giving us the shape of the metal needed to make the cube. As shown in Fig. 16.22, the pattern consists of six squares. The shape which can be folded to make a cube is called the *net* of the cube.

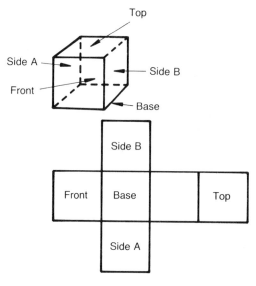

Fig. 16.22

It is possible for there to be more than one net for a solid object. For instance, the cube in Fig. 16.22 can be made from the net shown in Fig. 16.23.

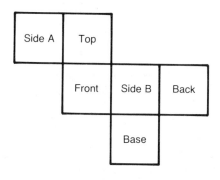

Fig. 16.23

Example 22

Sketch the net of the triangular prism shown in Fig. 16.24. As can be seen

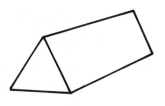

Fig. 16.24

from Fig. 16.25, the net consists of three rectangles representing the base and the two sides and two triangles representing the two ends.

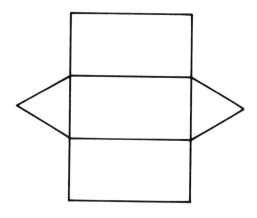

Fig. 16.25

Nets of Curved Surfaces

The net for a cylinder without a top and bottom is shown in Fig. 16.26. The length of the net is equal to the circumference of the cylinder.

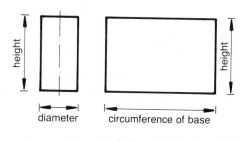

circle = $\pi \times$ diameter

Fig. 16.26

Example 23

Draw the net for the cone shown in Fig. 16.27.

The net is in the form of a sector of a circle. Note that the arms of the sector are equal to the slant height of the

127

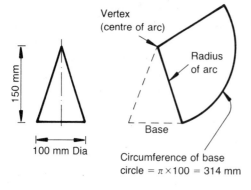

Fig. 16.27

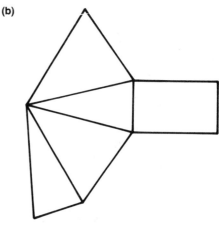

(b)

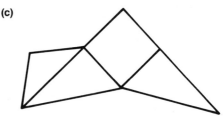

(c)

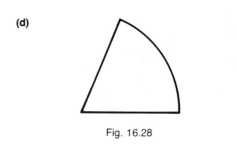

(d)

Fig. 16.28

cone and that the length of the arc is equal to the circumference of the base circle of the cone.

Exercise 118 — *All type B*

Sketch the nets for the following solids:

1) A cuboid 8 cm long, 3 cm wide and 4 cm high.

2) A triangular prism whose ends are right-angled triangles of base 3 cm and height 4 cm and whose length is 6 cm.

3) A pyramid with a square base of side 5 cm and a height (altitude) of 8 cm.

4) A cube with an edge of 4 cm.

5) A cylinder with a height of 5 cm and a diameter of 3 cm.

6) A cone with a vertical height of 8 cm and a base diameter of 7 cm. The diagrams (Fig. 16.28) show the nets of various solids. Name each solid.

(a)

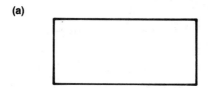

Exercise 119 — *Questions 1–5 type B, remainder C*

All the questions in this exercise have been taken from past C.S.E. examination papers.

1) The diagram (Fig. 16.29) shows the net from which the model of a prism was made. The prism stood on the horizontal rectangular base ABCD in which AB = 60 cm and AD = 24 cm. AE = DF = 15 cm.

(a) Make a sketch of the prism, marking the known lengths.

(b) By drawing the net to scale, find the vertical height of the prism.

128

(c) Find the total surface area of the prism.

(d) Find the volume of the prism.
(Y.R.)

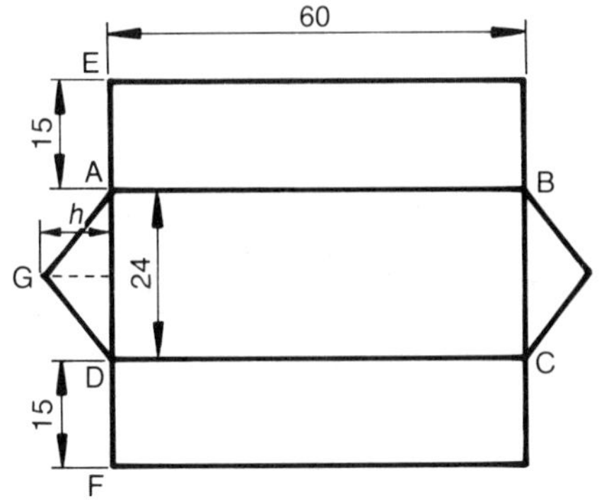

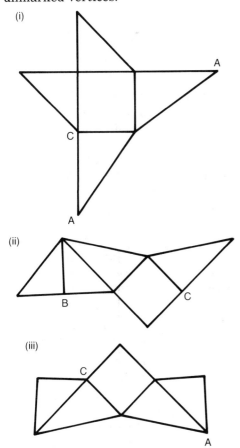

Fig. 16.29

2) The three diagrams in Fig. 16.30 are nets of a three dimensional shape. Complete the labelling of the unmarked vertices.

(i)

(ii)

(iii)

Fig. 16.30

3) The diagram below (Fig. 16.31), represents a prism of length 20 cm. The uniform cross-section of the prism is a right-angled triangle whose two shorter sides are 7 cm and 8 cm in length. Calculate the volume of the prism. (Y.R.)

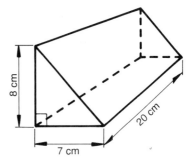

Fig. 16.31

4) Fig. 16.32 represents a length of guttering. The end ABC is in the shape of a quadrant of a circle.
AC = AB = EF = ED = 14 cm.
AE = BD = CF = 300 cm. Take the value of $\pi = \frac{22}{7}$.

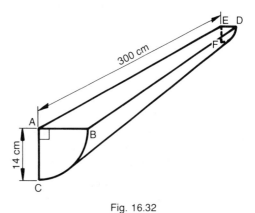

Fig. 16.32

(a) Calculate the area of the rectangle ABDE in square centimetres.

(b) Calculate the area of the curved surface BDFC in square centimetres.

(c) (i) Calculate the area of the end ABC in square centimetres.

129

(ii) Calculate the greatest volume
of water that the guttering
can hold in litres.   (*W.M.*)

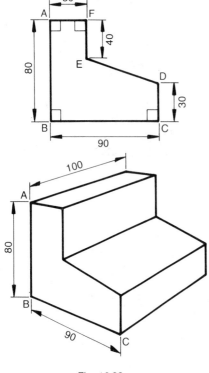

Fig. 16.33

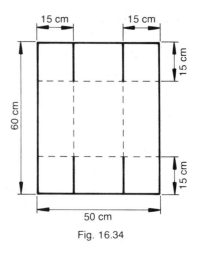

Fig. 16.34

5) Fig. 16.33 shows two views of a
wooden chair. All dimensions are
given in centimetres. Calculate:

(a)   The area ABCDEF of one side of
the chair, leaving your answer in
square centimetres.

(b)   The volume of the chair, leaving
your answer in cubic centimetres.
(*Y.R.*)

6) Cardboard boxes are made from
pieces of card, 60 cm by 50 cm, by
marking out as shown in Fig. 16.34,
cutting along the continuous lines and
folding along the dotted lines.

(a)   Calculate the amount of card
needed to make 800 boxes, leaving your answer in square
metres.

(b)   Calculate (i) the dimensions of
the cardboard box, (ii) the volume
of the box.

The box, when formed, is filled with
cylindrical tins, each tin being half the
height of the box. If the radius of the
base of each tin is 5 cm:

(c)   Calculate the maximum number
of tins the box will hold.

(d)   Express the amount of space
occupied by all the tins as a fraction of the total volume of the
box. (Take $\pi = \frac{22}{7}$)   (*S.W.*)

7) The diagram (Fig. 16.35), shows a
scale model of a church tower and
spire made from card. The tower of the
model has a square base with sides
5 cm and is 28 cm high. The spire is in
the form of a cone and the circular
base of the cone just reaches the edges
of the tower. The total height of the
spire and tower is 34 cm.

(a)   What is the height of the cone
used in the model as the spire?

(b)   What is the radius of the base of
the model of the spire?

(c)   Calculate the volume of air
enclosed between the cone and
the top of the tower. Give your
answer to the nearest cubic
centimetre taking $\pi = 3.14$.

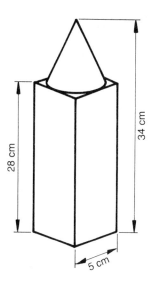

Fig. 16.35

(d) The cone was made by cutting and glueing from a single circle of card. What was the radius of the smallest possible circle?

(e) The church tower, of which this is a model, has a square base with sides 4.2 m. Estimate the height of the top of its spire above the ground to the nearest metre. (S)

8) An open cylindrical can whose internal dimensions are, radius 5 cm and height 20 cm, is completely filled with water.

(a) Calculate the volume of water in the can.

(b) A metal sphere of radius 3 cm is lowered into the can until it is completely covered. What volume of water is displaced by the sphere? Give your answer to the nearest whole number of cubic centimetres.

(c) The density of the metal from which the sphere is made is 11 g/cm³. If density is said to be equal to

$$\frac{\text{the mass of the sphere}}{\text{the volume of the sphere}}$$

find the total mass of the sphere to the nearest kilogramme.
(Take $\pi = 3.14$.)   (Y.R.)

9) Fig. 16.36 represents a solid triangular prism. The dimensions are given in centimetres.

(a) Find the area of the cross-section of the prism.

(b) If the volume of the prism is 1848 cm³, find the length l.

(c) If the material from which the prism is made weighs 17.5 g/cm³

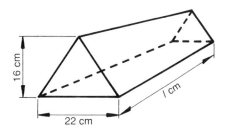

Fig. 16.36

and costs £2.10 per kilogramme, find:
(i)   The weight of the prism.
(ii) The cost of the prism, correct to the nearest whole pence.

(d) If the prism is recast into a cylindrical bar of length 12 cm, calculate the radius of the bar. (Take $\pi = \frac{22}{7}$.)

        (S.W.)

10)

(a) A rectangular tank has a base 72 cm long and 45 cm wide. When full it contains 81 litres. Find:
(i)   The volume of the tank in cubic centimetres.
(ii) The height of the tank.

(b) If water flows out of the tank through a pipe, at a rate of 18 cm/s, find the time, to the nearest second, it would take to empty the full tank if the pipe is of radius 2.3 cm.
(Take $\pi = 3.142$.)   (W)

Chapter 17   Graphs and Mappings

In newspapers, business reports and government publications, use is made of pictorial illustrations to compare quantities of the same kind. These diagrams help the reader to understand what deductions can be drawn from the quantities represented. One of the most common forms is the graph.

Axes of Reference

To plot a graph we first take two lines at right angles to each other as shown in Fig. 17.1. These lines are called the axes of reference. Their intersection, the point O, is called the origin. The vertical axis is often called the y-axis and the horizontal axis is then called the x-axis.

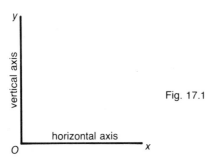

Fig. 17.1

Scales

The number of units represented by a unit length along an axis is called the scale on that axis. For instance 1 cm could represent 2 units. The scale is determined from the highest and lowest values to be plotted along an axis.

It should be as large as possible but it must be chosen so that it is easy to read. The most useful scales are 1, 2 and 5 units to 1 large square on the graph paper. Some multiples of these such as 10, 20, 100 units, etc. are also suitable. Note that the scales chosen need not be the same on both axes.

Coordinates

Coordinates are used to mark the points on a graph. In Fig. 17.2, values of x are to be plotted against values of y. The point P has been plotted so that $x = 8$ and $y = 10$. The values of 8 and 10 are said to be the rectangular coordinates of P.

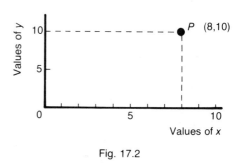

Fig. 17.2

For brevity we say that P is the point (8, 10). Note very carefully that the first number, it is 8, gives the value along the horizontal, or x-axis and the second number, it is 10, gives the coordinate along the vertical or y-axis. Because the order of the coordinates is very important we call the values (8, 10) an *ordered pair*. Thus, any pair of coordinates will constitute an ordered pair.

Drawing a Graph

Every graph shows a relation between two sets of numbers. The table below gives the cost of different quantities of oil.

Quantity (litres)	0	4	8	10	16
Cost £	0	2	4	5	8

To plot a graph we first draw the two axes of reference (Fig. 17.3). We then choose suitable scales to represent the quantity in litres along the horizontal axis and the cost in £ along the vertical axis. Scales of 5 mm = 2 litres (horizontally) and 5 mm = £1 (vertically) have been chosen. Having marked the number scales on both axes these should then be labelled as shown in the diagram. On plotting the points we see that a straight line passes through all of them.

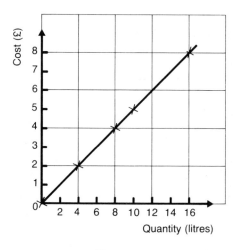

Fig. 17.3

In this example all the values were whole numbers but fractional and decimal values can also be represented on a graph as shown in the example which follows.

Example 1

The table below gives the average diameter of ash trees of varying ages. Plot a graph of this information with age plotted along the horizontal axis.

Age in years	5	10	15	20
Diameter (cm)	7.6	9.3	12.2	16.2

The graph is shown plotted in Fig. 17.4 and we see that it is a smooth curve which passes through all the plotted points.

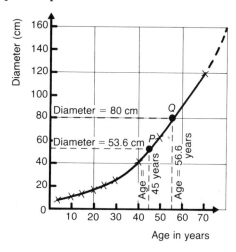

Fig. 17.4

When a graph is a smooth curve or a straight line we can use the graph to deduce corresponding values not given in the table of values from which the graph was plotted. Thus to find the diameter of a tree which is 45 years old we first find 45 on the horizontal axis and from this point we draw a vertical line to meet the curve at P. From P we now draw a horizontal line to the vertical axis and read off the value. It is found to be 53.6. Hence a tree which is 45 years old will have a diameter of 53.6 cm.

Suppose now that we wish to know the age of a tree with a diameter of 80 cm. We find 80 on the vertical axis and from this point we draw a horizontal

133

line to meet the curve at Q. From Q we draw a vertical line to the horizontal axis and read off the value. It is found to be 56.6. Hence a tree which is 80 cm in diameter will be 56.6 years old.

Using a graph in this way to find values which are not given in the original table is called *interpolation*. If we extend the curve so that it follows the general trend we can estimate values of the diameter and age which lie just beyond the range of the given values. Thus in Fig. 17.4 by extending the curve we can find the probable diameter of a tree which is 75 years old. This is found to be 136.4 cm. Finding a value in this way is called *extrapolation*. An extrapolated value can usually be relied upon, but in certain cases it may contain a substantial amount of error. Extrapolated values must therefore be used with care. It must be clearly understood that interpolation can only be used if the graph is a smooth curve or a straight line. It is no good using interpolation for the graph of Example 2.

Example 2

The table below gives the temperature at 12.00 noon on seven successive days. Plot a graph to illustrate this information with the day horizontal.

Day June	1	2	3	4
Temp. °C	16	20	16	18

As before we draw two axes at right-angles to each other, indicating the day on the horizontal axis. Since the temperatures range from 15° to 22 °C we can make 14 °C (say) our starting point on the vertical axis. This will allow us to use a larger scale on that axis which makes for greater accuracy in plotting the graph.

On plotting the points (Fig. 17.5) we see that it is impossible to join the points by means of a smooth curve.

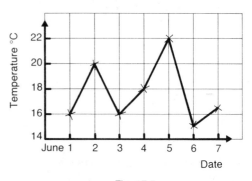

Fig. 17.5

The best we can do is to join the points by means of a series of straight lines. The graph then presents in pictorial form the variations in temperature and we can see at a glance that the 1st, 3rd and 6th June were cool days whilst the 2nd and 5th were warm days.

Example 3

The values in the table below give the speed of a body at certain times.

Time (min)	60	90	120	160	180	210
Speed (m/min)	11.2	9.5	9.0	8.7	8.5	8.4

Plot this information on a graph and from the graph estimate the speed of the body after 110 min and the time when the speed of the car was 9.7 m/min.

As before we draw two axes at right angles to each other indicating the time in minutes on the horizontal axus and the speed in metres per minute on the vertical axis. Since the time ranges from 60 to 210 we can make 60 our starting point on the horizontal axis. On the vertical axis we can make 8 our starting point. By doing this we can have larger scales on both axes and so plot the graph more accurately.

The graph is drawn in Fig. 17.6 and we see that it is a smooth curve. We can therefore use it to estimate values which are intermediate to those given in the table. From the graph we see that after a time of 110 min the speed of the body is 9.1 m/min and the speed is 9.7 m/min when the time is 84 min.

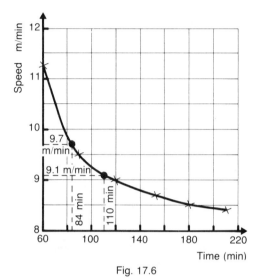

Fig. 17.6

Exercise 120 — *All type B*

1) The table below shows the amount of steel delivered to a factory during five successive weeks. Plot a graph to show this with the number of weeks on the horizontal axis.

Week number	1	2	3
Amount delivered (kg)	25 000	65 000	80 000
Week number	4	5	
Amount delivered (kg)	30 000	50 000	

2) The areas of circles for various diameters is shown in the table below. Plot a graph with the diameter on the horizontal axis and from it estimate the area of a circle whose diameter is 18 cm.

Diameter (cm)	5	10	15	20	25
Area (cm²)	19.6	78.5	177.6	314.2	492.2

3) The output of a factory in 8 successive weeks is given in the table below. Plot a graph to show this with the number of weeks on the horizontal axis.

Week number	1	2	3	4	5	6	7	8
Output (units)	83	65	78	89	96	88	73	69

4) The table below gives the amounts for £1 invested at 8% interest per annum for the periods stated.

Years	2	4	6	8	10	12	14
Amounts in £	1.17	1.36	1.59	1.85	2.16	2.52	2.94

Plot the years horizontally and find the amount after 7 years.

5) Two quantities W and P are connected as shown by the following table of values:

W	28	50	59	67	74	79	84
P	2.0	5.4	6.8	8.0	9.1	9.9	10.6

Plot a graph with P plotted horizontally and find the value of W when $P = 7.4$. What is the value of P when $W = 77$?

6) A quantity of gas is contained in a cylinder and is subjected to various pressures. The volume occupied by the gas under different pressures is shown below:

Pressure	1	2	3	4	5	6
Volume	2.4	1.2	0.8	0.6	0.48	0.4

Plot a graph of volume against pressure with pressure on the horizontal axis. Hence find:

(a) the volume when the pressure is 3.5.

(b) the increase in pressure needed to reduce the volume from 1.6 to 0.6.

135

Mapping

The relation between the quantity of oil in litres and its cost shown in the table on page 133 may also be represented in a diagram (Fig. 17.7).

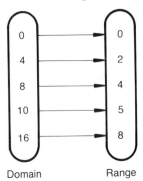

Fig. 17.7

Domain   Range

The set of starting elements, 0, 4, 8, 10 and 16 is called the *domain* and the set of finishing elements 0, 2, 4, 5 and 8 is called the *range*. The values connected by the arrowed lines constitute *ordered pairs* and the relation may be shown in a graph as before (Fig. 17.3).

Fig. 17.8 shows a relationship between the domain X and the range Y. X and Y are related by the relationship $x \rightarrow 3x+2$ which reads 'x is mapped onto $3x+2$'. The elements in Y are obtained by substituting the values in X into the expression $3x+2$. Thus, when

$x = 0$: $3x+2 = 3 \times 0+2 = 2$

$x = 1$: $3x+2 = 3 \times 1+2 = 5$

$x = 2$: $3x+2 = 3 \times 2+2 = 8$

and so on.

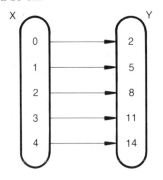

Fig. 17.8

1) Copy and complete Fig. 17.9 if the relation is:

(a) $x \rightarrow 2x+4$

(b) $x \rightarrow 6x$

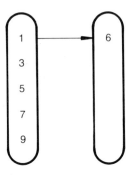

Fig. 17.9

2) For the relation $x \rightarrow x^2$

(a) What is 3 mapped onto?

(b) What is 6 mapped onto?

3) The diagram (Fig. 17.10) shows a relationship between A and B.

(a) What number should be in the position marked *?

(b) Give the relationship between an element, x, in A and the corresponding element in B.

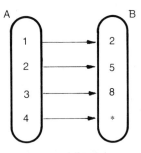

Fig. 17.10

4) With 2, 3, 4 and 5 as domain draw a mapping diagram for:

(a) $x \rightarrow 4-2x$.

(b) $x \rightarrow 2^x$.

5) The diagram (Fig. 17.11) shows a relationship between the domain X and the range Y. Find:

136

(a) The relationship between an element x in X and the corresponding element in Y.

(b) The numbers marked *.

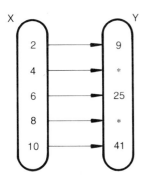

Fig. 17.11

6) If a relation from X to Y is defined by $y = x^2 - 3x + 2$ (i.e. $x \rightarrow x^2 - 3x + 2$) complete the mapping diagram shown in Fig. 17.12.

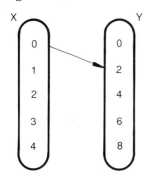

Fig. 17.12

7) State the relationship that gives the mapping shown in Fig. 17.13.

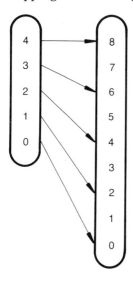

Fig. 17.13

Functions

A function is a relation in which one, and only one, arrowed line in the mapping diagram leaves each member of the domain. Hence the relation depicted in the mapping diagram of Fig. 17.7 is a function.

Consider the relation $x \rightarrow 2x + 5$ with domain $\{0, 1, 2, 3\}$. The range is found by substituting each element of the domain into $2x + 5$. Thus when

$$x = 0, \ 2x + 5 = 2 \times 0 + 5 = 5$$

$$x = 1, \ 2x + 5 = 2 \times 1 + 5 = 7$$

$$x = 2, \ 2x + 5 = 2 \times 2 + 5 = 9$$

$$x = 3, \ 2x + 5 = 2 \times 3 + 5 = 11$$

The mapping diagram is shown in Fig. 17.14(a).

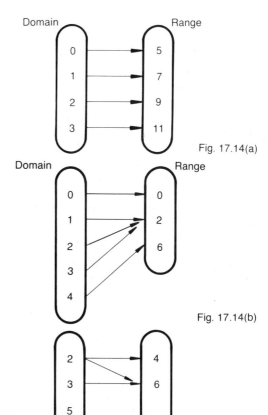

Fig. 17.14(a)

Fig. 17.14(b)

Fig. 17.14(c)

137

The relation $x \rightarrow 2x+5$ is a function and we therefore write $f:x \rightarrow 2x+5$ which is read as 'f maps x onto $2x+5$'.

The relation shown in Fig. 17.14(b) is also a function. The fact that there is more than one arrow arriving at one of the points (i.e. at the element 2) is immaterial. It is the 'one arrow leaving each element of the domain' which is important.

The relation 'is a factor of' shown in Fig. 17.14(c) is not a function because two arrows leave the element 2 of the domain.

A function such as $f:x \rightarrow 2x+5$ may be represented by an equation such as $y = 2x+5$. Corresponding values of x and y may then be placed in a table like the one below.

x	0	1	2	3
y	5	7	9	11

Since the values of y *depend* upon the values allocated to x, y is called the *dependent variable*. Since we can give x any value we please, x is called the *independent variable*. Note that in a mapping diagram, values of the independent variables appear in the domain whilst values of the dependent variable appear in the range.

To draw a graph of the equation $y = 2x+5$ we use the ordered pairs (coordinates) given in the table above.

Values of the dependent variable (y) are marked off along the vertical axis

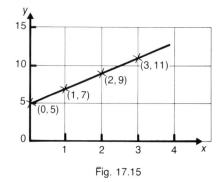

Fig. 17.15

whilst values of the independent variable (x) are marked off along the horizontal axis. The graph of $y = 2x+5$ is shown in Fig. 17.15.

Instead of writing a function $f:x \rightarrow 2x+5$ we often write $y = f(x)$ meaning that y is a function of x. Thus if $y = 3x^2-2x+5$ we may write $f(x) = 3x^2-2x+5$. The symbols F, g, h and φ are also used to represent functions and we may have

$$n = F(m)$$

m being the independent variable and n the dependent variable.

Example 4

If $f(x) = x^2+7x-5$ find the values of $f(2)$ and $f(-1)$.

To find $f(2)$ substitute $x = 2$ into the expression x^2+7x-5. Thus

$$f(2) = 2^2+7\times2-5$$
$$= 4+14-5 = 13$$
$$f(-1) = (-1)^2+7\times(-1)-5$$
$$= 1-7-5 = -11$$

Example 5

If $g:x \rightarrow 4x-1$, find the values of $g(3)$ and $g(-2)$.

$$g(3) = 4\times3-1 = 12-1 = 11$$
$$g(-2) = 4\times(-2)-1 = -8-1 = -9$$

Exercise 122 — *All type B*

1) If $f(x) = 3x^2-5x+2$ find:

(a) $f(2)$ (c) $f(-3)$
(b) $f(0)$ (d) $f(\frac{1}{2})$.

2) If $f(v) = 8v-7$ find:

(a) $f(3)$ (c) $f(0)$.
(b) $f(-2)$

3) If $M = \varphi(p) = 3p^2-2p$ find:

(a) $\varphi(1)$ (d) $\varphi(-1)$
(b) $\varphi(3)$ (e) $\varphi(-3)$.
(c) $\varphi(0)$

4) $F(h) = h^3 - 3h + 1$. Find $F(1), F(4)$ and $F(-2)$.

5) If $f: x \rightarrow \frac{1}{2}(4x+1)$ find the values of $f(3)$ and $f(-2)$.

6) $g: t \rightarrow \frac{1}{4}(1-5t)$. Find values of $g(-1), g(0)$ and $g(3)$.

Graphs of Functions

In plotting graphs of functions we may have to include coordinates which are positive and negative. To represent these on a graph we make use of the number scale used for directed numbers (Fig. 17.16).

Positive values of y are measured upwards above the origin.

Positive values of x are measured to the right of the origin.

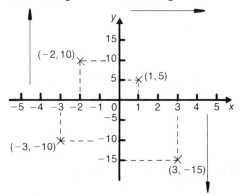

Negative values of x are measured to the left of the origin.

Negative values of y are measured downwards below the origin.

Fig. 17.16

Example 6

Draw the graph of $y = 2x - 5$ for values of x between -3 and 4.

Having decided on some values for x (these can be any numbers we like between -3 and 4, but the calculation of y and subsequent plotting is easier if we use whole numbers) we calculate corresponding values of y by substituting the chosen values of x into the expression $2x - 5$. Thus, when

$$x = -3,$$
$$y = 2 \times (-3) - 5 = -6 - 5 = -11$$

For convenience the calculations are tabulated as shown below:

x	-3	-2	-1	0	1	2	3	4
$2x$	-6	-4	-2	0	2	4	6	8
-5	-5	-5	-5	-5	-5	-5	-5	-5
y	-11	-9	-7	-5	-3	-1	1	3

The graph is now plotted using these values of x and y (Fig. 17.17) and it is seen to be a straight line.

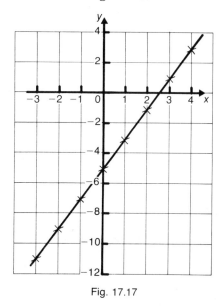

Fig. 17.17

Equations of the type $y = 2x - 5$ in which the highest power of the independent variable, x, is one, are called equations of the *first degree*. They are also called *linear equations* or *linear functions*.

All equations of this type give graphs which are straight lines hence the term 'linear'.

In order to draw graphs of linear functions we need only plot two points. It is safer, however, to plot three points, the third point acting as a check on the other two.

Example 7

Draw the graph of $f(x) = 5x + 3$ for values of x between -3 and 3.

139

Since $5x+3$ is a linear function we need only plot three points as follows:

x	−3	0	3
$f(x)$	−12	3	18

The graph is plotted in Fig. 17.18.

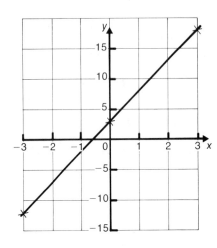

Fig. 17.18

Graphs of Quadratic Functions

The expression ax^2+bx+c where a, b and c are constants is called a quadratic function of x. When plotted, quadratic functions always give a smooth curve known as a *parabola*.

Example 8

Plot the graph of $y = 3x^2+10x-8$ between $x = -6$ and $x = 4$.

A table may be drawn up as follows giving corresponding values of y for chosen values of x.

x	−6	−5	−4	−3	−2	−1
$3x^2$	108	75	48	27	12	3
$10x$	−60	−50	−40	−30	−20	−10
−8	−8	−8	−8	−8	−8	−8
y	40	17	0	−11	−16	−15

x	0	1	2	3	4
$3x^2$	0	3	12	27	48
$10x$	0	10	20	30	40
−8	−8	−8	−8	−8	−8
y	−8	5	24	49	80

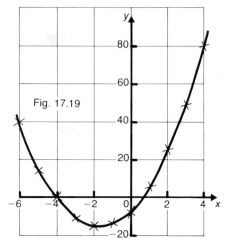

Fig. 17.19

The graph is shown in Fig. 17.19 and it is a smooth curve. Equations which are non-linear always give a graph which is a smooth curve.

Exercise 123 — *All type B*

Draw graphs of the following equations:

1) $y = x+2$ taking values of x between −3 and 2.

2) $y = 2x+5$ taking values of x between −4 and 4.

3) $y = 3x-4$ taking values of x between −4 and 3.

4) $y = 5-4x$ taking values of x between −2 and 4.

5) $y = 2x^2-7x-5$ between $x = -4$ and $x = 12$.

6) $y = x^2-4x+4$ between $x = -3$ and $x = 3$.

7) $y = 6x^2-11x-35$ between $x = -3$ and $x = 5$.

8) $y = 3x^2-5$ between $x = -2$ and $x = 4$.

9) $y = 1 + 3x - x^2$ between $x = -2$ and $x = 3$.

Gradient of a Straight Line

The gradient of a straight line graph is often required. For instance if a graph of distance is plotted against time, with time plotted on the horizontal axis, then the gradient of the resulting graph gives the speed.

Example 9

A car travels a distance of s kilometres in a time of t hours as shown in the table below:

t	0	0.5	1.0	1.5	2.0	3.0
s	0	30	60	90	120	180

Draw a graph of this information and by finding the gradient of the graph estimate the speed of the car. (Plot t horizontally.)

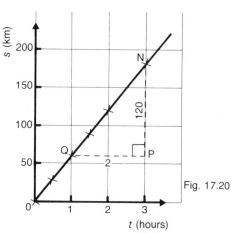

Fig. 17.20

The graph is shown in Fig. 17.20. To find the gradient draw the right angled triangle making the sides of the triangle reasonably long since a small triangle may give inaccurate results.

$$\text{Gradient} = \frac{\text{height of triangle}}{\text{base of triangle}}$$

$$= \frac{\text{NP}}{\text{QP}} = \frac{120}{2} = 60$$

Since speed $= \dfrac{\text{distance}}{\text{time}}$ the gradient

gives the speed of the car which is 60 km/h.

Exercise 124

1) The table below gives corresponding values of x and y. Plot the graph and from it find its gradient.

x	4	7	9	11	15
y	11	17	21	25	33

2) The following are observed values of P and Q.

P	5.0	7.0	8.8	11.6	15.0	19.2	24.0	32.0
Q	13.6	17.6	22.2	28.0	35.5	47.4	56.1	74.6

Plot a graph of these readings with P plotted vertically. Hence find the gradient of the graph.

3) In an experiment carried out with a lifting machine the effort E and the load W were found to have the values given in the table.

W	10	30	50	60	80	100
E	8.9	19.1	29	33	45	54

Plot a graph of this data with E vertically and hence find the gradient.

4) The following figures show how the resistance of a conductor varies as the temperature increases:

Temperature ($t°C$)	25	50	75	100	150
Resistance (R ohms)	20.7	21.5	22.3	23.0	24.5

Plot these results with R vertical and hence find the gradient.

5) Two quantities W and P are connected as shown in the following table of values:

W	28	50	59	67	74	79	84
P	2	5.4	6.9	8.0	9.1	9.9	10.7

Draw a graph of W against P, plotting W vertically. Hence find the gradient.

141

Chapter 18   Inequalities

Comparing Quantities

Whenever two quantities are compared they are often found to be unequal, that is, one quantity is larger than the other. Some examples are

      7 is greater than 5

      30 pence is less than £5

Statements such as these are called *inequalities*.

Symbols

The following symbols are used when dealing with inequalities:

  > means 'greater than'

  ≥ means 'equal to or greater than'

  < means 'less than'

  ≤ means 'equal to or less than'

Thus,

    $5 > 3$ means that 5 is greater than 3

    $x \geq 2$ means that x is equal to or greater than 2

    $2 < 4$ means that 2 is less than 4

    $m \leq 5$ means that m is equal to or less than 5

Note that the arrow always points to the smaller quantity.

Exercise 125 — *All type A*

Using the symbols >, < and =, fill in the gap between the following pairs of quantities:

1)   3   4

2)   10 mm   1 cm

3)   £1   80 p   **7)** $x+2$ x

4) $2x+2x$ $4x$ **8)** x^2-1 x^2

5) $\frac{1}{2}$ $\frac{1}{3}$ **9)** -3 -7

6) $5x-2x$ $3x$ **10)** x^2 $3+x^2$

Solutions of Simple Inequalities

If $x < 3$, what values of x could there be so that the inequality is true? Of course there are many different values which will make it true. Some of them are -5, 2.3 and $\frac{1}{2}$ but there are very many more, all of which are less than 3. However, if x has to be a positive whole number then the only possible solutions are 1 and 2.

Solutions of Inequalities on a Number Line

All real numbers can be shown on a number line. The arrowed line above the number line in Fig. 18.1, shows the solution for the inequality $x \leq 4$.

Fig. 18.1

The solid circle at the end of the arrowed line shows that $x = 4$ is included as a possible value of x.

Fig. 18.2 shows the solution for $x > -3$. The empty circle shows that -3 is not included as a possible value for x.

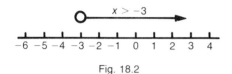

Fig. 18.2

Exercise 126 — *All type A*

Use number lines to show solutions for the following inequalities:

1) $x \leqslant 5$ **4)** $x \geqslant 2$

2) $x < 8$ **5)** $x \geqslant 100$

3) $x > 0$

Consider now, the inequality $2x + 3 > 11$. What is the solution for x? We proceed like this:

$$3x + 3 > 11$$

$$2x > 11 - 3$$

Subtracting 3 from each side of the inequality

$$2x > 8$$

$$x > 4$$

Dividing both sides of the inequality by 2.

The process is similar to that of solving a simple equation (see Chapter 15). The solution to the inequality can then be expressed on a number line (Fig. 18.3).

Fig. 18.3

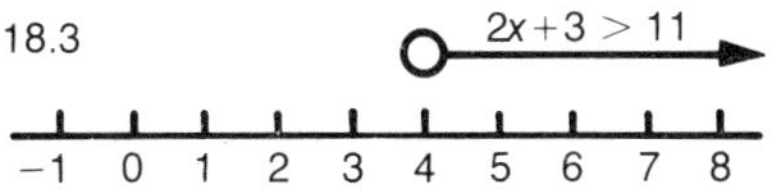

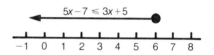

Example 1

Solve the inequality $5x - 7 \leqslant 3x + 5$.

$$5x - 7 \leqslant 3x + 5$$

$$5x - 3x \leqslant 5 + 7$$

$$2x \leqslant 12$$

$$x \leqslant 6$$

The solution is shown on the number line in Fig. 18.4.

Fig. 18.4

Exercise 127 — *All type B*

Solve the following inequalities and represent the solutions on a number line.

1) $x + 2 > 7$ **4)** $3x \leqslant 6$

2) $x - 3 < 5$ **5)** $2x + 5 > 7$

3) $2x \geqslant 4$ **6)** $3x - 2 \geqslant 10$

7) $5x - 4 > 2x + 8$

8) $3(2x + 5) \geqslant 3 - 2(x - 3)$

9) $3(x - 2) - 5(x - 7) < 12$

10) $2(3x + 5) \geqslant 22$

Example 2

If x has to be one of the numbers 0, 1, 2, 3, 4, 5, 6, 7, 8, 9 or 10, find the solution for $x < 6$ and $x \geqslant 3$.

Representing both inequalities on a number line (Fig. 18.5), we see that the solution is that x must equal 3, 4 or 5, because the arrowed lines representing the independent solutions for each inequality overlap.

143

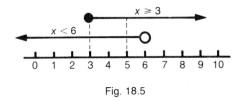

Fig. 18.5

given equalities true because the arrowed lines representing the independent solutions do not overlap. Note that the inequalities $x \leqslant 3$ and $x \geqslant 6$ is sometimes written $3 \leqslant x \geqslant 6$.

Example 3

If x must be one of the whole numbers, 0, 1, 2, 3, 4, 5, 6, 7, 8, 9 or 10, find the solution for the pair of inequalities $x \leqslant 3$ and $x \geqslant 6$.

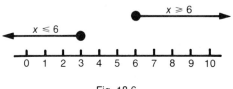

Fig. 18.6

From Fig. 18.6, we see that there are no numbers which make both the

Exercise 128 — *All type B*

Use number lines to find the solutions for the following pairs of inequalities:

1) $x < 4$ and $x > 2$

2) $x > 0$ and $x < 3$

3) $x < 4$ and $x > 7$

4) $x \geqslant 5$ and $x < 6$

5) $x < 0$ and $x > 8$

6) $x \geqslant 0$ and $x \leqslant 8$

7) $x \leqslant 4$ and $x > 2$

8) $x > 4$ and $x < 9$

Chapter 19   Time, Distance and Speed

Time

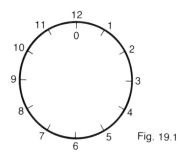

Fig. 19.1

The units of time are the second, minute, hour and day.

60 seconds (s)   = 1 minute (min)

60 minutes (min) = 1 hour (h)

24 hours (h)   = 1 day (d)

The symbols in brackets give the standard abbreviations for each of the units of time.

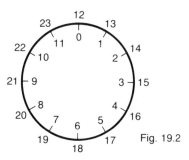

Fig. 19.2

The Clock

A standard clock face is marked off in hours from 1 to 12 (Fig. 19.1). However, since 1 day equals 24 hours we need a method of finding out if a stated time is between 12 midnight and 12 noon, or between 12 noon and 12 midnight. Traditionally times between 12 midnight and 12 noon were called a.m. (e.g. 9.15 a.m.) and times between 12 noon and 12 midnight were called p.m. (e.g. 9.30 p.m.). A second way is to use a 24 hour clock, see Fig. 19.2. Times between 12 midnight and 12 noon are given the times 00 hours to 12 hours and times between 12 noon and 12 midnight take the times 12 hours to 24 hours. Thus 3.30 a.m. is written 03 30 and 3.30 p.m. is written 15 30.

Example 1

Find the length of time, in hours, between:

(a)   2.15 a.m. and 7.30 p.m.,

(b)   04 25 and 17 12.

(a)   The easiest way is to use the 24 hour clock so that 7.30 p.m. becomes 19 30. The problem then becomes

$$19.30 - 2.15 = 17 \text{ hours}$$
$$\text{and 15 minutes}$$
$$= 17\tfrac{1}{4} \text{ hours}$$

(b)   The problem is

$$17\ 12 - 04\ 25 = 12 \text{ hours and 47}$$
$$\text{minutes}$$

Exercise 129 — *Questions 1–10 type A, 11 type B*

Find the length of time in hours and minutes, between the following times:

1) 0.36 a.m. and 9.27 a.m.

2) 2.15 p.m. and 8.38 p.m.

3) 1.36 a.m. and 12.00 noon.

4) 3.35 a.m. and 7.29 a.m.

5) 11.34 p.m. and 7.19 a.m.

6) 5.36 p.m. and 11.16 a.m.

7) 6.38 a.m. and 1.15 p.m.

8) 00 49 hours and 12 36 hours.

9) 17 45 hours and 01 16 hours.

10) 02 42 hours and 14 48 hours.

11) Below is part of a timetable for high tides for a certain week beginning on Saturday:

	Time of high tide	
Day of week	a.m.	p.m.
Saturday	07.18	19.57
Sunday	08.36	21.15
Monday	09.54	22.33

(a) A fishing boat can leave and return to harbour 30 minutes on either side of high tide. What is the earliest and latest that the boat can leave on Sunday? What is the longest time it can stay out if it returns on the same day?

(b) Assuming that the intervals between high tides are constant, on which day of the week is there only one high tide and at what time can it be expected?

Average Speed

The average speed of a vehicle is defined as *the total distance travelled* divided by the total time taken. The unit of speed depends upon the unit of distance and the unit of time. For instance if the distance is measured in kilometres (km) and the time is measured in hours (h) then the average speed will be stated in kilometres per hour (km/h). If the distance is measured in metres (m) and the time in seconds (s) then the average speed will be measured in metres per second (m/s).

Example 2

A car travels a total distance of 200 km in 4 hours. What is the average speed?

$$\text{Average speed} = \frac{\text{distance travelled}}{\text{time taken}}$$

$$= \frac{200 \text{ km}}{4 \text{ h}} = 50 \text{ km/h}$$

Example 3

A car travels 30 km at 40 km/h and 30 km at 50 km/h. Find its average speed.

Time taken to travel 30 km at 40 km/h

$$= \frac{30}{40} = 0.75 \text{ h}$$

Time taken to travel 30 km at 50 km/h

$$= \frac{30}{50} = 0.6 \text{ h}$$

∴ Total time taken
$$= 0.75 + 0.6 = 1.35 \text{ h}$$

Average speed
$$= \frac{\text{total distance travelled}}{\text{total time taken}}$$

$$= \frac{60}{1.35} = 44.44 \text{ km/h}$$

146

Example 4

A train travels for 4 hours at an average speed of 64 km/h. For the first 2 hours its average speed is 50 km/h. What is the average speed for the last 2 hours?

Total distance travelled in the 4 hours

$$= \text{average speed} \times \text{time taken}$$

$$= 64 \times 4 = 256 \text{ km}$$

Distance travelled in first 2 hours

$$= 50 \times 2 = 100 \text{ km}$$

Distance travelled in last 2 hours

$$= 256 - 100 = 156 \text{ km}$$

Average speed for the last 2 hours

$$= \frac{156}{2} = 78 \text{ km/h}$$

Exercise 130 — *Questions 1- 3 type A, remainder B*

1) A train travels 300 km in 4 hours. Calculate its average speed.

2) A car travels 200 km at an average speed of 50 km/h. How long does it take?

3) If a car travels for 5 hours at an average speed of 70 km/h how far has it gone?

4) For the first $1\frac{1}{2}$ hours of a 91 km journey the average speed was 30 km/h. If the average speed for the remainder of the journey was 23 km/h, calculate the average speed for the entire journey.

5) A motorist travelling at a steady speed of 90 km/h covers a section of motorway in 25 minutes. After a speed limit is imposed he finds that when travelling at the maximum speed allowed he takes 5 minutes longer than before to cover the same section. Calculate the speed limit.

6) In winter a train travels between two towns 264 km apart at an average speed of 72 km/h. In summer the journey takes 22 minutes less than in winter. Find the average speed in summer.

7) A train travels between two towns 135 km apart in $4\frac{1}{2}$ hours. If on the return journey the average speed is reduced by 3 km/h, calculate the time taken for the return journey.

8) A car travels 272 km at an average speed of 32 km/h. On the return journey the average speed is increased to 48 km/h. Calculate the average speed over the entire journey.

9) A cyclist travels from town A to town B, a distance of 140 km. Cycling non-stop his average speed is 24 km/h. A car travels the same journey, also travelling non-stop, and leaves town A 2 hours after the cyclist, arriving at town B 20 min before the cyclist. Calculate the average speed of the car in km/h.

10) A train left Cardiff at 13.27 and arrived in Crewe at 16.12. Find the time taken for the journey. If the average speed for the journey was 77 km/h, find the distance from Cardiff to Crewe.

Distance–Time Graphs

Since distance = speed×time, when the speed is constant the distance travelled is proportional to the time. This may be illustrated on a graph which will be a straight line.

Example 5

A car travels a distance of 180 km in a time of 3 hours. Draw a distance time graph to illustrate and from the graph find the average speed for the whole journey.

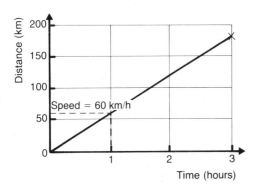

Fig. 19.3

The graph is shown in Fig. 19.3. Time (in hours) is plotted horizontally and distance vertically which is the usual way. Note that the straight line is obtained by taking the two points as follows: time = 0, distance = 0; time = 3 hours, distance = 180 km. To find the average speed we find the distance the car travelled in 1 hour. From the graph this is 60 km. Hence the average speed is 60 km/h.

Example 6

A train travels at a speed of 70 km/h. Draw a graph to illustrate and from the graph find the distance travelled in 2 hours and how long it will take to travel 175 km.

To draw the graph take the following points: time = 0, distance = 0; time = 1 hour, distance = 70 km (since speed is 70 km/h). The graph is drawn in Fig. 19.4.

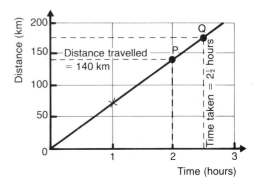

Fig. 19.4

To find the distance travelled in 2 hours we find 2 hours on the horizontal axis and draw a vertical line to meet the straight line graph at P. From P we draw a horizontal line to meet the vertical axis and read off the value which is 140 km.

To find how long it takes to travel 175 km we find 175 km on the vertical axis and draw a horizontal line to meet the graph at Q. From Q we draw a vertical line to meet the horizontal axis and read off the value which is $2\frac{1}{2}$ hours.

Example 7

A man travels a distance of 80 km by car at a speed of 40 km/h. He then cycles a distance of 20 km at a speed of 15 km/h and finally walks a distance of 8 km at a speed of 6 km/h. Draw a graph to illustrate and from it find the average speed for the entire journey.

148

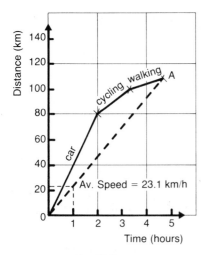

Fig. 19.5

(a) the average speed,

(b) the distance travelled in 2 hours,

(c) the time taken to travel 150 km.

2) A car travels at a speed of 60 km/h. Use a graph to find the distance travelled in 3 hours and the time taken to travel 40 km.

3) A car travels a distance of 80 km in 2 hours. It then changes speed and travels a further 80 km in $1\frac{1}{2}$ hours. Draw a time–distance graph and from it find the average speed for the entire journey.

4) A girl cycles a distance of 20 km at a speed of 12 km/h. She rests for 20 minutes and then continues the journey at 10 km/h for $1\frac{1}{2}$ hours. From the graph which you plot find the average speed for the entire journey and the total distance travelled.

5) A man travels a distance of 90 km by car at a speed of 60 km/h. He then cycles a distance of 18 km at a speed of 12 km/h. He then rests for 15 minutes before continuing on foot during which he walks a distance of 8 km in 2 hours. Find the average speed for the entire journey using a suitable graph.

The graph is drawn in the usual way (Fig. 19.5) and it consists of three straight lines to represent each stage of the journey. The average speed is found by drawing the straight line 0A. Using the line 0A we find the distance travelled in 1 hour, i.e. 23.1 km. The average speed is therefore 23.1 km/h.

Exercise 131 — *All type B*

1) A train travels a distance of 200 km in a time of 4 hours. Draw a graph to illustrate and find:

Chapter 20   Angles and Straight Lines

Angles

When two lines meet at a point they form an angle. The size of the angle depends only upon the amount of opening between the lines. It does not depend upon the lengths of the lines forming the angle. In Fig. 20.1 the angle A is larger than the angle B despite the fact that the lengths of the arms are shorter.

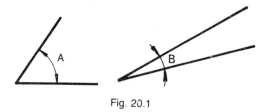

Fig. 20.1

Angular Measurement

An angle may be looked upon as the amount of rotation or turning. In Fig. 20.2 the line OA has been turned about O until it takes up the position OB. The angle through which the line has turned is the amount of opening between the lines OA and OB.

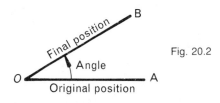

Fig. 20.2

If the line OA is rotated until it returns to its original position it will have described one revolution. Hence we can measure an angle as a fraction

of a revolution. Fig. 20.3 shows a circle divided up into 36 equal parts. The first division is split up into 10 equal parts so that each small division is $\frac{1}{360}$ of a complete revolution. We call this division a *degree*.

1 degree = $\frac{1}{360}$ of a revolution

360 degrees = 1 revolution

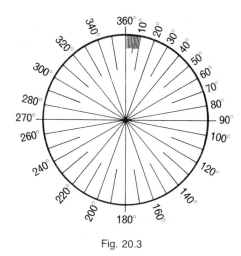

Fig. 20.3

When writing angles we write seventy degrees   70°. The small ° at the right hand corner of the figure replaces the word degrees. Thus 87° reads 87 degrees.

The right-angle is $\frac{1}{4}$ of a revolution and hence it contains $\frac{1}{4}$ of 360° = 90°. Two right-angles contain 180° and three right-angles contain 270°.

Example 1

Find the angle in degrees corresponding to $\frac{1}{8}$ of a revolution.

150

1 revolution = 360°

$\frac{1}{8}$ revolution = $\frac{1}{8}$×360° = 45°

Example 2

Find the angle in degrees corresponding to 0.6 of a revolution.

1 revolution = 360°

0.6 revolution = 0.6×360° = 216°

For some purposes the degree is too large a unit and it is sub-divided into minutes and seconds so that:

60 seconds = 1 minute

60 minutes = 1 degree

360 degrees = 1 revolution

An angle of 25 degrees 7 minutes 30 seconds is written 25° 7′ 30″.

Examples 3

(a) Add together 22° 35′ and 49° 42′.

22° 35′
49° 42′
———
72° 17′

The minutes 35 and 42 add up to 77 minutes which is 1°17′. The 17 is written in the minutes column and 1° carried over to the degrees column. The degrees 22, 49 and 1 add up to 72 degrees.

(b) Subtract 17° 49′ from 39° 27′.

39° 27′
17° 49′
———
21° 38′

We cannot subtract 49′ from 27′ so we borrow 1 from the 39° making it 38°. The 27′ now becomes 27′+60′ = 87′. Subtracting 49′ from 87′ gives 38′ which is written in the minutes column. The degree column is now 38°−17° = 21°.

Exercise 132 — *All type A*

1) How many degrees are there in 1$\frac{1}{2}$ right-angles?

2) How many degrees are there in $\frac{3}{5}$ of a right-angle?

3) How many degrees are there in $\frac{2}{3}$ of a right-angle?

4) How many degrees are there in 0.7 of a right-angle?

Find the angle in degrees corresponding to the following:

5) $\frac{1}{20}$ revolution

6) $\frac{3}{8}$ revolution

7) $\frac{4}{5}$ revolution

8) 0.8 revolution

9) 0.3 revolution

10) 0.25 revolution

Add together the following angles:

11) 11° 8′ and 17° 29′

12) 25° 38′ and 43° 45′

13) 8° 38′ 49″ and 5° 43′ 45″

14) 27° 4′ 52″ and 35° 43′ 19″

15) 72° 15′ 4″, 89° 27′ 38″ and 17° 28′ 43″

Subtract the following angles:

16) 8° 2′ from 29° 5′

17) 17° 28′ from 40° 16′

18) 4° 5′ 2″ from 11° 48′ 58″

19) 0° 7′ 15″ from 6° 2′ 5″

20) 48° 19′ 21″ from 85° 17′ 32″

151

Types of Angles

An *acute angle* (Fig. 20.4) is less than 90°.

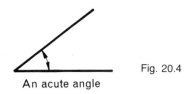

Fig. 20.4

An acute angle

An *obtuse angle* (Fig. 20.5) Lies between 90° and 180°.

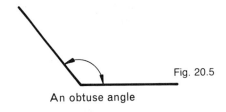

Fig. 20.5

An obtuse angle

A *reflex angle* (Fig. 20.6) is greater than 180°.

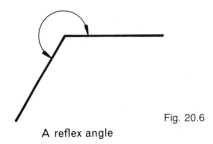

Fig. 20.6

A reflex angle

A *right angle* (Fig. 20.7) is equal to 90°.

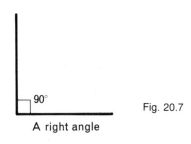

90°

Fig. 20.7

A right angle

Complementary angles are angles whose sum is 90°.

Supplementary angles are angles whose sum is 180°.

Properties of Angles and Straight Lines

1) *The total angle on a straight line is 180°* (Fig. 20.8). The angles A and B are called adjacent angles. They are also supplementary.

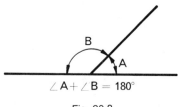

B

A

$\angle A + \angle B = 180°$

Fig. 20.8

2) *When two straight lines intersect the opposite angles are equal* (Fig. 20.9). The angles A and C are called vertically opposite angles. Similarly the angles B and D are also vertically opposite angles.

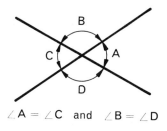

B

C

A

D

$\angle A = \angle C$ and $\angle B = \angle D$

Fig. 20.9

3) *When two parallel lines are cut by a transversal* (Fig. 20.10).

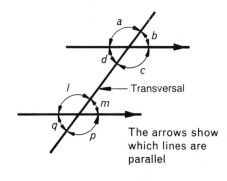

a

b

d

c

l

m

Transversal

q

p

The arrows show which lines are parallel

Fig. 20.10

(a) *The corresponding angles are equal* $a = l;$ $b = m;$ $c = p; d = q.$

(b) *The alternate angles are equal* $d = m;$ $c = l.$

(c) *The interior angles are supplementary* $d + l = 180°;$ $c + m = 180°.$

Conversely if two straight lines are cut by a transversal the lines are parallel if any *one* of the following is true:

(i) Two corresponding angles are equal.

(ii) Two alternate angles are equal.

(iii) Two interior angles are supplementary.

Examples 4

(a) Find the angle A shown in Fig. 20.11.

$$\angle B = 180° - 138° = 42°$$

$$\angle B = \angle A \text{ (corresponding angles)}$$

$$\angle A = 42°$$

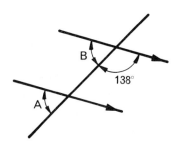

Fig. 20.11

(b) In Fig. 20.12 the line BF bisects $\angle$ABC. Find the value of the angle a.

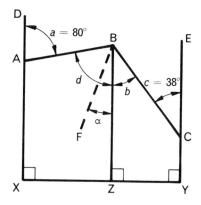

Fig. 20.12

The lines AX, BZ and EY are all parallel because they lie at right-angles to the line XY.

$$c = b \text{ (alternate angles: BZ} \| \text{EY)}$$

$$b = 38° \text{ (since } c = 38°)$$

$$a = d \text{ (alternate angles: XD} \| \text{BZ)}$$

$$d = 80° \text{ (since } a = 80°)$$

$$\angle ABC = b + d = 80° + 38° = 118°$$

$$\angle FBC = 118° \div 2 = 59° \text{ (since BF bisects } \angle ABC)$$

$$b + a = 59°$$

$$38° + a = 59°$$

$$a = 59° - 38° = 21°$$

Exercise 133 — *1–13 are Type A, remainder Type B*

1) Find x in Fig. 20.13.

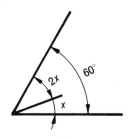

Fig. 20.13

153

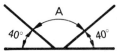

Fig. 20.14

2) Find A in Fig. 20.14.

3) Find x in Fig. 20.15.

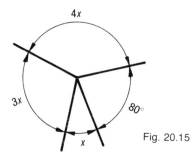

Fig. 20.15

4) In Fig. 20.16 find a, b, c and d.

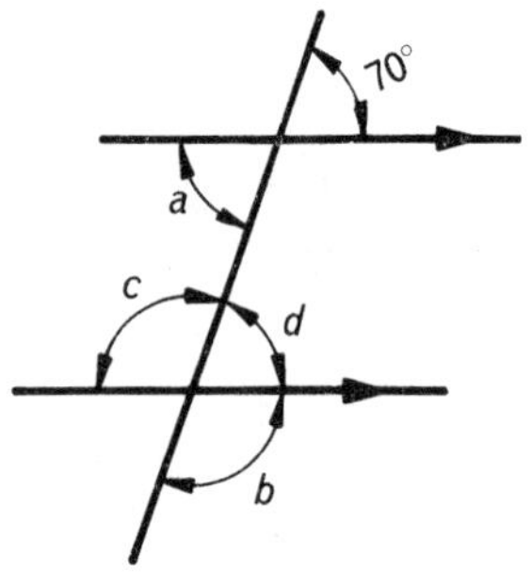

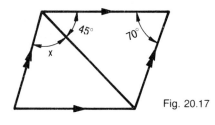

Fig. 20.16

5) Find the angle x in Fig. 20.17.

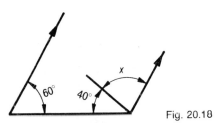

Fig. 20.17

6) Find x in Fig. 20.18.

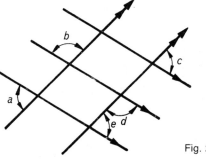

Fig. 20.18

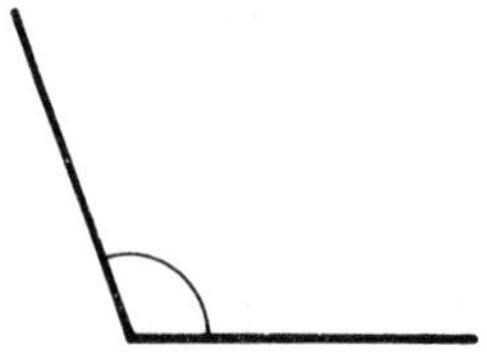

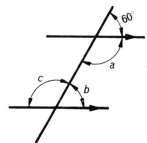

Fig. 20.19

7) The angle shown in Fig. 20.19 is:
a acute **b** right **c** reflex
d obtuse

Fig. 20.20

8) The angle a shown in Fig. 20.20 is equal to:

a 120° **b** 60° **c** neither of these

9) The angle b shown in Fig. 20.20 is equal to:
a 120° **b** 60° **c** neither of these

10) The angle c shown in Fig. 20.20 is equal to:

a 120° **b** 60° **c** neither of these

Fig. 20.21

11) In Fig. 20.21 which of the following is true?

a $a = d$ **b** $a = e$
c $e = b$ **d** $a = c$

12) A reflex angle is:
   a less than 90°
   b greater than 90°
   c greater than 180°
   d equal to 180°

13) Angles whose sum is 180° are called:
   a complementary angles
   b alternate angles
   c supplementary angles
   d corresponding angles

14) In Fig. 20.22 find A.

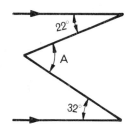

Fig. 20.22

15) In Fig. 20.23, AB is parallel to ED. Find the angle x.

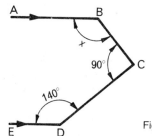

Fig. 20.23

16) Find A in Fig. 20.24.

Fig. 20.24

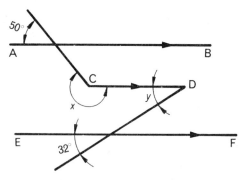

Fig. 20.25

17) In Fig. 20.25 the lines AB, CD and EF are parallel. Find the values of x and y.

18) In Fig. 20.26 which of the following is true?
   a $q = p + r$ **b** $p + q + r = 360°$
   c $q = r - p$ **d** $q = 360° - p - r$

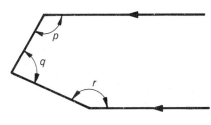

Fig. 20.26

19) In Fig. 20.27
   a $x = y$ **b** $x = 180° - y$
   c $x = y - 180°$ **d** $x + y = 180°$

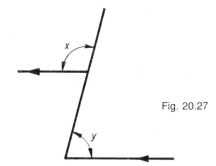

Fig. 20.27

155

Chapter 21 **Triangles**

Types of Triangles

1) An *acute-angled* triangle has all its angles less than 90° (Fig. 21.1).

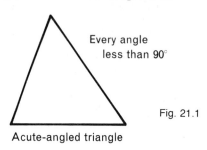

Every angle less than 90°

Fig. 21.1

Acute-angled triangle

2) A *right-angled* triangle has one of its angles equal to 90°. The side opposite to the right-angle is the longest side and it is called the hypotenuse (Fig. 21.2).

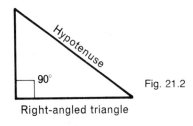

Fig. 21.2

Right-angled triangle

3) An *obtuse-angled* triangle has one angle greater than 90° (Fig. 21.3).

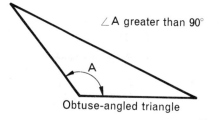

∠A greater than 90°

Obtuse-angled triangle

Fig. 21.3

4) A *scalene* triangle has all three sides of different length.

5) An *isosceles* triangle has two sides and two angles equal. The equal angles lie opposite to the equal sides (Fig. 21.4).

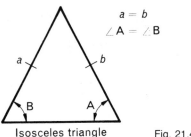

$a = b$
$\angle A = \angle B$

Isosceles triangle

Fig. 21.4

6) An *equilateral* triangle has all its sides and angles equal. Each angle of the triangle is 60° (Fig. 21.5).

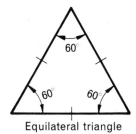

Equilateral triangle

Fig. 21.5

Angle Property of Triangles

1) *The sum of the angles of a triangle are equal to 180°* (Fig. 21.6).

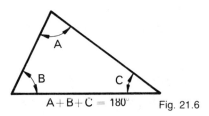

$A+B+C = 180°$

Fig. 21.6

2) *In every triangle the greatest angle is opposite to the longest side. The smallest angle is opposite to the shortest side.* In every triangle the sum of the lengths of any two sides is always greater than the length of the third side (Fig. 21.7).

a is the longest side since it lies opposite to the greatest angle A. c is the shortest side since it lies opposite to the smallest angle C. $a+b$ is greater than c, $a+c$ is greater than b and $b+c$ is greater than a.

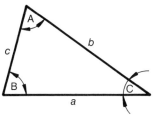

Fig. 21.7

3) *When the side of a triangle is produced the exterior angle so formed is equal to the sum of the opposite interior angles* (Fig. 21.8).

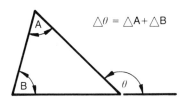

$$\triangle\theta = \triangle A + \triangle B$$

Fig. 21.8

Example 1

In Fig. 21.9, find the angles x and y.

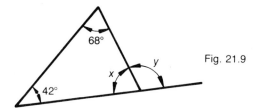

Fig. 21.9

Since the three angles of a triangle add up to 180°,

$$x+42+68 = 180$$
$$x = 180-42-68 = 70$$

Hence the angle x is 70°.

The exterior angle of a triangle is equal to the sum of the opposite interior angles. Hence:

$$y = 42+68 = 110$$

Therefore the angle y is 110°.

Exercise 134 — *All type A*

Find the angles x and y shown in Fig. 21.10.

1)

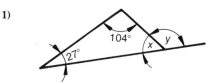

2)

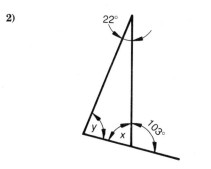

3)

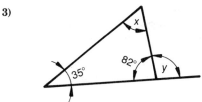

4)

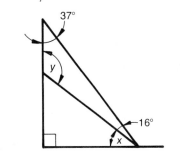

157

5)

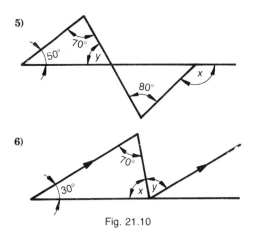

6)

Fig. 21.10

Standard Notation for a Triangle

Fig. 21.11 shows the *standard notation for a triangle*. The three vertices are marked A, B and C. The angles are called by the same letter as the vertices (see diagram). The side a lies opposite the angle A, b lies opposite the angle B and c lies opposite the angle C.

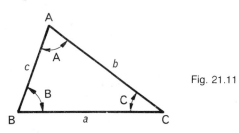

Fig. 21.11

Pythagoras' Theorem

In any right-angled triangle the square on the hypotenuse is equal to the sum of the squares on the other two sides. In the diagram (Fig. 21.12)

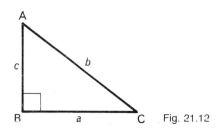

Fig. 21.12

$$AC^2 = AB^2 + BC^2$$

or $$b^2 = a^2 + c^2$$

The hypotenuse is the longest side and it always lies opposite to the right-angle. Thus in Fig. 21.12 the side b is the hypotenuse since it lies opposite to the right-angle at B. It is worth remembering that triangles with sides of 3, 4, 5; 5, 12, 13; 7, 24, 25 are right-angled triangles.

Example 2

1) In $\triangle$ABC, $\angle$B = 90°, $a = 4.2$ cm and $c = 3.7$ cm. Find b (Fig. 21.13).

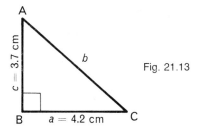

Fig. 21.13

By Pythagoras' Theorem,

$$b^2 = a^2 + c^2$$

$$b^2 = 4.2^2 + 3.7^2$$

$$= 17.64 + 13.69$$

$$= 31.33$$

$$b = \sqrt{31.33} = 5.598 \text{ cm}$$

2) In $\triangle$ABC, $\angle$A = 90°, $a = 6.4$ cm and $b = 5.2$ cm. Find c (Fig. 21.14).

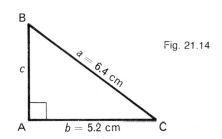

Fig. 21.14

158

$$a^2 = b^2 + c^2$$

or $\quad c^2 = a^2 - b^2 = 6.4^2 - 5.2^2$

$$= 40.96 - 27.04 = 13.92$$

$$c = \sqrt{13.92} = 3.731 \text{ cm}$$

Properties of the Isosceles Triangle

The most important properties of an isosceles triangle is that the perpendicular dropped from the apex to the unequal side:

(i) Bisects the unequal side. Thus in Fig. 21.15, BD = CD.

(ii) Bisects the apex angle. Thus in Fig. 21.15, angle BAD = angle CAD.

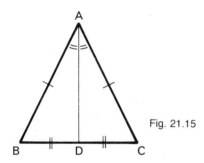

Fig. 21.15

Example 3

An isosceles triangle has equal sides 6 cm long and a base 4 cm long.

(a) Find the altitude of the triangle.

(b) Calculate the area of the triangle.

(a) The triangle is shown in Fig. 21.16. The altitude AD is perpendicular to the base and hence it bisects the base.

In triangle ABD, by Pythagoras' theorem,

$$AD^2 = AB^2 - BD^2 = 6^2 - 2^2 = 32$$

$$AD = \sqrt{32} = 5.66$$

Hence the altitude of the triangle is 5.66 cm

(b) Area of triangle
$$= \tfrac{1}{2} \times \text{base} \times \text{altitude}$$
$$= \tfrac{1}{2} \times 4 \times 5.66 = 11.32 \text{ cm}^2$$

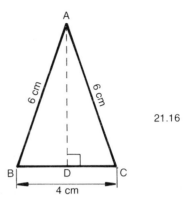

21.16

Exercise 135 — *All type B*

1) Find the side a in Fig. 21.17.

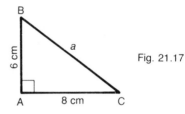

Fig. 21.17

2) Find the side b in Fig. 21.18.

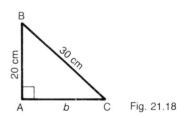

Fig. 21.18

3) Find the side c in Fig. 21.19.

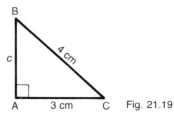

Fig. 21.19

159

4) Find the sides marked x in Fig. 21.20.

(a) **(b)**

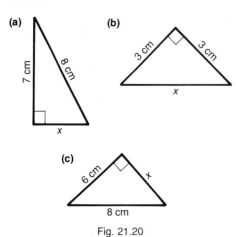

(c)

Fig. 21.20

5) Find the altitudes of the triangles shown in Fig. 21.21. All the triangles are isosceles.

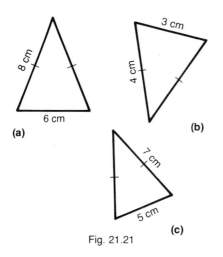

(a)

(b)

(c)

Fig. 21.21

6) Find the angles marked θ for each of the isosceles triangles in Fig. 21.22.

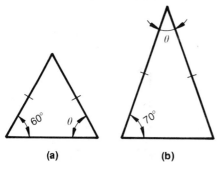

(a) **(b)**

(c)

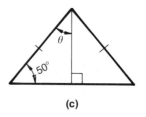

Fig. 21.22

7) Find the angles marked x, y and z in Fig. 21.23.

(a)

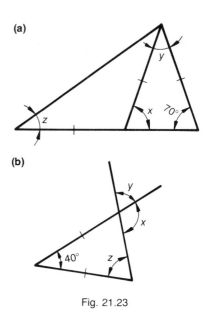

(b)

Fig. 21.23

Congruent Triangles

Two triangles are said to be congruent if they are equal in every respect.

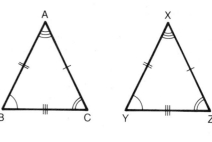

Fig. 21.24

160

Thus in Fig. 21.24 the triangles ABC and XYZ are congruent because:

$$AC = XZ \qquad \angle B = \angle Y$$

$$AB = XY \quad \text{and} \quad \angle C = \angle Z$$

$$BC = ZY \qquad \angle A = \angle X$$

Note that the angles which are equal lie opposite to the corresponding sides.

If two triangles are congruent they will also be equal in area. The notation used to express the fact that $\triangle ABC$ is congruent to $\triangle XYZ$ is $\triangle ABC \equiv \triangle XYZ$.

For two triangles to be congruent the six elements of one triangle (three sides and three angles) must be equal to the six elements of the second triangle. However to prove that two triangles are congruent it is not necessary to prove all six equalities. Any of the following are sufficient to prove that two triangles are congruent:

1) *One side and two angles in one triangle equal to one side and two similarly located angles in the second triangle* (Fig. 21.25).

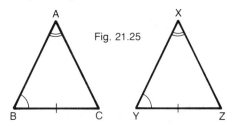
Fig. 21.25

2) *Two sides and the angle between them in one triangle equal to two sides and the angle between them in the second triangle* (Fig. 21.26).

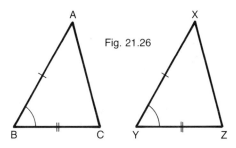
Fig. 21.26

3) *Three sides of one triangle equal to three sides of the other triangle* (Fig. 21.27).

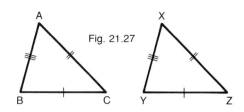
Fig. 21.27

4) *In right-angled triangles if the hypotenuses are equal and one other side in each triangle are also equal* (Fig. 21.28).

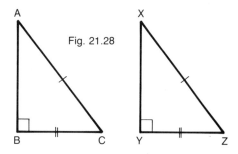
Fig. 21.28

Note that three equal angles are not sufficient to prove congruency and neither are two sides and a non-included angle. An included angle is an angle between the two equal sides of the triangles (e.g., $\angle ABC$ and $\angle XYZ$ in Fig. 21.27 and $\angle ACB$ and $\angle XYZ$ in Fig. 21.28).

Example 4

1) The mid-points of the sides MP and ST of $\triangle LMP$ and $\triangle RST$ are X and Y respectively. If $LM = RS$, $MP = ST$ and $LX = RY$ show that $\triangle LMP \equiv \triangle RST$.

Referring to Fig. 21.29:

$$\triangle LMX \equiv \triangle RSY \text{ (condition}$$
$$\text{(3) above)}$$

therefore $\qquad \angle M = \angle S$

161

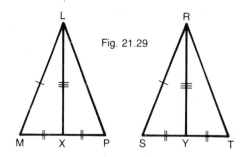

Fig. 21.29

In △s LMP and RST

LM = RS;   MP = ST;   ∠M = ∠S.

That is, two sides and the included angle in △LMP equal the two sides and the included angle in △RST. Hence   △LMP≡△RST.

2)   The diagonals of the quadrilateral XYZW intersect at O. Given that OX = OW   and   OY = OZ   show that XY = WZ.

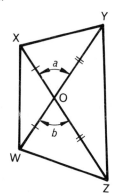

Fig. 21.30

Referring to Fig. 21.30:

In △s XOY and WOZ

OX = OW   and   OY = OZ (given)

a = b (vertically opposite angles)

Hence the two sides and the included angle in △XOY equal two sides and the included angle in △WOZ. Hence △XOY≡△WOZ.

therefore   XY = WZ

Exercise 136 — *All type B*

1)   In Fig. 21.31 state the letter which

corresponds to those triangles which are definitely congruent.

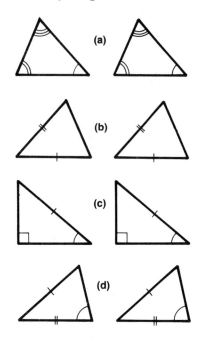

Fig. 21.31

2)   In Fig. 21.32 state the letter which corresponds to those triangles which are definitely congruent.

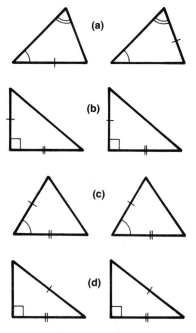

Fig. 21.32

3) In Fig. 21.33 find the lengths of RQ and SX. The diagram is not drawn to scale. What is the magnitude of ∠SXP?

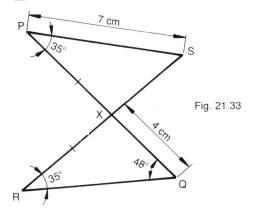

7 cm

P

35°

S

Fig. 21.33

X

4 cm

48°

Q

35°

R

4) In Fig. 21.34 find the length of PY.

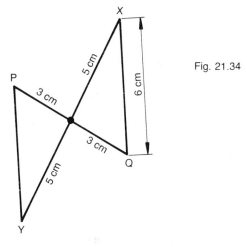

X

5 cm

Fig. 21.34

P

3 cm

6 cm

3 cm

Q

5 cm

Y

5) In Fig. 21.35 AB is parallel to CD and each is 4 cm long. If AD = 5 cm, find the length of BC. If ∠DAC = 42°, find ∠BCA.

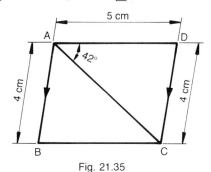

5 cm

A

42°

D

4 cm

4 cm

B

C

Fig. 21.35

6) In Fig. 21.36 name all the triangles which are congruent. G is the mid-point of DE, H is the mid-point of DF and J is the mid-point of EF.

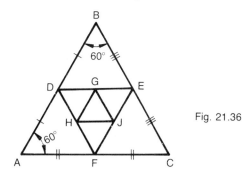

B

60°

D

G

E

H

J

Fig. 21.36

60°

A

F

C

Similar Triangles

Triangles which are equi-angular are called *similar triangles*. Thus in Fig. 21.37 if:

$$\angle A = \angle X, \quad \angle B = \angle Y \quad \text{and}$$
$$\angle C = \angle Z$$

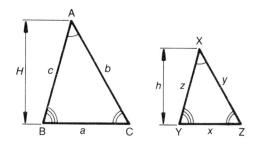

A

H

c

b

B

a

C

X

h

z

y

Y

x

Z

Fig. 21.37

the triangles ABC and ZYX are similar. In similar triangles the ratios of corresponding sides are equal. Thus for the triangles shown in Fig. 21.37.

$$\frac{a}{x} = \frac{b}{y} = \frac{c}{z} = \frac{H}{h}$$

Note that by corresponding sides we mean the sides opposite to the equal angles. It helps in solving problems on similar triangles if we write the two

163

triangles with the equal angles under each other. Thus in △s ABC and XYZ if $\angle A = \angle X$, $\angle B = \angle Y$ and $\angle C = \angle Z$

we write $\dfrac{ABC}{XYZ}$

The equations connecting the sides of the triangles are then easily obtained by writing any two letters in the first triangle over any two corresponding letters in the second triangle. Thus,

$$\frac{AB}{XY} = \frac{AC}{XZ} = \frac{BC}{YZ}$$

In Fig. 21.38 to prove △ABC is similar to △XYZ it is sufficient to prove any one of the following:

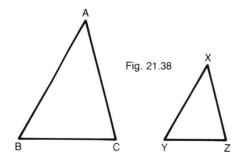

Fig. 21.38

(i) *Two angles in △ABC equal to two angles in △XYZ.* For instance, the triangles are similar if $\angle A = \angle X$ and $\angle B = \angle Y$, since it follows that $\angle C = \angle Z$.

(ii) *The three sides of △ABC are proportional to the corresponding sides of △XYZ.* Thus △ABC is similar to △XYZ if,

$$\frac{AB}{XY} = \frac{AC}{XZ} = \frac{BC}{YZ}$$

(iii) *Two sides in △ABC are proportional to two sides in △XYZ and the angles included between these sides in each triangle are equal.* Thus △ABC is similar to △XYZ if,

$\dfrac{AB}{XY} = \dfrac{AC}{XZ}$ and $\angle A = \angle X$.

164

Example 5

1) In Fig. 21.39 find the dimension marked x.

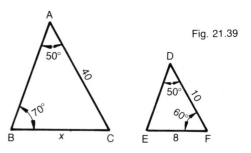

Fig. 21.39

In △ABC,
  angle C = $180° - 50° - 70° = 60°$
In △DEF,
  angle E = $180° - 50° - 60° = 70°$

therefore △ABC and △DEF are similar.

$$\frac{40}{10} = \frac{x}{8} \quad \text{or} \quad 320 = 10x$$

$$x = \frac{320}{10} = 32 \text{ mm}$$

2) In Fig. 21.40 prove that △s PTS and PQR are similar and calculate the length of TS.

In △s PTS and PQR

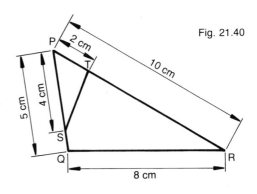

Fig. 21.40

$$\frac{PS}{PR} = \frac{4}{10} = 0.4$$

$$\frac{PT}{PQ} = \frac{2}{5} = 0.4$$

therefore $\dfrac{PS}{PR} = \dfrac{PT}{PQ}$

Also ∠P is common to both triangles and it is the included angle between PS and PT in △PTS and PR and PQ in △PQR. Hence △s PTS and PQR are similar.

Writing $\dfrac{\triangle \text{PTS}}{\triangle \text{PQR}}$ we see that

$$\frac{\text{TS}}{\text{QR}} = \frac{\text{PT}}{\text{PQ}}$$

$$\frac{\text{TS}}{8} = \frac{2}{5}$$

$$\text{TS} = \frac{2 \times 8}{5} = 3.2 \text{ cm}$$

Exercise 137 — *Questions 1–4 type B, remainder C*

1) Fig. 21.41 shows a large number of triangles. Write down the letters representing triangles which are similar. You should be able to find four sets of similar triangles.

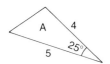

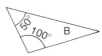

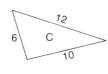

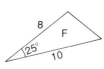

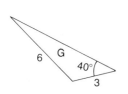

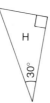

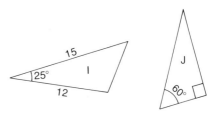

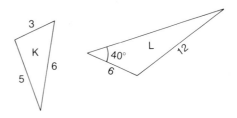

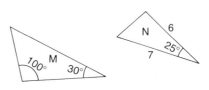

Fig. 21.41

2) The triangles shown in Fig. 21.42 are

    a congruent   **b** similar
    c neither of these

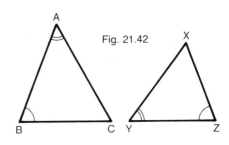

Fig. 21.42

3) If the triangles ABC and XYZ shown in Fig. 21.42 are similar then

  a $\dfrac{\text{AC}}{\text{XY}} = \dfrac{\text{XZ}}{\text{BC}}$ **b** $\dfrac{\text{AC}}{\text{XY}} = \dfrac{\text{BC}}{\text{XZ}}$

  c $\dfrac{\text{BC}}{\text{AB}} = \dfrac{\text{YZ}}{\text{XZ}}$ **d** $\dfrac{\text{BC}}{\text{AB}} = \dfrac{\text{XZ}}{\text{YZ}}$

165

4) In Fig. 21.43 if
$$\frac{AB}{XY} = \frac{AC}{XZ} \quad \text{and} \quad \angle B = \angle Y$$
then

a $\dfrac{AB}{XY} = \dfrac{BC}{YZ}$ **b** $\angle A = \angle X$

c $\angle C = \angle Z$

d none of the foregoing are necessarily true.

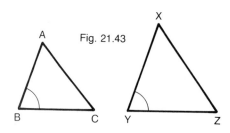
Fig. 21.43

5) In Fig. 21.44, $\angle A = \angle X$ and $\angle B = \angle Y$. Hence

a $XY = 6\frac{7}{8}$ cm **b** $XY = 17\frac{3}{5}$ cm

c $YZ = 19\frac{1}{5}$ cm **d** $YZ = 7\frac{1}{2}$ cm

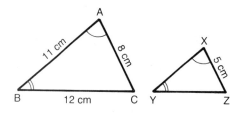
Fig. 21.44

6) In Fig. 21.45, $PS = 8$ cm and $QS = 2$ cm.
Hence $\dfrac{ST}{QR}$ is equal to

a $\dfrac{1}{4}$ **b** $\dfrac{4}{1}$ **c** $\dfrac{4}{5}$ **d** $\dfrac{5}{4}$

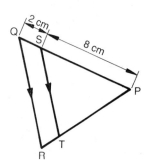
Fig. 21.45

7) In Fig. 21.46, XY is parallel to BC and AB is parallel to YZ. Hence:

a $\angle ABC = \angle YZC$

b $\triangle$s ABC and YZC are similar

c $\dfrac{YZ}{ZC} = \dfrac{AC}{BC}$ **d** $\dfrac{ZC}{AC} = \dfrac{YZ}{AB}$

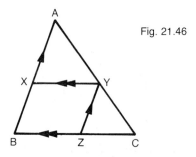
Fig. 21.46

8) In Fig. 21.47, AB is parallel to DC and $AB = 3$ cm and $DC = 5$ cm.
Hence $\dfrac{XD}{XB}$ is equal to

a $\dfrac{3}{5}$ **b** $\dfrac{5}{3}$ **c** $\dfrac{5}{8}$

d none of these

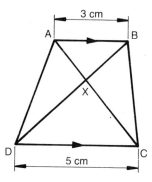
Fig. 21.47

9) In Fig. 21.48 find BC, AB and DE if possible.

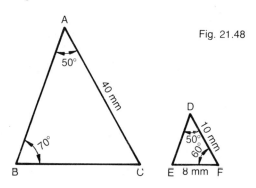
Fig. 21.48

166

10) In Fig. 21.49, find EC and AB.

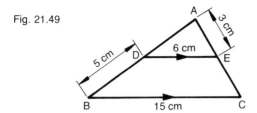

Fig. 21.49

Areas of Similar Triangles

The ratio of the areas of similar triangles is equal to the ratio of the squares on corresponding sides.

If in Fig. 21.50 △s ABC and XYZ are similar then,

$$\frac{\text{area of }\triangle\text{ABC}}{\text{area of }\triangle\text{XYZ}} = \frac{\text{AB}^2}{\text{XY}^2} = \frac{\text{AC}^2}{\text{XZ}^2}$$

$$= \frac{\text{BC}^2}{\text{YZ}^2} = \frac{\text{AD}^2}{\text{WX}^2}$$

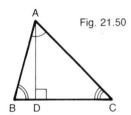

Fig. 21.50

Example 6

Find the area of triangle XYZ given that the area of triangle ABC is 12 cm² (see Fig. 21.51).

Fig. 21.51

In triangle XYZ, $\angle$ Y = 70° and in triangle ABC, $\angle$ A = 50°. Hence the two triangles are similar because they are equi-angular. BC and YZ correspond, hence;

$$\frac{\text{Area of }\triangle\text{XYZ}}{\text{Area of }\triangle\text{ABC}} = \frac{\text{YZ}^2}{\text{BC}^2}$$

$$\frac{\text{Area of }\triangle\text{XYZ}}{12} = \frac{10^2}{5^2} = \frac{100}{25} = 4$$

Area of $\triangle$XYZ = 4×12 = 48 cm²

Exercise 138 — *All type C*

1) In Fig. 21.52, the triangles ABC and EFG are similar. If the area of △ABC is 8 cm², calculate the area of △EFG.

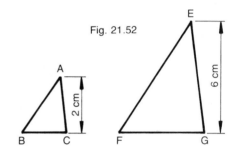

Fig. 21.52

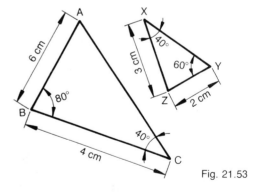

Fig. 21.53

2) In Fig. 21.53 if the area of △XYZ is 10 cm² then the area of △ABC is

    a impossible to find from the given information
    b 40 cm² **c** 80 cm² **d** 160 cm²

167

3) In Fig. 21.54, △s ABC and DEF are similar triangles. If the area of △ABC is 20 cm² then the area of △DEF is

    a 10 cm² **b** 5 cm² **c** 8 cm²

    d none of these

Fig. 21.54

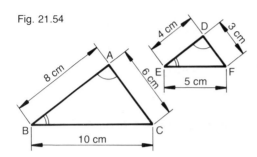

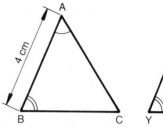

Fig. 21.55

5) In Fig. 21.56, $\dfrac{\text{AX}}{\text{XB}} = \dfrac{2}{1}$. The area of △ABC is 36 cm². Hence the area of XYBC is

    a 12 cm² **b** 18 cm² **c** 20 cm²

    d 16 cm²

4) In Fig. 21.55, ∠A = ∠X and ∠B = ∠Y. △ABC has an area of 36 cm² and △XYZ has an area of 4 cm². If AB = 4 cm then XY is equal to

    a $\frac{3}{4}$ cm   **b** $\frac{4}{3}$ cm   **c** $\frac{4}{9}$ cm

    d $\frac{9}{4}$ cm

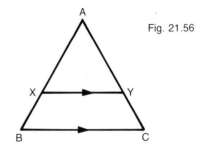

Fig. 21.56

Chapter 22   **Quadrilaterals and Polygons**

Quadrilaterals

A quadrilateral is any four sided figure (Fig. 22.1). Since it can be split up into two triangles the sum of its angles is 360°.

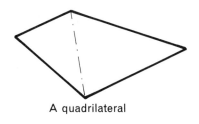

A quadrilateral

Fig. 22.1

Parallelogram

A parallelogram (Fig. 22.2) has both pairs of opposite sides parallel. It has the following properties:

(i)   The sides which are opposite to each other are equal in length.

(ii) The angles which are opposite to each other are equal.

(iii) The diagonals bisect each other.

(iv) The diagonals bisect the parallelogram so that two congruent triangles are formed.

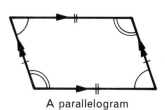

A parallelogram

Fig. 22.2

Rectangle

A rectangle (Fig. 22.3) is a parallelogram with each of its angles equal to 90°. A rectangle has all the properties of a parallelogram but, in addition, the diagonals are equal in length.

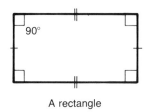

90°

Fig. 22.3

A rectangle

Rhombus

A rhombus is a parallelogram with all its sides equal in length (Fig. 22.4). It

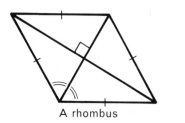

Fig. 22.4

A rhombus

has all the properties of a parallelogram but, in addition, it has the following properties:

(i)   The diagonals bisect at right-angles.

(ii) The diagonal bisects the angle through which it passes.

Square

A square (Fig. 22.5) is a rectangle with all its sides equal in length. It has all the properties of a parallelogram, rectangle and rhombus.

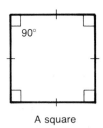

Fig. 22.5

A square

Trapezium

A trapezium (Fig. 22.6) is a quadrilateral with one pair of sides parallel.

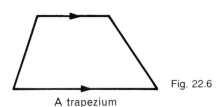

Fig. 22.6

A trapezium

Exercise 139 — *All type B*

1) Calculate the angle x in Fig. 22.7.

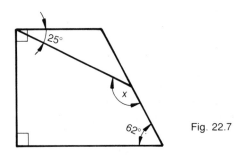

Fig. 22.7

2) Find the angle x in Fig. 22.8.

170

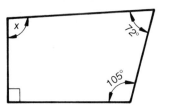

Fig. 22.8

3) In Fig. 22.9, ABCD is a parallelogram. Calculate the angles x and y.

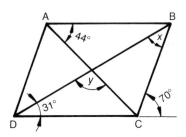

Fig. 22.9

4) A quadrilateral has one pair of sides parallel. It is therefore a

    a rhombus   **b** parallelogram

    c rectangle   **d** trapezium

5) A quadrilateral has diagonals which bisect at right-angles. It is therefore a

    a rhombus   **b** square

    c rectangle   **d** parallelogram

6) In Fig. 22.10, x is equal to

    a $a+b+c$

    b $360°-(a+b+c)$

    c $a+b+c+180°$

    d $360°-a+b+c$

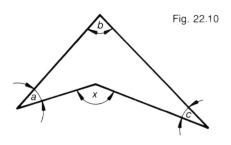

Fig. 22.10

7) In Fig. 22.11, y is equal to

    a 80° **b** 70° **c** 40° **d** 100°

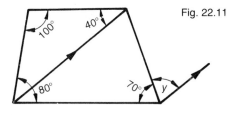

Fig. 22.11

8) In Fig. 22.12, find p.

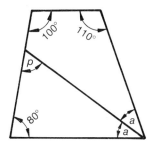

Fig. 22.12

9) In a quadrilateral one angle is equal to 60°. The other three angles are equal. What is the size of the equal angles?

10) Fig. 22.13 shows a rhombus. Are △s ABE and DEC congruent? Does ∠ DAC equal ∠ DCA? Is the angle DAB bisected by AC?

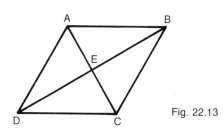

Fig. 22.13

Polygons

Any plane closed figure bounded by straight lines is called a polygon.

1) A *convex* polygon (Fig. 22.14) has no interior angle greater than 180°.

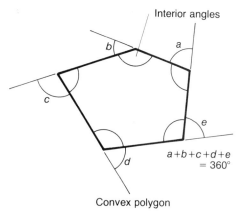

Interior angles

$a+b+c+d+e$ $= 360°$

Convex polygon

Fig. 22.14

2) A *re-entrant* polygon (Fig. 22.15) has at least one interior angle greater than 180°.

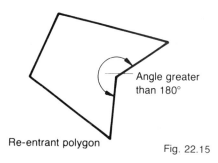

Angle greater than 180°

Re-entrant polygon

Fig. 22.15

3) A *regular* polygon (Fig. 22.16) has all of its sides and all of its angles equal.

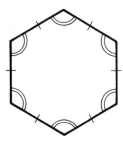

Fig. 22.16

4) A *pentagon* is a polygon with 5 sides.

5) A *hexagon* is a polygon with 6 sides.

6) An *octagon* is a polygon with 8 sides.

In a convex polygon having n sides the sum of the interior angles is $(2n-4)$ *right-angles. The sum of the exterior angles is 360°, no matter how many sides the polygon has.* Note that these statements apply to all polygons not just regular polygons.

Example 1

Each interior angle of a regular polygon is 140°. How many sides has it?

Let the polygon have n sides.

The sum of the interior angles is then $140n$ degrees. But the sum of the interior angles is also $(2n-4)$ right-angles or $90(2n-4)$ degrees.

$$\therefore \qquad 90(2n-4) = 140n$$

$$180n - 360 = 140n$$

$$40n = 360$$

$$n = 9$$

Hence the polygon has 9 sides.

Exercise 140 — *All type B*

1) Find the sum of the interior angles of a convex polygon with

   a 5 **b** 8 **c** 10 **d** 12 sides.

2) If the polygons in Question 1 are all regular find the size of the interior angle of each.

3) A hexagon has interior angles of 100°, 110°, 120° and 128°. If the remaining two angles are equal, what is their size?

4) Each interior angle of a regular polygon is 150°. How many sides has it?

5) ABCDE is a regular pentagon. Find the size of each exterior angle.

6) A regular polygon has each interior angle greater by 90° than each exterior angle. How many sides has the polygon?

7) A polygon has all its interior angles less than 180°. Hence it is definitely a

   a convex polygon

   b regular polygon

   c re-entrant polygon

   d quadrilateral

8) A regular polygon has each interior angle equal to 108°. It therefore has

   a 4 sides   **b** 5 sides

   c 6 sides   **d** 7 sides

9) A regular polygon has each exterior angle equal to 40°. It therefore has

   a 7 sides   **b** 8 sides

   c 9 sides   **d** 10 sides

10) A regular polygon has each interior angle greater by 60° than each exterior angle. It therefore has

   a 4 sides   **b** 6 sides

   c 7 sides   **d** 8 sides

Chapter 23 Symmetry

Line Symmetry

If the rectangle ABCD (Fig. 23.1) is folded along the line GH, the rectangle ABHG will fit exactly over the rectangle GHCD. The rectangle ABCD is

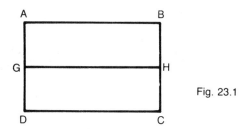

Fig. 23.1

said to be symmetrical about the line GH which is called an *axis of symmetry*. An alternative is to say that the rectangle has *line symmetry*. GH is only one of the axes of symmetry of the rectangle ABCD. The line EF is another axis of symmetry (Fig. 23.2). The rectangle, therefore, has two axes of symmetry.

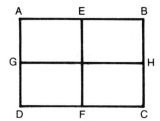

Fig. 23.2

Planes of Symmetry

If a solid figure, such as a sphere, is cut into two equal parts as shown in Fig. 23.3, the plane of the cut is called a *plane of symmetry*. The cuboid (Fig. 23.4) has been cut into two equal parts

by the plane ABCD. Hence the plane ABCD is a plane of symmetry for the cuboid.

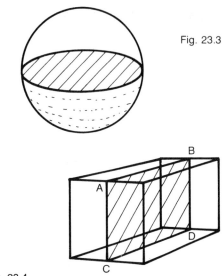

Fig. 23.3

Fig. 23.4

Point Symmetry

A parallelogram has no axes of symmetry. If we draw the diagonals AC and BD to intersect at O (Fig. 23.5) this point is called a *point of symmetry*.

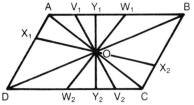

Fig. 23.5

This is because if we draw the lines V_1V_2, W_1W_2, X_1X_2 and Y_1Y_2, $OV_1 = OV_2$, $OW_1 = OW_2$, $OX_1 = OX_2$ and $OY_1 = OY_2$. That is,

173

for any line passing through O, there are two points, one on each side of O which are equidistant from O. The parallelogram is said to have *point symmetry*.

Many shapes have both line and point symmetry. Some examples are the square, rectangle and circle.

Rotational Symmetry

Consider the square shown in Fig. 23.6. O is the point where the diagonals intersect. Let us draw this square on a piece of cardboard, cut it out and place it exactly over a congruent square drawn on a piece of paper. If we

Fig. 23.6

stick a pin through O and rotate the cardboard square we see that it will fit exactly over the paper square when the angle of rotation is 90°. We say that the square has *rotational symmetry of order 4* because the angle of rotation when the shape is exactly repeated in $\frac{1}{4}$ of a revolution or $\frac{360°}{4}$

The shape shown in Fig. 23.7 has rotational symmetry of order 2, because

Fig. 23.7

the shape is exactly repeated when the shape is rotated, about O, through $180° = \frac{360°}{2}$. The shape shown in Fig. 23.8 has rotational symmetry of order 5.

Fig. 23.8

Rotational symmetry is sometimes said to be *radial symmetry*.

Exercise 141 — *All type B*

1) Fig. 23.9 shows a square, a rhombus, an isosceles trapezium, an isosceles triangle, an equilateral triangle and a hexagon. Copy the diagrams and on each draw all the axes of symmetry. Hence write down the number of axes of symmetry that each shape possesses.

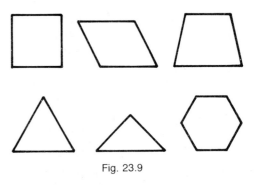

Fig. 23.9

2) Plot the points given below on graph paper and then join them up in alphabetical order. State which of the shapes has (a) line symmetry, (b) point symmetry.

(a) A(2, 5), B(4, 12), and C(6, 10).
(b) A(4, 5), B(6, 5), C(6, 10) and D(4, 10).
(c) A(4, 5), B(6, 5), C(6, 10) and D(4, 10).
(d) A(4, 10), B(8, 10), C(10, 15) and D(6, 15).
(e) A(4, 3), B(6, 10) and D(8, 3).
(f) A(2, 2), B(6, 5), C(6, 15) and D(2, 15).

174

(g) A(0, 10), B(5, 5), C(10, 5),
D(15, 10), E(15, 15), F(10, 20),
G(5, 20) and E(0, 15).

(h) A(0, 5), B(5, 0), C(0, −5) and
D(−5, 0).

(i) A(0, 2), B(2, 3), C(6, 3), D(6, 1)
and E(2, 1).

3) Write down the order of the rotational symmetry for each of the shapes in Question 2. If the shape does not have rotational symmetry then write 'none'.

4) How many axes of symmetry has

(a) a regular hexagon,

(b) a regular pentagon and

(c) a regular octagon.

5) How many planes of symmetry has

(a) a cube,

(b) a sphere,

(c) a cone,

(d) a pyramid with a square base.

Fig. 23.10

6) Fig. 23.10 shows some letters. For each

(a) write down the number of axes of symmetry,

(b) show the point of symmetry if any,

(c) state the order of rotational symmetry.

Chapter 24 Geometrical Constructions

1) *To divide a line AB into two equal parts*

Construction: With A and B as centres and a radius greater than $\frac{1}{2}$AB, draw circular arcs which intersect at X and Y (Fig. 24.1). Join XY. The line XY divides AB into two equal parts and it is also perpendicular to AB.

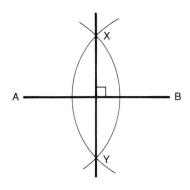

Fig. 24.1

2) *To draw a perpendicular from a given point A on a straight line.*

Construction: With centre A and any radius draw a circle to cut the straight line at points P and Q (Fig. 24.2). With

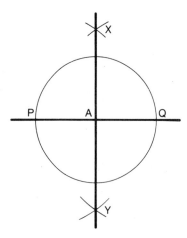

Fig. 24.2

centres P and Q and a radius greater than AP (or AQ) draw circular arcs to intersect at X and Y. Join XY. This line will pass through A and it is perpendicular to the given line.

3) *To draw a perpendicular from a point A at the end of a line* (Fig. 24.3).

Construction: From any point O outside the line and radius OA draw a circle to cut the line at B. Draw the diameter BC and join AC. AC is perpendicular to the straight line (because the angle in a semi-circle is 90°).

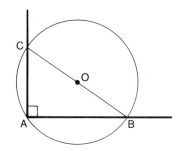

Fig. 24.3

4) *To draw the perpendicular to a line AB from a given point P which is not on the line.*

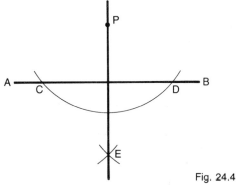

Fig. 24.4

Construction: With P as centre draw a circular arc to cut AB at points C and D. With C and D as centres and a radius greater than ½CD, draw circular arcs to intersect at E. Join PE. The line PE is the required perpendicular (Fig. 24.4).

5) *To construct an angle of 60°*

Construction: Draw a line AB. With A as centre and any radius draw a circular arc to cut AB at D. With D as centre and the *same* radius draw a second arc to cut the first arc at C. Join AC. The angle CAD is then 60° (Fig. 24.5).

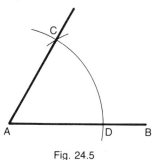

Fig. 24.5

6) *To bisect a given angle ∠BAC*

Construction: With centre A and any radius draw an arc to cut AB at D and AC at E. With centres D and E and a radius greater than ½DE draw arcs to intersect at F. Join AF, then AF bisects ∠BAC (Fig. 24.6). Note that by bisecting an angle of 60°, an angle of 30° is obtained. An angle of 45° is obtained by bisecting a right-angle.

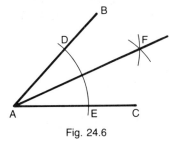

Fig. 24.6

7) *To construct an angle equal to a given angle BAC*

Construction: With centre A and any radius draw an arc to cut AB at D and AC at E. Draw the line XY. With centre X and the same radius draw an arc to cut XY at W. With centre W and radius equal to DE draw an arc to cut the first arc at V. Join VX, then ∠VXW = ∠BAC (Fig. 24.7).

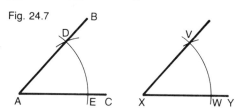

Fig. 24.7

8) *To draw a line through a point P parallel to a given line AB.*

Construction: Mark off any two points X and Y on AB. With centre P and radius XY draw an arc. With centre Y and radius XP draw a second arc to cut the first arc at Q. Join PQ, then PQ is parallel to AB (Fig. 24.8).

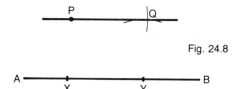

Fig. 24.8

9) *To divide a straight line AB into a number of equal parts.*

Construction: Suppose that AB has to be divided into four equal parts. Draw AC at any angle to AB. Set off on AC, four equal parts AP, PQ, QR, RS of any convenient length. Join SB. Draw RV, QW and PX each parallel to SB. Then AX = XW = WV = VB (Fig. 24.9).

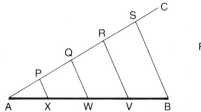

Fig. 24.9

177

10) *To draw the circumscribed circle of a given triangle ABC.*

Construction: Construct the perpendicular bisectors of the sides AB and AC (using construction 1) so that they intersect at O. With centre O and radius AO draw a circle which is the required circumscribed circle (Fig. 24.10).

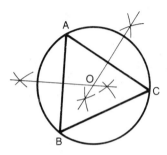

Fig. 24.10

11) *To draw the inscribed circle of a given triangle ABC.*

Construction: Construct the internal bisectors of ∠B and ∠C (using construction 6) to intersect at O. With centre O draw the inscribed circle of the triangle ABC (Fig. 24.11).

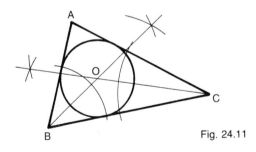

Fig. 24.11

12) *To draw a triangle whose area is equal to that of a given quadrilateral ABCD.*

Construction: Join BD and draw CE parallel to BD to meet AB produced at E. Then ADE is a triangle whose area is equal to that of the quadrilateral ABCD (Fig. 24.12).

Proof: As DBE and CDB are equal in

area. Add to each of these triangles the area ADB.

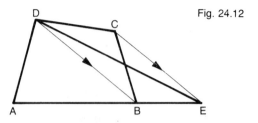

Fig. 24.12

13) *To draw a square whose area is equal to that of a given rectangle ABCD.*

Construction: Produce AB to E so that BC is equal to BE. Draw a circle with AE as diameter to meet BC (or BC produced) at F. Then BF is a side of the required square (Fig. 24.13).

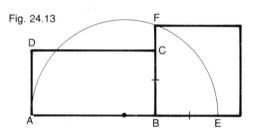

Fig. 24.13

14) *To draw a tangent to a circle at a given point P on the circumference of the circle.*

Construction: O is the centre of the given circle. Join OP. Using construction 3 draw the line PT which is perpendicular to OP. PT is the required tangent, since at the point of tangency, a tangent is perpendicular to a radius (Fig. 24.14).

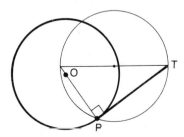

Fig. 24.14

178

15) *To draw the segment of a circle so that it contains a given angle θ.*

Construction: Draw the lines AB and AX so that $\angle BAX = \theta$. From A draw AM perpendicular to AX. Draw the perpendicular bisector of AB to meet AM at O. With centre O and radius OA draw the circular arc which terminates at A and B. This is the required segment (Fig. 24.15).

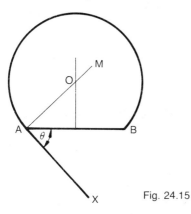

Fig. 24.15

16) *To construct a triangle given the lengths of each of the three sides.*

Construction: Suppose $a = 6$ cm, $b = 3$ cm and $c = 4$ cm. Draw BC = 6 cm. With centre B and radius 4 cm draw a circular arc. With centre C and radius 3 cm draw a circular arc to cut the first arc at A. Join AB and AC. Then ABC is the required triangle (Fig. 24.16).

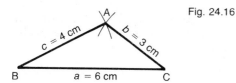

Fig. 24.16

17) *To construct a triangle given two sides and the included angle between the two sides.*

Construction: Suppose $b = 5$ cm and $c = 6$ m and $\angle A = 60°$. Draw AB = 6 cm and draw AX such that $\angle BAX = 60°$. Along AX mark off

AC = 5 cm. Then ABC is the required triangle (Fig. 24.17).

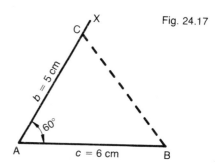

Fig. 24.17

18) *To construct a triangle (or triangles) given the lengths of two of the sides and an angle which is not the included angle between the two given sides.*

Construction: (a) Suppose $a = 5$ cm, $b = 6$ cm and $\angle B = 60°$. Draw BC = 5 cm and draw BX such that $\angle CBX = 60°$. With centre C and radius of 6 cm describe a circular arc to cut BX at A. Join CA then ABC is the required triangle ABC (Fig. 24.18).

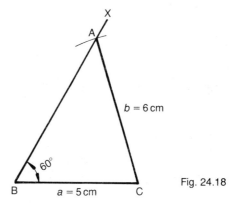

Fig. 24.18

(b) Suppose that $a = 5$ cm, $b = 4.5$ cm and $\angle B = 60°$. The construction is the same as before but the circular arc drawn with C as centre now cuts BX at two points A and A_1. This means that there are two triangles which meet the given conditions, i.e., $\triangle$s ABC and A_1BC (Fig. 24.19). For this reason this case is often called the *ambiguous case*.

179

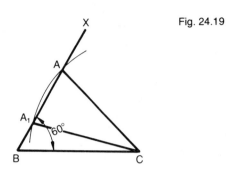

Fig. 24.19

Construction: It is required to draw a pair of tangents from the point P to the circle centre O. Join OP. With OP as diameter draw an arc to cut the given circle at points A and B. Join PA and PB which are the required pair of tangents.

19) *To construct a common tangent to two given circles.*

Construction: The two given circles have centres X and Y and radii x and y respectively (Fig. 24.20). With centre X draw a circle whose radius is $(x-y)$. With diameter XY draw an arc to cut the previously drawn circle at M. Join XM and produce to P at the circumference of the circle. Draw YQ parallel to XP, Q being at the circumference of the circle. Join PQ which is the required tangent.

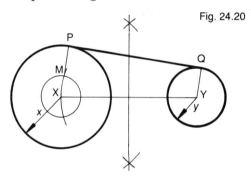

Fig. 24.20

20) *To construct a pair of tangents from an external point P to a given circle* (Fig. 24.21).

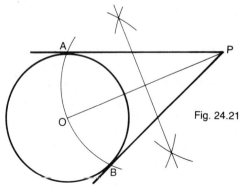

Fig. 24.21

Exercise 142A — *All type A*

1) Construct a triangle ABC with AB = 5 cm, AC = 4 cm and $\angle$ CAB = 45°.

2) Construct the point P inside the triangle ABC in Question 1, so that it is equi-distant from the three sides of the triangle.

3) Draw the line AB 4.6 cm long and construct the isosceles triangle ABC with AC = 7.2 cm. Hence construct the rhombus ABCD.

4) Draw the line AB = 8 cm. At A construct an angle of 60° and at B an angle of 45°. Hence complete the triangle ABC.

5) Construct an angle of 60°. Bisect this angle and so obtain an angle of 30°.

6) Draw a line AB = 8 cm. Construct the perpendicular bisector of AB to cut AB at E. Mark off EC = 3 cm and ED = 3 cm. Join A and C, C and B, B and D and D and A to form the quadrilateral ABCD.

(a) Name the quadrilateral ABCD.

(b) State the number of axes of symmetry that ABCD possesses.

7) Construct an angle of 60° and hence construct a regular hexagon.

8) Draw a line AB = 10 cm. At A construct a right angle and hence construct a rectangle having dimensions 10 cm by 5 cm.

180

9) Draw WX = 5 cm. At W construct an angle of 60°. Along the inclined arm of this angle mark off WZ = 4 cm. Hence complete a drawing of the parallelogram WXYZ.

10) Construct a rectangle ABCD in which AB = 5.8 cm and the diagonal AC = 7.4 cm.

11) Construct a trapezium AXBC in which BX is parallel to AC and ∠CAX = 60°. Measure the distance AX.

12) Construct an equilateral triangle having sides 5 cm long.

13) Construct △ABC with AB = 8 cm, BC = 6 cm and AC = 11.2 cm.

14) Construct the inscribed circle of △ABC (Question 13).

15) Construct △ABC in which AB = 8 cm, AC = 7 cm and ∠CAB = 45°. Construct the circumcircle of this triangle.

16) Draw a line AB = 9 cm and divide it into 7 equal parts.

17) Draw the line XY = 7 cm. Mark off PX = 3 cm. Erect a perpendicular through P. Mark off PZ = 5 cm, Z being above XY. Hence complete the triangle XYZ.

18) Draw the rectangle ABCD with AB = 6 cm and AD = 4 cm. Construct a square whose area is equal to that of the rectangle ABCD. Measure the side of your square.

19) Draw two circles whose centres are 8 cm apart and whose diameters are 6 cm and 8 cm. Draw the common tangent to these circles.

20) Draw a circle, centre O, whose radius is 4 cm. Mark off any point P so that OP = 8 cm. Construct a pair of tangents from P to the circle.

Chapter 25 **Trigonometry**

The Notation for a Right-angled Triangle

The sides of a right-angled triangle are given special names. In Fig. 25.1 the side AB lies opposite the right-angle and it is called the *hypotenuse*. The side BC lies opposite to the angle A and it is called the *side opposite to A*. The side AC is called the *side adjacent to A*.

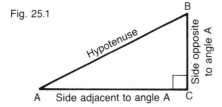

Fig. 25.1

When we consider the angle B (Fig. 25.2) the side AB is still the hypotenuse but AC is now the side opposite to B and BC is the side adjacent to B.

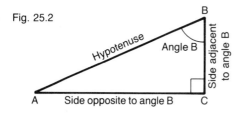

Fig. 25.2

The Trigonometrical Ratios

Consider any angle θ which is bounded by the lines OA and OB as shown in Fig. 25.3. Take any point P on the boundary line OB. From P draw line PM perpendicular to OA to meet it at the point M. Then,

the ratio $\dfrac{MP}{OP}$ is called the sine of $\angle AOB$

the ratio $\dfrac{OM}{OP}$ is called the cosine of $\angle AOB$

and

the ratio $\dfrac{MP}{OM}$ is called the tangent of $\angle AOB$

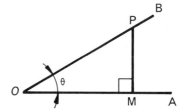

Fig. 25.3

The Sine of an Angle

The abbreviation 'sin' is usually used for sine. In any right-angled triangle (Fig. 25.4).

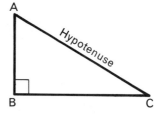

Fig. 25.4

the sine of angle =
$$\dfrac{\text{side opposite the angle}}{\text{hypotenuse}}$$

$$\sin A = \dfrac{BC}{AC}$$

$$\sin C = \dfrac{AB}{AC}$$

Example 1

Find by drawing a suitable triangle the value of sin 30°.

Draw the lines AX and AY which intersect at A so that the angle $\angle YAX = 30°$ as shown in Fig. 25.5. Along AY measure off AC equal to 1 unit (say 10 cm) and from C draw CB perpendicular to AX. Measure CB which will be found to be 0.5 units (5 cm in this case.)

Therefore $\sin 30° = \dfrac{5}{10} = 0.5$.

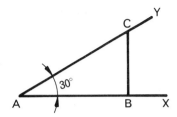

Fig. 25.5

Although it is possible to find the sines of angles by drawing this is inconvenient and not very accurate. Tables of sines have been calculated which allow us to find the sine of any angle. This table is reproduced below.

Natural Sines

°	0' 0.0°	6' 0.1°	12' 0.2°	18' 0.3°	24' 0.4°	30' 0.5°	36' 0.6°	42' 0.7°	48' 0.8°	54' 0.9°	1'	2'	3'	4'	5'
0	0.0000	0.0017	0.0035	0.0052	0.0070	0.0087	0.0105	0.0122	0.0140	0.0157	3	6	9	12	15
1	0.0175	0.0192	0.0209	0.0227	0.0244	0.0262	0.0279	0.0297	0.0314	0.0332	3	6	9	12	15
2	0.0349	0.0366	0.0384	0.0401	0.0419	0.0436	0.0454	0.0471	0.0488	0.0506	3	6	9	12	15
3	0.0523	0.0541	0.0558	0.0576	0.0593	0.0610	0.0628	0.0645	0.0663	0.0680	3	6	9	12	15
4	0.0698	0.0715	0.0732	0.0750	0.0767	0.0785	0.0802	0.0819	0.0837	0.0854	3	6	9	12	14
5	0.0872	0.0889	0.0906	0.0924	0.0941	0.0958	0.0976	0.0993	0.1011	0.1028	3	6	9	12	14
6	0.1045	0.1063	0.1080	0.1097	0.1115	0.1132	0.1149	0.1167	0.1184	0.1201	3	6	9	12	14
7	0.1219	0.1236	0.1253	0.1271	0.1288	0.1305	0.1323	0.1340	0.1357	0.1374	3	6	9	12	14
8	0.1392	0.1409	0.1426	0.1444	0.1461	0.1478	0.1495	0.1513	0.1530	0.1547	3	6	9	11	14
9	0.1564	0.1582	0.1599	0.1616	0.1633	0.1650	0.1668	0.1685	0.1702	0.1719	3	6	9	11	14
10	0.1736	0.1754	0.1771	0.1788	0.1805	0.1822	0.1840	0.1857	0.1874	0.1891	3	6	9	11	14
11	0.1908	0.1925	0.1942	0.1959	0.1977	0.1994	0.2011	0.2028	0.2045	0.2062	3	6	9	11	14
12	0.2079	0.2096	0.2113	0.2130	0.2147	0.2164	0.2181	0.2198	0.2215	0.2232	3	6	9	11	14
13	0.2250	0.2267	0.2284	0.2300	0.2317	0.2334	0.2351	0.2368	0.2385	0.2402	3	6	8	11	14
14	0.2419	0.2436	0.2453	0.2470	0.2487	0.2504	0.2521	0.2538	0.2554	0.2571	3	6	8	11	14
15	0.2588	0.2605	0.2622	0.2639	0.2656	0.2672	0.2689	0.2706	0.2723	0.2740	3	6	8	11	14
16	0.2756	0.2773	0.2790	0.2807	0.2823	0.2840	0.2857	0.2874	0.2890	0.2907	3	6	8	11	14
17	0.2924	0.2940	0.2957	0.2974	0.2990	0.3007	0.3024	0.3040	0.3057	0.3074	3	6	8	11	14
18	0.3090	0.3107	0.3123	0.3140	0.3156	0.3173	0.3190	0.3206	0.3223	0.3239	3	6	8	11	14
19	0.3256	0.3272	0.3289	0.3305	0.3322	0.3338	0.3355	0.3371	0.3387	0.3404	3	5	8	11	14
20	0.3420	0.3437	0.3453	0.3469	0.3486	0.3502	0.3518	0.3535	0.3551	0.3567	3	5	8	11	14
21	0.3584	0.3600	0.3616	0.3633	0.3649	0.3665	0.3681	0.3697	0.3714	0.3730	3	5	8	11	14
22	0.3746	0.3762	0.3778	0.3795	0.3811	0.3827	0.3843	0.3859	0.3875	0.3891	3	5	8	11	13
23	0.3907	0.3923	0.3939	0.3955	0.3971	0.3987	0.4003	0.4019	0.4035	0.4051	3	5	8	11	13
24	0.4067	0.4083	0.4099	0.4115	0.4131	0.4147	0.4163	0.4179	0.4195	0.4210	3	5	8	11	13
25	0.4226	0.4242	0.4258	0.4274	0.4289	0.4305	0.4321	0.4337	0.4352	0.4368	3	5	8	11	13
26	0.4384	0.4399	0.4415	0.4431	0.4446	0.4462	0.4478	0.4493	0.4509	0.4524	3	5	8	10	13
27	0.4540	0.4555	0.4571	0.4586	0.4602	0.4617	0.4633	0.4648	0.4664	0.4679	3	5	8	10	13
28	0.4695	0.4710	0.4726	0.4741	0.4756	0.4772	0.4787	0.4802	0.4818	0.4833	3	5	8	10	13
29	0.4848	0.4863	0.4879	0.4894	0.4909	0.4924	0.4939	0.4955	0.4970	0.4985	3	5	8	10	13
30	0.5000	0.5015	0.5030	0.5045	0.5060	0.5075	0.5090	0.5105	0.5120	0.5135	3	5	8	10	13
31	0.5150	0.5165	0.5180	0.5195	0.5210	0.5225	0.5240	0.5255	0.5270	0.5284	2	5	7	10	12
32	0.5299	0.5314	0.5329	0.5344	0.5358	0.5373	0.5388	0.5402	0.5417	0.5432	2	5	7	10	12
33	0.5446	0.5461	0.5476	0.5490	0.5505	0.5519	0.5534	0.5548	0.5563	0.5577	2	5	7	10	12
34	0.5592	0.5606	0.5621	0.5635	0.5650	0.5664	0.5678	0.5693	0.5707	0.5721	2	5	7	10	12
35	0.5736	0.5750	0.5764	0.5779	0.5793	0.5807	0.5821	0.5835	0.5850	0.5864	2	5	7	9	12
36	0.5878	0.5892	0.5906	0.5920	0.5934	0.5948	0.5962	0.5976	0.5990	0.6004	2	5	7	9	12
37	0.6018	0.6032	0.6046	0.6060	0.6074	0.6088	0.6101	0.6115	0.6129	0.6143	2	5	7	9	12
38	0.6157	0.6170	0.6184	0.6198	0.6211	0.6225	0.6239	0.6252	0.6266	0.6280	2	5	7	9	11
39	0.6293	0.6307	0.6320	0.6334	0.6347	0.6361	0.6374	0.6388	0.6401	0.6414	2	4	7	9	11
40	0.6428	0.6441	0.6455	0.6468	0.6481	0.6494	0.6508	0.6521	0.6534	0.6547	2	4	7	9	11
41	0.6561	0.6574	0.6587	0.6600	0.6613	0.6626	0.6639	0.6652	0.6665	0.6678	2	4	7	9	11
42	0.6691	0.6704	0.6717	0.6730	0.6743	0.6756	0.6769	0.6782	0.6794	0.6807	2	4	6	9	11
43	0.6820	0.6833	0.6845	0.6858	0.6871	0.6884	0.6896	0.6909	0.6921	0.6934	2	4	6	8	11
44	0.6947	0.6959	0.6972	0.6984	0.6997	0.7009	0.7022	0.7034	0.7046	0.7059	2	4	6	8	10

183

Reading the Table of Sines of Angles

1) *To find* sin 12°. The sine of an angle with an exact number of degrees is shown in the column headed 0. Thus sin 12° = 0.2079.

2) *To find* sin 12° 36′. The value will be found under the column headed 36′. Thus sin 12° 36′ = 0.2181.

3) *To find* sin 12° 40′. If the number of minutes is not an exact multiple of 6 we use the table of mean differences. Now 12° 36′ = 0.2181 and 40′ is 4′ more than 36′. Looking in the mean difference column headed 4 we find the value 11. This is *added* on to the sine of 12° 36′ and we have sin 12° 40′ = 0.2181 + 0.0011 = 0.2192.

4) *To find the angle whose sine is* 0.1711. Look in the table of sines to find the nearest number *lower* than 0.1711. This is found to be 0.1702 which corresponds to an angle of 9° 48′.

Natural Sines

°	0′ 0.0°	6′ 0.1°	12′ 0.2°	18′ 0.3°	24′ 0.4°	30′ 0.5°	36′ 0.6°	42′ 0.7°	48′ 0.8°	54′ 0.9°	1′	2′	3′	4′	5′
45	0.7071	0.7083	0.7096	0.7108	0.7120	0.7133	0.7145	0.7157	0.7169	0.7181	2	4	6	8	10
46	0.7193	0.7206	0.7218	0.7230	0.7242	0.7254	0.7266	0.7278	0.7290	0.7302	2	4	6	8	10
47	0.7314	0.7325	0.7337	0.7349	0.7361	0.7373	0.7385	0.7396	0.7408	0.7420	2	4	6	8	10
48	0.7431	0.7443	0.7455	0.7466	0.7478	0.7490	0.7501	0.7513	0.7524	0.7536	2	4	6	8	10
49	0.7547	0.7558	0.7570	0.7581	0.7593	0.7604	0.7615	0.7627	0.7638	0.7649	2	4	6	8	9
50	0.7660	0.7672	0.7683	0.7694	0.7705	0.7716	0.7727	0.7738	0.7749	0.7760	2	4	6	7	9
51	0.7771	0.7782	0.7793	0.7804	0.7815	0.7826	0.7837	0.7848	0.7859	0.7869	2	4	5	7	9
52	0.7880	0.7891	0.7902	0.7912	0.7923	0.7934	0.7944	0.7955	0.7965	0.7976	2	4	5	7	9
53	0.7986	0.7997	0.8007	0.8018	0.8028	0.8039	0.8049	0.8059	0.8070	0.8080	2	3	5	7	9
54	0.8090	0.8100	0.8111	0.8121	0.8131	0.8141	0.8151	0.8161	0.8171	0.8181	2	3	5	7	8
55	0.8192	0.8202	0.8211	0.8221	0.8231	0.8241	0.8251	0.8261	0.8271	0.8281	2	3	5	7	8
56	0.8290	0.8300	0.8310	0.8320	0.8329	0.8339	0.8348	0.8358	0.8368	0.8377	2	3	5	6	8
57	0.8387	0.8396	0.8406	0.8415	0.8425	0.8434	0.8443	0.8453	0.8462	0.8471	2	3	5	6	8
58	0.8480	0.8490	0.8499	0.8508	0.8517	0.8526	0.8536	0.8545	0.8554	0.8563	2	3	5	6	8
59	0.8572	0.8581	0.8590	0.8599	0.8607	0.8616	0.8625	0.8634	0.8643	0.8652	1	3	4	6	7
60	0.8660	0.8669	0.8678	0.8686	0.8695	0.8704	0.8712	0.8721	0.8729	0.8738	1	3	4	6	7
61	0.8746	0.8755	0.8763	0.8771	0.8780	0.8788	0.8796	0.8805	0.8813	0.8821	1	3	4	6	7
62	0.8829	0.8838	0.8846	0.8854	0.8862	0.8870	0.8878	0.8886	0.8894	0.8902	1	3	4	5	7
63	0.8910	0.8918	0.8926	0.8934	0.8942	0.8949	0.8957	0.8965	0.8973	0.8980	1	3	4	5	6
64	0.8988	0.8996	0.9003	0.9011	0.9018	0.9026	0.9033	0.9041	0.9048	0.9056	1	3	4	5	6
65	0.9063	0.9070	0.9078	0.9085	0.9092	0.9100	0.9107	0.9114	0.9121	0.9128	1	2	4	5	6
66	0.9135	0.9143	0.9150	0.9157	0.9164	0.9171	0.9178	0.9184	0.9191	0.9198	1	2	3	5	6
67	0.9205	0.9212	0.9219	0.9225	0.9232	0.9239	0.9245	0.9252	0.9259	0.9265	1	2	3	4	6
68	0.9272	0.9278	0.9285	0.9291	0.9298	0.9304	0.9311	0.9317	0.9323	0.9330	1	2	3	4	5
69	0.9336	0.9342	0.9348	0.9354	0.9361	0.9367	0.9373	0.9379	0.9385	0.9391	1	2	3	4	5
70	0.9397	0.9403	0.9409	0.9415	0.9421	0.9426	0.9432	0.9438	0.9444	0.9449	1	2	3	4	5
71	0.9455	0.9461	0.9466	0.9472	0.9478	0.9483	0.9489	0.9494	0.9500	0.9505	1	2	3	4	5
72	0.9511	0.9516	0.9521	0.9527	0.9532	0.9537	0.9542	0.9548	0.9553	0.9558	1	2	3	3	4
73	0.9563	0.9568	0.9573	0.9578	0.9583	0.9588	0.9593	0.9598	0.9603	0.9608	1	2	2	3	4
74	0.9613	0.9617	0.9622	0.9627	0.9632	0.9636	0.9641	0.9646	0.9650	0.9655	1	2	2	3	4
75	0.9659	0.9664	0.9668	0.9673	0.9677	0.9681	0.9686	0.9690	0.9694	0.9699	1	1	2	3	4
76	0.9703	0.9707	0.9711	0.9715	0.9720	0.9724	0.9728	0.9732	0.9736	0.9740	1	1	2	3	3
77	0.9744	0.9748	0.9751	0.9755	0.9759	0.9763	0.9767	0.9770	0.9774	0.9778	1	1	2	2	3
78	0.9781	0.9785	0.9789	0.9792	0.9796	0.9799	0.9803	0.9806	0.9810	0.9813	1	1	2	2	3
79	0.9816	0.9820	0.9823	0.9826	0.9829	0.9833	0.9836	0.9839	0.9842	0.9845	1	1	2	2	3
80	0.9848	0.9851	0.9854	0.9857	0.9860	0.9863	0.9866	0.9869	0.9871	0.9874	0	1	1	2	2
81	0.9877	0.9880	0.9882	0.9885	0.9888	0.9890	0.9893	0.9895	0.9898	0.9900	0	1	1	2	2
82	0.9903	0.9905	0.9907	0.9910	0.9912	0.9914	0.9917	0.9919	0.9921	0.9923	0	1	1	1	2
83	0.9925	0.9928	0.9930	0.9932	0.9934	0.9936	0.9938	0.9940	0.9942	0.9943	0	1	1	1	2
84	0.9945	0.9947	0.9949	0.9951	0.9952	0.9954	0.9956	0.9957	0.9959	0.9960	0	1	1	1	1
85	0.9962	0.9963	0.9965	0.9966	0.9968	0.9969	0.9971	0.9972	0.9973	0.9974	0	0	1	1	1
86	0.9976	0.9977	0.9978	0.9979	0.9980	0.9981	0.9982	0.9983	0.9984	0.9985	0	0	1	1	1
87	0.9986	0.9987	0.9988	0.9989	0.9990	0.9990	0.9991	0.9992	0.9993	0.9993	0	0	0	1	1
88	0.9994	0.9995	0.9995	0.9996	0.9996	0.9997	0.9997	0.9997	0.9998	0.9998	0	0	0	0	0
89	0.9998	0.9999	0.9999	0.9999	0.9999	1.0000	1.0000	1.0000	1.0000	1.0000	0	0	0	0	0
90	1.0000														

Now 0.1702 is 0.0009 less than 0.1711 so we look in the mean difference table in the row marked 9° and find 9 in the column headed 3'. The angle whose sine is 0.1711 is then $9°48' + 3' = 9°51'$ or $\sin 9°51' = 0.1711$.

Example 2

(a) Find the length of AB in Fig. 25.6.

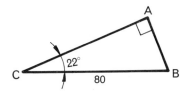

Fig. 25.6

AB is the side opposite $\angle$ACB. BC is the hypotenuse since it is opposite to the right-angle.

Therefore

$$\frac{AB}{BC} = \sin 20°$$

$$AB = BC \times \sin 22° = 80 \times 0.3746$$

$$= 29.97 \text{ mm}$$

(b) Find the length of AB in Fig. 25.7.

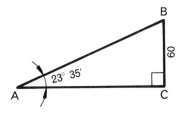

Fig. 25.7

BC is the side opposite to $\angle$BAC and AB is the hypotenuse.

Therefore

$$\frac{BC}{AB} = \sin 23° 35'$$

$$AB = \frac{BC}{\sin 23° 35'} = \frac{60}{0.4000}$$

$$= 150 \text{ mm}$$

(c) Find the angles CAB and ABC in $\triangle$ABC which is shown in Fig. 25.8.

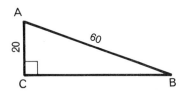

Fig. 25.8

$$\sin B = \frac{AC}{AB} = \frac{20}{60} = 0.3333$$

From the sine tables

$$\angle B = 19° 28'$$

$$\angle A = 90° - 19° 28' = 70° 32'$$

Exercise 142 — All type A

1) Find, by drawing, the sines of the following angles:

(a) 30°   (b) 45°   (c) 68°

2) Find, by drawing, the angles whose sines are:

(a) $\frac{1}{3}$ (b) $\frac{3}{4}$ (c) 0.72

3) Use the tables to write down the values of:

(a) $\sin 12°$ (d) $\sin 7° 23'$
(b) $\sin 18° 12'$ (e) $\sin 87° 35'$
(c) $\sin 74° 42'$ (f) $\sin 0° 11'$

4) Use the tables to write down the angles whose sines are:

(a) 0.1564   (e) 0.9814
(b) 0.9135   (f) 0.7395
(c) 0.9880   (g) 0.0500
(d) 0.0802   (h) 0.2700

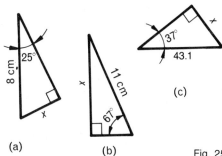

Fig. 25.9

185

5) Find the lengths of the sides marked x in Fig. 25.9 the triangles being right-angled.

6) Find the angles marked θ in Fig. 25.10, the triangles being right-angled.

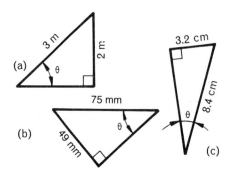

Fig. 25.10

7) In $\triangle ABC$, $\angle C = 90°$, $\angle B = 23°\,17'$ and $AC = 11.2$ cm. Find AB.

8) In $\triangle ABC$, $\angle B = 90°$, $\angle A = 67°28'$ and $AC = 0.86$ m. Find BC.

9) An equilateral triangle has an altitude of 18.7 cm. Find the length of the equal sides.

10) Find the altitude of an isosceles triangle whose vertex angle is 38° and whose equal sides are 7.9 m long.

11) The equal sides of an isosceles triangle are each 27 cm long and the altitude is 19 cm. Find the angles of the triangle.

The Cosine of an Angle

In any right-angled triangle (Fig. 25.11):

the cosine of an angle

$$= \frac{\text{side adjacent to the angle}}{\text{hypotenuse}}$$

$$\cos A = \frac{AB}{AC}$$

$$\cos C = \frac{BC}{AC}$$

The abbreviation 'cos' is usually used for cosine.

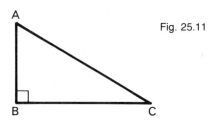

Fig. 25.11

The cosine of an angle may be found by drawing, the construction being similar to that used for the sine of an angle. However, tables of cosines are available and these are used in a similar way to the table of sines except that the mean differences are now *subtracted*.

Example 3

(a) Find the length of the side BC in Fig. 25.12.

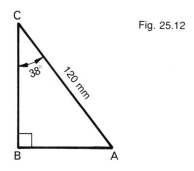

Fig. 25.12

BC is the side adjacent to $\angle BCA$ and AC is the hypotenuse.

Therefore

$$\frac{BC}{AC} = \cos 38°$$

$$BC = AC \times \cos 38° = 120 \times 0.7880$$

$$- 94.56 \text{ mm}$$

(b) Find the length of the side AC in Fig. 25.13.

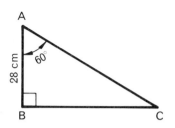

Fig. 25.13

AB is the side adjacent to $\angle$ BAC and AC is the hypotenuse.

Therefore

$$\frac{AB}{AC} = \cos 60°$$

$$AC = \frac{AB}{\cos 60°} = \frac{28}{0.5000} = 56 \text{ cm}$$

(c) Find the angle θ shown in Fig. 25.14.

Natural Cosines

Numbers in difference columns to be *subtracted*, not added.

°	0' 0.0°	6' 0.1°	12' 0.2°	18' 0.3°	24' 0.4°	30' 0.5°	36' 0.6°	42' 0.7°	48' 0.8°	54' 0.9°	1'	2'	3'	4'	5'
0	1.0000	1.0000	1.0000	1.0000	1.0000	1.0000	0.9999	0.9999	0.9999	0.9999	0	0	0	0	0
1	0.9998	0.9998	0.9998	0.9997	0.9997	0.9997	0.9996	0.9996	0.9995	0.9995	0	0	0	0	0
2	0.9994	0.9993	0.9993	0.9992	0.9991	0.9990	0.9990	0.9989	0.9988	0.9987	0	0	0	1	1
3	0.9986	0.9985	0.9984	0.9983	0.9982	0.9981	0.9980	0.9979	0.9978	0.9977	0	0	1	1	1
4	0.9976	0.9974	0.9973	0.9972	0.9971	0.9969	0.9968	0.9966	0.9965	0.9963	0	0	1	1	1
5	0.9962	0.9960	0.9959	0.9957	0.9956	0.9954	0.9952	0.9951	0.9949	0.9947	0	1	1	1	1
6	0.9945	0.9943	0.9942	0.9940	0.9938	0.9936	0.9934	0.9932	0.9930	0.9928	0	1	1	1	2
7	0.9925	0.9923	0.9921	0.9919	0.9917	0.9914	0.9912	0.9910	0.9907	0.9905	0	1	1	1	2
8	0.9903	0.9900	0.9898	0.9895	0.9893	0.9890	0.9888	0.9885	0.9882	0.9880	0	1	1	2	2
9	0.9877	0.9874	0.9871	0.9869	0.9866	0.9863	0.9860	0.9857	0.9854	0.9851	0	1	1	2	2
10	0.9848	0.9845	0.9842	0.9839	0.9836	0.9833	0.9829	0.9826	0.9823	0.9820	1	1	2	2	3
11	0.9816	0.9813	0.9810	0.9806	0.9803	0.9799	0.9796	0.9792	0.9789	0.9785	1	1	2	2	3
12	0.9781	0.9778	0.9774	0.9770	0.9767	0.9763	0.9759	0.9755	0.9751	0.9748	1	1	2	2	3
13	0.9744	0.9740	0.9736	0.9732	0.9728	0.9724	0.9720	0.9715	0.9711	0.9707	1	1	2	3	3
14	0.9703	0.9699	0.9694	0.9690	0.9686	0.9681	0.9677	0.9673	0.9668	0.9664	1	1	2	3	4
15	0.9659	0.9655	0.9650	0.9646	0.9641	0.9636	0.9632	0.9627	0.9622	0.9617	1	2	2	3	4
16	0.9613	0.9608	0.9603	0.9598	0.9593	0.9588	0.9583	0.9578	0.9573	0.9568	1	2	2	3	4
17	0.9563	0.9558	0.9553	0.9548	0.9542	0.9537	0.9532	0.9527	0.9521	0.9516	1	2	3	3	4
18	0.9511	0.9505	0.9500	0.9494	0.9489	0.9483	0.9478	0.9472	0.9466	0.9461	1	2	3	4	5
19	0.9455	0.9449	0.9444	0.9438	0.9432	0.9426	0.9421	0.9415	0.9409	0.9403	1	2	3	4	5
20	0.9397	0.9391	0.9385	0.9379	0.9373	0.9367	0.9361	0.9354	0.9348	0.9342	1	2	3	4	5
21	0.9336	0.9330	0.9323	0.9317	0.9311	0.9304	0.9298	0.9291	0.9285	0.9278	1	2	3	4	5
22	0.9272	0.9265	0.9259	0.9252	0.9245	0.9239	0.9232	0.9225	0.9219	0.9212	1	2	3	4	6
23	0.9205	0.9198	0.9191	0.9184	0.9178	0.9171	0.9164	0.9157	0.9150	0.9143	1	2	3	5	6
24	0.9135	0.9128	0.9121	0.9114	0.9107	0.9100	0.9092	0.9085	0.9078	0.9070	1	2	4	5	6
25	0.9063	0.9056	0.9048	0.9041	0.9033	0.9026	0.9018	0.9011	0.9003	0.8996	1	3	4	5	6
26	0.8988	0.8980	0.8973	0.8965	0.8957	0.8949	0.8942	0.8934	0.8926	0.8918	1	3	4	5	6
27	0.8910	0.8902	0.8894	0.8886	0.8878	0.8870	0.8862	0.8854	0.8846	0.8838	1	3	4	5	7
28	0.8829	0.8821	0.8813	0.8805	0.8796	0.8788	0.8780	0.8771	0.8763	0.8755	1	3	4	6	7
29	0.8746	0.8738	0.8729	0.8721	0.8712	0.8704	0.8695	0.8686	0.8678	0.8669	1	3	4	6	7
30	0.8660	0.8652	0.8643	0.8634	0.8625	0.8616	0.8607	0.8599	0.8590	0.8581	1	3	4	6	7
31	0.8572	0.8563	0.8554	0.8545	0.8536	0.8526	0.8517	0.8508	0.8499	0.8490	2	3	5	6	8
32	0.8480	0.8471	0.8462	0.8453	0.8443	0.8434	0.8425	0.8415	0.8406	0.8396	2	3	5	6	8
33	0.8387	0.8377	0.8368	0.8358	0.8348	0.8339	0.8329	0.8320	0.8310	0.8300	2	3	5	6	8
34	0.8290	0.8281	0.8271	0.8261	0.8251	0.8241	0.8231	0.8221	0.8211	0.8202	2	3	5	7	8
35	0.8192	0.8181	0.8171	0.8161	0.8151	0.8141	0.8131	0.8121	0.8111	0.8100	2	3	5	7	8
36	0.8090	0.8080	0.8070	0.8059	0.8049	0.8039	0.8028	0.8018	0.8007	0.7997	2	3	5	7	9
37	0.7986	0.7976	0.7965	0.7955	0.7944	0.7934	0.7923	0.7912	0.7902	0.7891	2	4	5	7	9
38	0.7880	0.7869	0.7859	0.7848	0.7837	0.7826	0.7815	0.7804	0.7793	0.7782	2	4	5	7	9
39	0.7771	0.7760	0.7749	0.7738	0.7727	0.7716	0.7705	0.7694	0.7683	0.7672	2	4	6	7	9
40	0.7660	0.7649	0.7638	0.7627	0.7615	0.7604	0.7593	0.7581	0.7570	0.7559	2	4	6	8	9
41	0.7547	0.7536	0.7524	0.7513	0.7501	0.7490	0.7478	0.7466	0.7455	0.7443	2	4	6	8	10
42	0.7431	0.7420	0.7408	0.7396	0.7385	0.7373	0.7361	0.7349	0.7337	0.7325	2	4	6	8	10
43	0.7314	0.7302	0.7290	0.7278	0.7266	0.7254	0.7242	0.7230	0.7218	0.7206	2	4	6	8	10
44	0.7193	0.7181	0.7169	0.7157	0.7145	0.7133	0.7120	0.7108	0.7096	0.7083	2	4	6	8	10

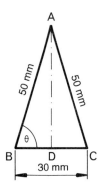

A

50 mm   50 mm

θ

B   D   C
30 mm

Fig. 25.14

Since △ABC is isosceles the perpendicular AD bisects the base BC and hence   BD = 15 mm.

$$\cos\theta = \frac{BD}{AB} = \frac{15}{50} = 0.3$$

$$\theta = 72°\,32'$$

Natural Cosines

Numbers in difference columns to be *subtracted*, not added.

°	0' 0.0°	6' 0.1°	12' 0.2°	18' 0.3°	24' 0.4°	30' 0.5°	36' 0.6°	42' 0.7°	48' 0.8°	54' 0.9°	1'	2'	3'	4'	5'
45	0.7071	0.7059	0.7046	0.7034	0.7022	0.7009	0.6997	0.6984	0.6972	0.6959	2	4	6	8	10
46	0.6947	0.6934	0.6921	0.6909	0.6896	0.6884	0.6871	0.6858	0.6845	0.6833	2	4	6	8	11
47	0.6820	0.6807	0.6794	0.6782	0.6769	0.6756	0.6743	0.6730	0.6717	0.6704	2	4	6	9	11
48	0.6691	0.6678	0.6665	0.6652	0.6639	0.6626	0.6613	0.6600	0.6587	0.6574	2	4	7	9	11
49	0.6561	0.6547	0.6534	0.6521	0.6508	0.6494	0.6481	0.6468	0.6455	0.6441	2	4	7	9	11
50	0.6428	0.6414	0.6401	0.6388	0.6374	0.6361	0.6347	0.6334	0.6320	0.6307	2	4	7	9	11
51	0.6293	0.6280	0.6266	0.6252	0.6239	0.6225	0.6211	0.6198	0.6184	0.6170	2	5	7	9	11
52	0.6157	0.6143	0.6129	0.6115	0.6101	0.6088	0.6074	0.6060	0.6046	0.6032	2	5	7	9	12
53	0.6018	0.6004	0.5990	0.5976	0.5962	0.5948	0.5934	0.5920	0.5906	0.5892	2	5	7	9	12
54	0.5878	0.5864	0.5850	0.5835	0.5821	0.5807	0.5793	0.5779	0.5764	0.5750	2	5	7	9	12
55	0.5736	0.5721	0.5707	0.5693	0.5678	0.5664	0.5650	0.5635	0.5621	0.5606	2	5	7	10	12
56	0.5592	0.5577	0.5563	0.5548	0.5534	0.5519	0.5505	0.5490	0.5476	0.5461	2	5	7	10	12
57	0.5446	0.5432	0.5417	0.5402	0.5388	0.5373	0.5358	0.5344	0.5329	0.5314	2	5	7	10	12
58	0.5299	0.5284	0.5270	0.5255	0.5240	0.5225	0.5210	0.5195	0.5180	0.5165	2	5	7	10	12
59	0.5150	0.5135	0.5120	0.5105	0.5090	0.5075	0.5060	0.5045	0.5030	0.5015	3	5	8	10	13
60	0.5000	0.4985	0.4970	0.4955	0.4939	0.4924	0.4909	0.4894	0.4879	0.4863	3	5	8	10	13
61	0.4848	0.4833	0.4818	0.4802	0.4787	0.4772	0.4756	0.4741	0.4726	0.4710	3	5	8	10	13
62	0.4695	0.4679	0.4664	0.4648	0.4633	0.4617	0.4602	0.4586	0.4571	0.4555	3	5	8	10	13
63	0.4540	0.4524	0.4509	0.4493	0.4478	0.4462	0.4446	0.4431	0.4415	0.4399	3	5	8	10	13
64	0.4384	0.4368	0.4352	0.4337	0.4321	0.4305	0.4289	0.4274	0.4258	0.4242	3	5	8	11	13
65	0.4226	0.4210	0.4195	0.4179	0.4163	0.4147	0.4131	0.4115	0.4099	0.4083	3	5	8	11	13
66	0.4067	0.4051	0.4035	0.4019	0.4003	0.3987	0.3971	0.3955	0.3939	0.3923	3	5	8	11	13
67	0.3907	0.3891	0.3875	0.3859	0.3843	0.3827	0.3811	0.3795	0.3778	0.3762	3	5	8	11	13
68	0.3746	0.3730	0.3714	0.3697	0.3681	0.3665	0.3649	0.3633	0.3616	0.3600	3	5	8	11	14
69	0.3584	0.3567	0.3551	0.3535	0.3518	0.3502	0.3486	0.3469	0.3453	0.3437	3	5	8	11	14
70	0.3420	0.3404	0.3387	0.3371	0.3355	0.3338	0.3322	0.3305	0.3289	0.3272	3	5	8	11	14
71	0.3256	0.3239	0.3223	0.3206	0.3190	0.3173	0.3156	0.3140	0.3123	0.3107	3	6	8	11	14
72	0.3090	0.3074	0.3057	0.3040	0.3024	0.3007	0.2990	0.2974	0.2957	0.2940	3	6	8	11	14
73	0.2924	0.2907	0.2890	0.2874	0.2857	0.2840	0.2823	0.2807	0.2790	0.2773	3	6	8	11	14
74	0.2756	0.2740	0.2723	0.2706	0.2689	0.2672	0.2656	0.2639	0.2622	0.2605	3	6	8	11	14
75	0.2588	0.2571	0.2554	0.2538	0.2521	0.2504	0.2487	0.2470	0.2453	0.2436	3	6	8	11	14
76	0.2419	0.2402	0.2385	0.2368	0.2351	0.2334	0.2317	0.2300	0.2284	0.2267	3	6	8	11	14
77	0.2250	0.2233	0.2215	0.2198	0.2181	0.2164	0.2147	0.2130	0.2113	0.2096	3	6	9	11	14
78	0.2079	0.2062	0.2045	0.2028	0.2011	0.1994	0.1977	0.1959	0.1942	0.1925	3	6	9	11	14
79	0.1908	0.1891	0.1874	0.1857	0.1840	0.1822	0.1805	0.1788	0.1771	0.1754	3	6	9	11	14
80	0.1736	0.1719	0.1702	0.1685	0.1668	0.1650	0.1633	0.1616	0.1599	0.1582	3	6	9	11	14
81	0.1564	0.1547	0.1530	0.1513	0.1495	0.1478	0.1461	0.1444	0.1426	0.1409	3	6	9	11	14
82	0.1392	0.1374	0.1357	0.1340	0.1323	0.1305	0.1288	0.1271	0.1253	0.1236	3	6	9	12	14
83	0.1219	0.1201	0.1184	0.1167	0.1149	0.1132	0.1115	0.1097	0.1080	0.1063	3	6	9	12	14
84	0.1045	0.1028	0.1011	0.0993	0.0976	0.0958	0.0941	0.0924	0.0906	0.0889	3	6	9	12	14
85	0.0872	0.0854	0.0837	0.0819	0.0802	0.0785	0.0767	0.0750	0.0732	0.0715	3	6	9	12	14
86	0.0698	0.0680	0.0663	0.0645	0.0628	0.0610	0.0593	0.0576	0.0558	0.0541	3	6	9	12	15
87	0.0523	0.0506	0.0488	0.0471	0.0454	0.0436	0.0419	0.0401	0.0384	0.0366	3	6	9	12	15
88	0.0349	0.0332	0.0314	0.0297	0.0279	0.0262	0.0244	0.0227	0.0209	0.0192	3	6	9	12	15
89	0.0175	0.0157	0.0140	0.0122	0.0105	0.0087	0.0070	0.0052	0.0035	0.0017	3	6	9	12	15
90	0.0000														

Exercise 143 — *All type A*

1) Use the tables to write down the values of:

(a) cos 15°   (d) cos 0° 11′
(b) cos 24° 18′   (e) cos 73° 22′
(c) cos 78° 24′   (f) cos 39° 59′

2) Use the tables to write down the angles whose cosine are:

(a) 0.9135   (e) 0.9586
(b) 0.3420   (f) 0.0084
(c) 0.9673   (g) 0.2611
(d) 0.4289   (h) 0.4700

3) Find the lengths of the sides marked *x* in Fig. 25.15, the triangles being right-angled.

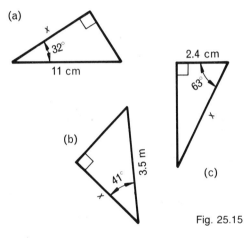

Fig. 25.15

4) Find the angles marked θ in Fig. 25.16, the triangles being right-angled.

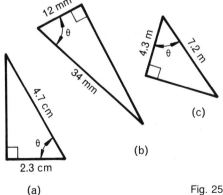

Fig. 25.16

5) An isosceles triangle has a base of 3.4 cm and the equal sides are each

4.2 cm long. Find the angles of the triangle and also its altitude.

6) In △ABC, ∠C = 90°, ∠B = 33° 27′ and   BC = 2.4 cm. Find AB.

7) In △ABC, ∠B = 90°, ∠A = 62° 45′ and   AC = 4.3 cm. Find AB.

8) In Fig. 25.17, calculate ∠BAC and the length BC.

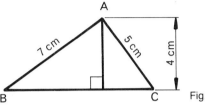

Fig. 25.17

9) In Fig. 25.18 calculate BD, AD, AC and BC.

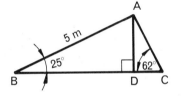

Fig. 25.18

The Tangent of an Angle

In any right-angled triangle (Fig. 25.19),

the tangent of an angle

$$= \frac{\text{side opposite to the angle}}{\text{side adjacent to the angle}}$$

$$\tan A = \frac{BC}{AB}$$

$$\tan C = \frac{AB}{BC}$$

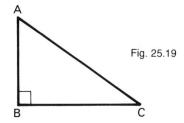

Fig. 25.19

189

The abbreviation 'tan' is usually used for tangent. From the table of tangents the tangents of angles from 0° to 90° can be read directly. For example:

$$\tan 37° = 0.7536 \quad \text{and}$$

$$\tan 62° 29' = 1.9196$$

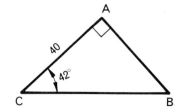

Fig. 25.20

Example 4

(a) Find the length of the side AB in Fig. 25.20.

AB is the side opposite $\angle$ C and AC is the side adjacent to $\angle$ C. Hence,

$$\frac{AB}{AC} = \tan \angle C$$

Natural Tangents

°	0' 0.0°	6' 0.1°	12' 0.2°	18' 0.3°	24' 0.4°	30' 0.5°	36' 0.6°	42' 0.7°	48' 0.8°	54' 0.9°	1'	2'	3'	4'	5'
0	0.0000	0.0017	0.0035	0.0052	0.0070	0.0087	0.0105	0.0122	0.0140	0.0157	3	6	9	12	15
1	0.0175	0.0192	0.0209	0.0227	0.0244	0.0262	0.0279	0.0297	0.0314	0.0332	3	6	9	12	15
2	0.0349	0.0367	0.0384	0.0402	0.0419	0.0437	0.0454	0.0472	0.0489	0.0507	3	6	9	12	15
3	0.0524	0.0542	0.0559	0.0577	0.0594	0.0612	0.0629	0.0647	0.0664	0.0682	3	6	9	12	15
4	0.0699	0.0717	0.0734	0.0752	0.0769	0.0787	0.0805	0.0822	0.0840	0.0857	3	6	9	12	15
5	0.0875	0.0892	0.0910	0.0928	0.0945	0.0963	0.0981	0.0998	0.1016	0.1033	3	6	9	12	15
6	0.1051	0.1069	0.1086	0.1104	0.1122	0.1139	0.1157	0.1175	0.1192	0.1210	3	6	9	12	15
7	0.1228	0.1246	0.1263	0.1281	0.1299	0.1317	0.1334	0.1352	0.1370	0.1388	3	6	9	12	15
8	0.1405	0.1423	0.1441	0.1459	0.1477	0.1495	0.1512	0.1530	0.1548	0.1566	3	6	9	12	15
9	0.1584	0.1602	0.1620	0.1638	0.1655	0.1673	0.1691	0.1709	0.1727	0.1745	3	6	9	12	15
10	0.1763	0.1781	0.1799	0.1817	0.1835	0.1853	0.1871	0.1890	0.1908	0.1926	3	6	9	12	15
11	0.1944	0.1962	0.1980	0.1998	0.2016	0.2035	0.2053	0.2071	0.2089	0.2107	3	6	9	12	15
12	0.2126	0.2144	0.2162	0.2180	0.2199	0.2217	0.2235	0.2254	0.2272	0.2290	3	6	9	12	15
13	0.2309	0.2327	0.2345	0.2364	0.2382	0.2401	0.2419	0.2438	0.2456	0.2475	3	6	9	12	15
14	0.2493	0.2512	0.2530	0.2549	0.2568	0.2586	0.2605	0.2623	0.2642	0.2661	3	6	9	12	16
15	0.2679	0.2698	0.2717	0.2736	0.2754	0.2773	0.2792	0.2811	0.2830	0.2849	3	6	9	13	16
16	0.2867	0.2886	0.2905	0.2924	0.2943	0.2962	0.2981	0.3000	0.3019	0.3038	3	6	9	13	16
17	0.3057	0.3076	0.3096	0.3115	0.3134	0.3153	0.3172	0.3191	0.3211	0.3230	3	6	10	13	16
18	0.3249	0.3269	0.3288	0.3307	0.3327	0.3346	0.3365	0.3385	0.3404	0.3424	3	6	10	13	16
19	0.3443	0.3463	0.3482	0.3502	0.3522	0.3541	0.3561	0.3581	0.3600	0.3620	3	7	10	13	16
20	0.3640	0.3659	0.3679	0.3699	0.3719	0.3739	0.3759	0.3779	0.3799	0.3819	3	7	10	13	17
21	0.3839	0.3859	0.3879	0.3899	0.3919	0.3939	0.3959	0.3979	0.4000	0.4020	3	7	10	13	17
22	0.4040	0.4061	0.4081	0.4101	0.4122	0.4142	0.4163	0.4183	0.4204	0.4224	3	7	10	14	17
23	0.4245	0.4265	0.4286	0.4307	0.4327	0.4348	0.4369	0.4390	0.4411	0.4431	3	7	10	14	17
24	0.4452	0.4473	0.4494	0.4515	0.4536	0.4557	0.4578	0.4599	0.4621	0.4642	4	7	11	14	18
25	0.4663	0.4684	0.4706	0.4727	0.4748	0.4770	0.4791	0.4813	0.4834	0.4856	4	7	11	14	18
26	0.4877	0.4899	0.4921	0.4942	0.4964	0.4986	0.5008	0.5029	0.5051	0.5073	4	7	11	15	18
27	0.5095	0.5117	0.5139	0.5161	0.5184	0.5206	0.5228	0.5250	0.5272	0.5295	4	7	11	15	18
28	0.5317	0.5340	0.5362	0.5384	0.5407	0.5430	0.5452	0.5475	0.5498	0.5520	4	8	11	15	19
29	0.5543	0.5566	0.5589	0.5612	0.5635	0.5658	0.5681	0.5704	0.5727	0.5750	4	8	12	15	19
30	0.5774	0.5797	0.5820	0.5844	0.5867	0.5890	0.5914	0.5938	0.5961	0.5985	4	8	12	16	20
31	0.6009	0.6032	0.6056	0.6080	0.6104	0.6128	0.6152	0.6176	0.6200	0.6224	4	8	12	16	20
32	0.6249	0.6273	0.6297	0.6322	0.6346	0.6371	0.6395	0.6420	0.6445	0.6469	4	8	12	16	20
33	0.6494	0.6519	0.6544	0.6569	0.6594	0.6619	0.6644	0.6669	0.6694	0.6720	4	8	13	17	21
34	0.6745	0.6771	0.6796	0.6822	0.6847	0.6873	0.6899	0.6924	0.6950	0.6976	4	9	13	17	21
35	0.7002	0.7028	0.7054	0.7080	0.7107	0.7133	0.7159	0.7186	0.7212	0.7239	4	9	13	17	22
36	0.7265	0.7292	0.7319	0.7346	0.7373	0.7400	0.7427	0.7454	0.7481	0.7508	5	9	14	18	23
37	0.7536	0.7563	0.7590	0.7618	0.7646	0.7673	0.7701	0.7729	0.7757	0.7785	5	9	14	18	23
38	0.7813	0.7841	0.7869	0.7898	0.7926	0.7954	0.7983	0.8012	0.8040	0.8069	5	9	14	19	24
39	0.8098	0.8127	0.8156	0.8185	0.8214	0.8243	0.8273	0.8302	0.8332	0.8361	5	10	15	20	24
40	0.8391	0.8421	0.8451	0.8481	0.8511	0.8541	0.8571	0.8601	0.8632	0.8662	5	10	15	20	25
41	0.8693	0.8724	0.8754	0.8785	0.8816	0.8847	0.8878	0.8910	0.8941	0.8972	5	10	16	21	26
42	0.9004	0.9036	0.9067	0.9099	0.9131	0.9163	0.9195	0.9228	0.9260	0.9293	5	11	16	21	27
43	0.9325	0.9358	0.9391	0.9424	0.9457	0.9490	0.9523	0.9556	0.9590	0.9623	6	11	17	22	28
44	0.9657	0.9691	0.9725	0.9759	0.9793	0.9827	0.9861	0.9896	0.9930	0.9965	6	11	17	23	28

$$\frac{AB}{AC} = \tan 42°$$

$$AB = AC \times \tan 42° = 40 \times 0.9004$$

$$= 36.02 \text{ mm}$$

(b) Find the length of the side BC in Fig. 25.21.

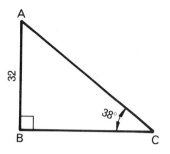

Fig. 25.21

Natural Tangents

°	0′ 0.0°	6′ 0.1°	12′ 0.2°	18′ 0.3°	24′ 0.4°	30′ 0.5°	36′ 0.6°	42′ 0.7°	48′ 0.8°	54′ 0.9°	1′	2′	3′	4′	5′
45	1.0000	1.0035	1.0070	1.0105	1.0141	1.0176	1.0212	1.0247	1.0283	1.0319	6	12	18	24	30
46	1.0355	1.0392	1.0428	1.0464	1.0501	1.0538	1.0575	1.0612	1.0649	1.0686	6	12	18	25	31
47	1.0724	1.0761	1.0799	1.0837	1.0875	1.0913	1.0951	1.0990	1.1028	1.1067	6	13	19	25	32
48	1.1106	1.1145	1.1184	1.1224	1.1263	1.1303	1.1343	1.1383	1.1423	1.1463	7	13	20	27	33
49	1.1504	1.1544	1.1585	1.1626	1.1667	1.1708	1.1750	1.1792	1.1833	1.1875	7	14	21	28	34
50	1.1918	1.1960	1.2002	1.2045	1.2088	1.2131	1.2174	1.2218	1.2261	1.2305	7	14	22	29	36
51	1.2349	1.2393	1.2437	1.2482	1.2527	1.2572	1.2617	1.2662	1.2708	1.2753	8	15	23	30	38
52	1.2799	1.2846	1.2892	1.2938	1.2985	1.3032	1.3079	1.3127	1.3175	1.3222	8	16	24	31	39
53	1.3270	1.3319	1.3367	1.3416	1.3465	1.3514	1.3564	1.3613	1.3663	1.3713	8	16	25	33	41
54	1.3764	1.3814	1.3865	1.3916	1.3968	1.4019	1.4071	1.4124	1.4176	1.4229	9	17	26	34	43
55	1.4281	1.4335	1.4388	1.4442	1.4496	1.4550	1.4605	1.4659	1.4715	1.4770	9	18	27	36	45
56	1.4826	1.4882	1.4938	1.4994	1.5051	1.5108	1.5166	1.5224	1.5282	1.5340	10	19	29	38	48
57	1.5399	1.5458	1.5517	1.5577	1.5637	1.5697	1.5757	1.5818	1.5880	1.5941	10	20	30	40	50
58	1.6003	1.6066	1.6128	1.6191	1.6255	1.6319	1.6383	1.6447	1.6512	1.6577	11	21	32	43	53
59	1.6643	1.6709	1.6775	1.6842	1.6909	1.6977	1.7045	1.7113	1.7182	1.7251	11	23	34	45	56
60	1.7321	1.7391	1.7461	1.7532	1.7603	1.7675	1.7747	1.7820	1.7893	1.7966	12	24	36	48	60
61	1.8040	1.8115	1.8190	1.8265	1.8341	1.8418	1.8495	1.8572	1.8650	1.8728	13	26	38	51	64
62	1.8807	1.8887	1.8967	1.9047	1.9128	1.9210	1.9292	1.9375	1.9458	1.9542	14	27	41	55	68
63	1.9626	1.9711	1.9797	1.9883	1.9970	2.0057	2.0145	2.0233	2.0323	2.0413	15	29	44	58	73
64	2.0503	2.0594	2.0686	2.0778	2.0872	2.0965	2.1060	2.1155	2.1251	2.1348	16	31	47	63	78
65	2.1445	2.1543	2.1642	2.1742	2.1842	2.1943	2.2045	2.2148	2.2251	2.2355	17	34	51	68	85
66	2.2460	2.2566	2.2673	2.2781	2.2889	2.2998	2.3109	2.3220	2.3332	2.3445	18	37	55	73	92
67	2.3559	2.3673	2.3789	2.3906	2.4023	2.4142	2.4262	2.4383	2.4504	2.4627	20	40	60	79	99
68	2.4751	2.4876	2.5002	2.5129	2.5257	2.5386	2.5517	2.5649	2.5782	2.5916	22	43	65	87	108
69	2.6051	2.6187	2.6325	2.6464	2.6605	2.6746	2.6889	2.7034	2.7179	2.7326	24	47	71	95	119
70	2.7475	2.7625	2.7776	2.7929	2.8083	2.8329	2.8397	2.8556	2.8716	2.8878	26	52	78	104	131
71	2.9042	2.9208	2.9375	2.9544	2.9714	2.9887	3.0061	3.0237	3.0415	3.0595	29	58	87	116	145
72	3.0777	3.0961	3.1146	3.1334	3.1524	3.1716	3.1910	3.2106	3.2305	3.2506	32	64	96	129	161
73	3.2709	3.2914	3.3122	3.3332	3.3544	3.3759	3.3977	3.4197	3.4420	3.4646	36	72	108	144	180
74	3.4874	3.5105	3.5339	3.5576	3.5816	3.6059	3.6305	3.6554	3.6806	3.7062	41	81	122	163	204
75	3.7321	3.7583	3.7848	3.8118	3.8391	3.8667	3.8947	3.9232	3.9520	3.9812	46	93	139	186	232
76	4.0108	4.0408	4.0713	4.1022	4.1335	4.1653	4.1976	4.2303	4.2635	4.2972	53	107	160	213	267
77	4.3315	4.3662	4.4015	4.4374	4.4737	4.5107	4.5483	4.5864	4.6252	4.6646					
78	4.7046	4.7453	4.7867	4.8288	4.8716	4.9152	4.9594	5.0045	5.0504	5.0970					
79	5.1446	5.1929	5.2422	5.2924	5.3435	5.3955	5.4486	5.5026	5.5578	5.6140					
80	5.6713	5.7297	5.7894	5.8502	5.9124	5.9758	6.0405	6.1066	6.1742	6.2432			Differences		
81	6.3138	6.3859	6.4596	6.5350	6.6122	6.6912	6.7720	6.8548	6.9395	7.0264			untrustworthy		
82	7.1154	7.2066	7.3002	7.3962	7.4947	7.5958	7.6996	7.8062	7.9158	8.0285			here		
83	8.1443	8.2636	8.3863	8.5126	8.6427	8.7769	8.9152	9.0579	9.2052	9.3572					
84	9.5144	9.677	9.845	10.02	10.20	10.39	10.58	10.78	10.99	11.20					
85	11.43	11.66	11.91	12.16	12.43	12.71	13.00	13.30	13.62	13.95					
86	14.30	14.67	15.06	15.46	15.89	16.35	16.83	17.34	17.89	18.46					
87	19.08	19.74	20.45	21.20	22.02	22.90	23.86	24.90	26.03	27.27					
88	28.64	30.14	31.82	33.69	35.80	38.19	40.92	44.07	47.74	52.08					
89	57.29	63.66	71.62	81.85	95.49	114.6	143.2	191.0	286.5	57.30					
90	∞														

There are two ways of doing this problem.

(i) $\dfrac{AB}{BC} = \tan 38°$ or $BC = \dfrac{AB}{\tan 38°}$

Therefore $BC = \dfrac{32}{0.7813} = 40.96$ mm

(ii) Since $\angle C = 38°$,

$$\angle A = 90° - 38° = 52°$$

now

$\dfrac{BC}{AB} = \tan A$ or $BC = AB \times \tan A$

$BC = 32 \times 1.2799 = 40.96$ mm

Both methods produce the same answer but method (ii) is better because it is quicker and more convenient to multiply than divide. Whenever possible the ratio should be arranged so that the quantity to be found is the numerator of the ratio.

Exercise 144 — *All type A*

1) Use tables to write down the values of:

(a) $\tan 18°$ (d) $\tan 39° 27'$
(b) $\tan 32° 24'$ (e) $\tan 11° 20'$
(c) $\tan 53° 42'$ (f) $\tan 69° 23'$

2) Use tables to write down the angles whose tangents are:

(a) 0.4452   (e) 0.3568
(b) 3.2709   (f) 0.8263
(c) 0.0769   (g) 1.9251
(d) 0.3977   (h) 0.0163

Fig. 25.22

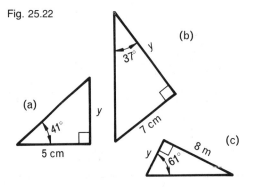

3) Find the lengths of the sides marked y in Fig. 25.22, the triangles being right-angled.

4) Find the angles marked a in Fig. 25.23, the triangles being right-angled.

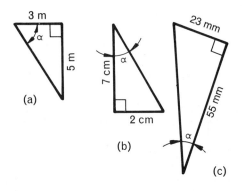

Fig. 25.23

5) An isosceles triangle has a base 10 cm long and the two equal angles are each 57°. Calculate the altitude of the triangle.

6) In $\triangle ABC$, $\angle B = 90°$, $\angle C = 49°$ and $AB = 3.2$ cm. Find BC.

7) In $\triangle ABC$, $\angle A = 12° 23'$, $\angle B = 90°$ and $BC = 7.31$ cm. Find AB.

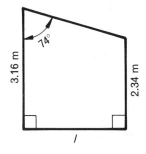

Fig. 25.24

8) Calculate the distance l in Fig. 25.24.

9) Calculate the distance d in Fig. 25.25.

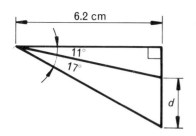

6.2 cm

11°
17°

d

Fig. 25.25

Logarithms of the Trigonometrical Ratios

Tables are used to find the log of a trig

ratio in the same way as to find the ratio itself.

Example 5

(a)   Find the value of $28.25 \times \sin 39° 17'$.

	number	log
	28.25	1.4510
	sin 39° 17′	$\bar{1}.8015$
Answer =	17.88	1.2525

Logarithms of Sines

°	0′ 0.0°	6′ 0.1°	12′ 0.2°	18′ 0.3°	24′ 0.4°	30′ 0.5°	36′ 0.6°	42′ 0.7°	48′ 0.8°	54′ 0.9°	1′	2′	3′	4′	5′
0	$-\infty$	$\bar{3}.2419$	$\bar{3}.5429$	$\bar{3}.7190$	$\bar{3}.8439$	$\bar{3}.9408$	$\bar{2}.0200$	$\bar{2}.0870$	$\bar{2}.1450$	$\bar{2}.1961$			Differences		
1	$\bar{2}.2419$	$\bar{2}.2832$	$\bar{2}.3210$	$\bar{2}.3558$	$\bar{2}.3880$	$\bar{2}.4179$	$\bar{2}.4459$	$\bar{2}.4723$	$\bar{2}.4971$	$\bar{2}.5206$			untrustworthy		
2	$\bar{2}.5428$	$\bar{2}.5640$	$\bar{2}.5842$	$\bar{2}.6035$	$\bar{2}.6220$	$\bar{2}.6397$	$\bar{2}.6567$	$\bar{2}.6731$	$\bar{2}.6889$	$\bar{2}.7041$			here		
3	$\bar{2}.7188$	$\bar{2}.7330$	$\bar{2}.7468$	$\bar{2}.7602$	$\bar{2}.7731$	$\bar{2}.7857$	$\bar{2}.7979$	$\bar{2}.8098$	$\bar{2}.8213$	$\bar{2}.8326$					
4	$\bar{2}.8436$	$\bar{2}.8543$	$\bar{2}.8647$	$\bar{2}.8749$	$\bar{2}.8849$	$\bar{2}.8946$	$\bar{2}.9042$	$\bar{2}.9135$	$\bar{2}.9226$	$\bar{2}.9315$	16	32	48	64	80
5	$\bar{2}.9403$	$\bar{2}.9489$	$\bar{2}.9573$	$\bar{2}.9655$	$\bar{2}.9736$	$\bar{2}.9816$	$\bar{2}.9894$	$\bar{2}.9970$	$\bar{1}.0046$	$\bar{1}.0120$	13	26	39	52	65
6	$\bar{1}.0192$	$\bar{1}.0264$	$\bar{1}.0334$	$\bar{1}.0403$	$\bar{1}.0472$	$\bar{1}.0539$	$\bar{1}.0605$	$\bar{1}.0670$	$\bar{1}.0734$	$\bar{1}.0797$	11	22	33	44	55
7	$\bar{1}.0859$	$\bar{1}.0920$	$\bar{1}.0981$	$\bar{1}.1040$	$\bar{1}.1099$	$\bar{1}.1157$	$\bar{1}.1214$	$\bar{1}.1271$	$\bar{1}.1326$	$\bar{1}.1381$	10	19	29	38	48
8	$\bar{1}.1436$	$\bar{1}.1489$	$\bar{1}.1542$	$\bar{1}.1594$	$\bar{1}.1646$	$\bar{1}.1697$	$\bar{1}.1747$	$\bar{1}.1797$	$\bar{1}.1847$	$\bar{1}.1895$	8	17	25	34	42
9	$\bar{1}.1943$	$\bar{1}.1991$	$\bar{1}.2038$	$\bar{1}.2085$	$\bar{1}.2131$	$\bar{1}.2176$	$\bar{1}.2221$	$\bar{1}.2266$	$\bar{1}.2310$	$\bar{1}.2353$	8	15	23	30	38
10	$\bar{1}.2397$	$\bar{1}.2439$	$\bar{1}.2482$	$\bar{1}.2524$	$\bar{1}.2565$	$\bar{1}.2606$	$\bar{1}.2647$	$\bar{1}.2687$	$\bar{1}.2727$	$\bar{1}.2767$	7	14	20	27	34
11	$\bar{1}.2806$	$\bar{1}.2845$	$\bar{1}.2883$	$\bar{1}.2921$	$\bar{1}.2959$	$\bar{1}.2997$	$\bar{1}.3034$	$\bar{1}.3070$	$\bar{1}.3107$	$\bar{1}.3143$	6	12	19	25	31
12	$\bar{1}.3179$	$\bar{1}.3214$	$\bar{1}.3250$	$\bar{1}.3284$	$\bar{1}.3319$	$\bar{1}.3353$	$\bar{1}.3387$	$\bar{1}.3421$	$\bar{1}.3455$	$\bar{1}.3488$	6	11	17	23	28
13	$\bar{1}.3521$	$\bar{1}.3554$	$\bar{1}.3586$	$\bar{1}.3618$	$\bar{1}.3650$	$\bar{1}.3682$	$\bar{1}.3713$	$\bar{1}.3745$	$\bar{1}.3775$	$\bar{1}.3806$	5	11	16	21	26
14	$\bar{1}.3837$	$\bar{1}.3867$	$\bar{1}.3897$	$\bar{1}.3927$	$\bar{1}.3957$	$\bar{1}.3986$	$\bar{1}.4015$	$\bar{1}.4044$	$\bar{1}.4073$	$\bar{1}.4102$	5	10	15	20	24
15	$\bar{1}.4130$	$\bar{1}.4158$	$\bar{1}.4186$	$\bar{1}.4214$	$\bar{1}.4242$	$\bar{1}.4269$	$\bar{1}.4296$	$\bar{1}.4323$	$\bar{1}.4350$	$\bar{1}.4377$	5	9	14	18	23
16	$\bar{1}.4403$	$\bar{1}.4430$	$\bar{1}.4456$	$\bar{1}.4482$	$\bar{1}.4508$	$\bar{1}.4533$	$\bar{1}.4559$	$\bar{1}.4584$	$\bar{1}.4609$	$\bar{1}.4634$	4	9	13	17	21
17	$\bar{1}.4659$	$\bar{1}.4684$	$\bar{1}.4709$	$\bar{1}.4733$	$\bar{1}.4757$	$\bar{1}.4781$	$\bar{1}.4805$	$\bar{1}.4829$	$\bar{1}.4853$	$\bar{1}.4876$	4	8	12	16	20
18	$\bar{1}.4900$	$\bar{1}.4923$	$\bar{1}.4946$	$\bar{1}.4969$	$\bar{1}.4992$	$\bar{1}.5015$	$\bar{1}.5037$	$\bar{1}.5060$	$\bar{1}.5082$	$\bar{1}.5104$	4	8	11	15	19
19	$\bar{1}.5126$	$\bar{1}.5148$	$\bar{1}.5170$	$\bar{1}.5192$	$\bar{1}.5213$	$\bar{1}.5235$	$\bar{1}.5256$	$\bar{1}.5278$	$\bar{1}.5299$	$\bar{1}.5320$	4	7	11	14	18
20	$\bar{1}.5341$	$\bar{1}.5361$	$\bar{1}.5382$	$\bar{1}.5402$	$\bar{1}.5423$	$\bar{1}.5443$	$\bar{1}.5463$	$\bar{1}.5484$	$\bar{1}.5504$	$\bar{1}.5523$	3	7	10	13	17
21	$\bar{1}.5543$	$\bar{1}.5563$	$\bar{1}.5583$	$\bar{1}.5602$	$\bar{1}.5621$	$\bar{1}.5641$	$\bar{1}.5660$	$\bar{1}.5679$	$\bar{1}.5698$	$\bar{1}.5717$	3	6	10	13	16
22	$\bar{1}.5736$	$\bar{1}.5754$	$\bar{1}.5773$	$\bar{1}.5792$	$\bar{1}.5810$	$\bar{1}.5828$	$\bar{1}.5847$	$\bar{1}.5865$	$\bar{1}.5883$	$\bar{1}.5901$	3	6	9	12	15
23	$\bar{1}.5919$	$\bar{1}.5937$	$\bar{1}.5954$	$\bar{1}.5972$	$\bar{1}.5990$	$\bar{1}.6007$	$\bar{1}.6024$	$\bar{1}.6042$	$\bar{1}.6059$	$\bar{1}.6076$	3	6	9	12	14
24	$\bar{1}.6093$	$\bar{1}.6110$	$\bar{1}.6127$	$\bar{1}.6144$	$\bar{1}.6161$	$\bar{1}.6177$	$\bar{1}.6194$	$\bar{1}.6210$	$\bar{1}.6227$	$\bar{1}.6243$	3	6	8	11	14
25	$\bar{1}.6259$	$\bar{1}.6276$	$\bar{1}.6292$	$\bar{1}.6308$	$\bar{1}.6324$	$\bar{1}.6340$	$\bar{1}.6356$	$\bar{1}.6371$	$\bar{1}.6387$	$\bar{1}.6403$	3	5	8	11	13
26	$\bar{1}.6418$	$\bar{1}.6434$	$\bar{1}.6449$	$\bar{1}.6465$	$\bar{1}.6480$	$\bar{1}.6495$	$\bar{1}.6510$	$\bar{1}.6526$	$\bar{1}.6541$	$\bar{1}.6556$	3	5	8	10	13
27	$\bar{1}.6570$	$\bar{1}.6585$	$\bar{1}.6600$	$\bar{1}.6615$	$\bar{1}.6629$	$\bar{1}.6644$	$\bar{1}.6659$	$\bar{1}.6673$	$\bar{1}.6687$	$\bar{1}.6702$	2	5	7	10	12
28	$\bar{1}.6716$	$\bar{1}.6730$	$\bar{1}.6744$	$\bar{1}.6759$	$\bar{1}.6773$	$\bar{1}.6787$	$\bar{1}.6801$	$\bar{1}.6814$	$\bar{1}.6828$	$\bar{1}.6842$	2	5	7	9	12
29	$\bar{1}.6856$	$\bar{1}.6869$	$\bar{1}.6883$	$\bar{1}.6896$	$\bar{1}.6910$	$\bar{1}.6923$	$\bar{1}.6937$	$\bar{1}.6950$	$\bar{1}.6963$	$\bar{1}.6977$	2	4	7	9	11
30	$\bar{1}.6990$	$\bar{1}.7003$	$\bar{1}.7016$	$\bar{1}.7029$	$\bar{1}.7042$	$\bar{1}.7055$	$\bar{1}.7068$	$\bar{1}.7080$	$\bar{1}.7093$	$\bar{1}.7106$	2	4	6	9	11
31	$\bar{1}.7118$	$\bar{1}.7131$	$\bar{1}.7144$	$\bar{1}.7156$	$\bar{1}.7168$	$\bar{1}.7181$	$\bar{1}.7193$	$\bar{1}.7205$	$\bar{1}.7218$	$\bar{1}.7230$	2	4	6	8	10
32	$\bar{1}.7242$	$\bar{1}.7254$	$\bar{1}.7266$	$\bar{1}.7278$	$\bar{1}.7290$	$\bar{1}.7302$	$\bar{1}.7314$	$\bar{1}.7326$	$\bar{1}.7338$	$\bar{1}.7349$	2	4	6	8	10
33	$\bar{1}.7361$	$\bar{1}.7373$	$\bar{1}.7384$	$\bar{1}.7396$	$\bar{1}.7407$	$\bar{1}.7419$	$\bar{1}.7430$	$\bar{1}.7442$	$\bar{1}.7453$	$\bar{1}.7464$	2	4	6	8	10
34	$\bar{1}.7476$	$\bar{1}.7487$	$\bar{1}.7498$	$\bar{1}.7509$	$\bar{1}.7520$	$\bar{1}.7531$	$\bar{1}.7542$	$\bar{1}.7553$	$\bar{1}.7564$	$\bar{1}.7575$	2	4	6	7	9
35	$\bar{1}.7586$	$\bar{1}.7597$	$\bar{1}.7607$	$\bar{1}.7618$	$\bar{1}.7629$	$\bar{1}.7640$	$\bar{1}.7650$	$\bar{1}.7661$	$\bar{1}.7671$	$\bar{1}.7682$	2	4	5	7	9
36	$\bar{1}.7692$	$\bar{1}.7703$	$\bar{1}.7713$	$\bar{1}.7723$	$\bar{1}.7734$	$\bar{1}.7744$	$\bar{1}.7754$	$\bar{1}.7764$	$\bar{1}.7774$	$\bar{1}.7785$	2	3	5	7	9
37	$\bar{1}.7795$	$\bar{1}.7805$	$\bar{1}.7815$	$\bar{1}.7825$	$\bar{1}.7835$	$\bar{1}.7844$	$\bar{1}.7854$	$\bar{1}.7864$	$\bar{1}.7874$	$\bar{1}.7884$	2	3	5	7	8
38	$\bar{1}.7893$	$\bar{1}.7903$	$\bar{1}.7913$	$\bar{1}.7922$	$\bar{1}.7932$	$\bar{1}.7941$	$\bar{1}.7951$	$\bar{1}.7960$	$\bar{1}.7970$	$\bar{1}.7979$	2	3	5	6	8
39	$\bar{1}.7989$	$\bar{1}.7998$	$\bar{1}.8007$	$\bar{1}.8017$	$\bar{1}.8026$	$\bar{1}.8035$	$\bar{1}.8044$	$\bar{1}.8053$	$\bar{1}.8063$	$\bar{1}.8072$	2	3	5	6	8
40	$\bar{1}.8081$	$\bar{1}.8090$	$\bar{1}.8099$	$\bar{1}.8108$	$\bar{1}.8117$	$\bar{1}.8125$	$\bar{1}.8134$	$\bar{1}.8143$	$\bar{1}.8152$	$\bar{1}.8161$	1	3	4	6	7
41	$\bar{1}.8169$	$\bar{1}.8178$	$\bar{1}.8187$	$\bar{1}.8195$	$\bar{1}.8204$	$\bar{1}.8213$	$\bar{1}.8221$	$\bar{1}.8230$	$\bar{1}.8238$	$\bar{1}.8247$	1	3	4	6	7
42	$\bar{1}.8255$	$\bar{1}.8264$	$\bar{1}.8272$	$\bar{1}.8280$	$\bar{1}.8289$	$\bar{1}.8297$	$\bar{1}.8305$	$\bar{1}.8313$	$\bar{1}.8322$	$\bar{1}.8330$	1	3	4	6	7
43	$\bar{1}.8338$	$\bar{1}.8346$	$\bar{1}.8354$	$\bar{1}.8362$	$\bar{1}.8370$	$\bar{1}.8378$	$\bar{1}.8386$	$\bar{1}.8394$	$\bar{1}.8402$	$\bar{1}.8410$	1	3	4	5	7
44	$\bar{1}.8418$	$\bar{1}.8426$	$\bar{1}.8433$	$\bar{1}.8441$	$\bar{1}.8449$	$\bar{1}.8457$	$\bar{1}.8464$	$\bar{1}.8472$	$\bar{1}.8480$	$\bar{1}.8487$	1	3	4	5	6

(b)   Find the angle A given that

$\cos \angle A = \dfrac{20.23}{29.86}$

number	log
20.23	1.3060
29.86	1.4751
cos A	$\bar{1}.8309$

The angle A is found directly from the log cos table:

$\angle A = 47° 21'$

(c)   If $b = \dfrac{c \sin \angle B}{\sin \angle C}$ find b when

$c = 19.28$, $\angle B = 61°$ and $\angle C = 22° 7'$.

number	log
19.28	1.2851
sin 61°	$\bar{1}.9418$
	1.2269
sin 22° 7′	$\bar{1}.5757$
Answer = 44.79	1.6512

Logarithms of Sines

°	0′ 0.0°	6′ 0.1°	12′ 0.2°	18′ 0.3°	24′ 0.4°	30′ 0.5°	36′ 0.6°	42′ 0.7°	48′ 0.8°	54′ 0.9°	1′	2′	3′	4′	5′
45	1̄.8495	1̄.8502	1̄.8510	1̄.8517	1̄.8525	1̄.8532	1̄.8540	1̄.8547	1̄.8555	1̄.8562	1	2	4	5	6
46	1̄.8569	1̄.8577	1̄.8584	1̄.8591	1̄.8598	1̄.8606	1̄.8613	1̄.8620	1̄.8627	1̄.8634	1	2	4	5	6
47	1̄.8641	1̄.8648	1̄.8655	1̄.8662	1̄.8669	1̄.8676	1̄.8683	1̄.8690	1̄.8697	1̄.8704	1	2	3	5	6
48	1̄.8711	1̄.8718	1̄.8724	1̄.8731	1̄.8738	1̄.8745	1̄.8751	1̄.8758	1̄.8765	1̄.8771	1	2	3	4	6
49	1̄.8778	1̄.8784	1̄.8791	1̄.8797	1̄.8804	1̄.8810	1̄.8817	1̄.8823	1̄.8830	1̄.8836	1	2	3	4	5
50	1̄.8843	1̄.8849	1̄.8855	1̄.8862	1̄.8868	1̄.8874	1̄.8880	1̄.8887	1̄.8893	1̄.8899	1	2	3	4	5
51	1̄.8905	1̄.8911	1̄.8917	1̄.8923	1̄.8929	1̄.8935	1̄.8941	1̄.8947	1̄.8953	1̄.8959	1	2	3	4	5
52	1̄.8965	1̄.8971	1̄.8977	1̄.8983	1̄.8989	1̄.8995	1̄.9000	1̄.9006	1̄.9012	1̄.9018	1	2	3	4	5
53	1̄.9023	1̄.9029	1̄.9035	1̄.9041	1̄.9046	1̄.9052	1̄.9057	1̄.9063	1̄.9069	1̄.9074	1	2	3	4	5
54	1̄.9080	1̄.9085	1̄.9091	1̄.9096	1̄.9101	1̄.9107	1̄.9112	1̄.9118	1̄.9123	1̄.9128	1	2	3	4	5
55	1̄.9134	1̄.9139	1̄.9144	1̄.9149	1̄.9155	1̄.9160	1̄.9165	1̄.9170	1̄.9175	1̄.9181	1	2	3	3	4
56	1̄.9186	1̄.9191	1̄.9196	1̄.9201	1̄.9206	1̄.9211	1̄.9216	1̄.9221	1̄.9226	1̄.9231	1	2	3	3	4
57	1̄.9236	1̄.9241	1̄.9246	1̄.9251	1̄.9255	1̄.9260	1̄.9265	1̄.9270	1̄.9275	1̄.9279	1	2	2	3	4
58	1̄.9284	1̄.9289	1̄.9294	1̄.9298	1̄.9303	1̄.9308	1̄.9312	1̄.9317	1̄.9322	1̄.9326	1	2	2	3	4
59	1̄.9331	1̄.9335	1̄.9340	1̄.9344	1̄.9349	1̄.9353	1̄.9358	1̄.9362	1̄.9367	1̄.9371	1	1	2	3	4
60	1̄.9375	1̄.9380	1̄.9384	1̄.9388	1̄.9393	1̄.9397	1̄.9401	1̄.9406	1̄.9410	1̄.9414	1	1	2	3	4
61	1̄.9418	1̄.9422	1̄.9427	1̄.9431	1̄.9435	1̄.9439	1̄.9443	1̄.9447	1̄.9451	1̄.9455	1	1	2	3	3
62	1̄.9459	1̄.9463	1̄.9467	1̄.9471	1̄.9475	1̄.9479	1̄.9483	1̄.9487	1̄.9491	1̄.9495	1	1	2	3	3
63	1̄.9499	1̄.9503	1̄.9506	1̄.9510	1̄.9514	1̄.9518	1̄.9522	1̄.9525	1̄.9529	1̄.9533	1	1	2	3	3
64	1̄.9537	1̄.9540	1̄.9544	1̄.9548	1̄.9551	1̄.9555	1̄.9558	1̄.9562	1̄.9566	1̄.9569	1	1	2	2	3
65	1̄.9573	1̄.9576	1̄.9580	1̄.9583	1̄.9587	1̄.9590	1̄.9594	1̄.9597	1̄.9601	1̄.9604	1	1	2	2	3
66	1̄.9607	1̄.9611	1̄.9614	1̄.9617	1̄.9621	1̄.9624	1̄.9627	1̄.9631	1̄.9634	1̄.9637	1	1	2	2	3
67	1̄.9640	1̄.9643	1̄.9647	1̄.9650	1̄.9653	1̄.9656	1̄.9659	1̄.9662	1̄.9666	1̄.9669	1	1	2	2	3
68	1̄.9672	1̄.9675	1̄.9678	1̄.9681	1̄.9684	1̄.9687	1̄.9690	1̄.9693	1̄.9696	1̄.9699	1	1	2	2	2
69	1̄.9702	1̄.9704	1̄.9707	1̄.9710	1̄.9713	1̄.9716	1̄.9719	1̄.9722	1̄.9724	1̄.9727	0	1	1	2	2
70	1̄.9730	1̄.9733	1̄.9735	1̄.9738	1̄.9741	1̄.9743	1̄.9746	1̄.9749	1̄.9751	1̄.9754	0	1	1	2	2
71	1̄.9757	1̄.9759	1̄.9762	1̄.9764	1̄.9767	1̄.9770	1̄.9772	1̄.9775	1̄.9777	1̄.9780	0	1	1	2	2
72	1̄.9782	1̄.9785	1̄.9787	1̄.9789	1̄.9792	1̄.9794	1̄.9797	1̄.9799	1̄.9801	1̄.9804	0	1	1	2	2
73	1̄.9806	1̄.9808	1̄.9811	1̄.9813	1̄.9815	1̄.9817	1̄.9820	1̄.9822	1̄.9824	1̄.9826	0	1	1	1	2
74	1̄.9828	1̄.9831	1̄.9833	1̄.9835	1̄.9837	1̄.9839	1̄.9841	1̄.9843	1̄.9845	1̄.9847	0	1	1	1	2
75	1̄.9849	1̄.9851	1̄.9853	1̄.9855	1̄.9857	1̄.9859	1̄.9861	1̄.9863	1̄.9865	1̄.9867	0	1	1	1	2
76	1̄.9869	1̄.9871	1̄.9873	1̄.9875	1̄.9876	1̄.9878	1̄.9880	1̄.9882	1̄.9884	1̄.9885	0	1	1	1	2
77	1̄.9887	1̄.9889	1̄.9891	1̄.9892	1̄.9894	1̄.9896	1̄.9897	1̄.9899	1̄.9901	1̄.9902	0	1	1	1	1
78	1̄.9904	1̄.9906	1̄.9907	1̄.9909	1̄.9910	1̄.9912	1̄.9913	1̄.9915	1̄.9916	1̄.9918	0	1	1	1	1
79	1̄.9919	1̄.9921	1̄.9922	1̄.9924	1̄.9925	1̄.9927	1̄.9928	1̄.9929	1̄.9931	1̄.9932	0	0	1	1	1
80	1̄.9934	1̄.9935	1̄.9936	1̄.9937	1̄.9939	1̄.9940	1̄.9941	1̄.9943	1̄.9944	1̄.9945	0	0	1	1	1
81	1̄.9946	1̄.9947	1̄.9949	1̄.9950	1̄.9951	1̄.9952	1̄.9953	1̄.9954	1̄.9955	1̄.9956	0	0	1	1	1
82	1̄.9958	1̄.9959	1̄.9960	1̄.9961	1̄.9962	1̄.9963	1̄.9964	1̄.9965	1̄.9966	1̄.9967	0	0	0	1	1
83	1̄.9968	1̄.9968	1̄.9969	1̄.9970	1̄.9971	1̄.9972	1̄.9973	1̄.9974	1̄.9975	1̄.9975	0	0	0	1	1
84	1̄.9976	1̄.9977	1̄.9978	1̄.9978	1̄.9979	1̄.9980	1̄.9981	1̄.9981	1̄.9982	1̄.9983	0	0	0	0	1
85	1̄.9983	1̄.9984	1̄.9985	1̄.9985	1̄.9986	1̄.9987	1̄.9987	1̄.9988	1̄.9988	1̄.9989	0	0	0	0	0
86	1̄.9989	1̄.9990	1̄.9990	1̄.9991	1̄.9991	1̄.9992	1̄.9992	1̄.9993	1̄.9993	1̄.9994	0	0	0	0	0
87	1̄.9994	1̄.9994	1̄.9995	1̄.9995	1̄.9996	1̄.9996	1̄.9996	1̄.9996	1̄.9997	1̄.9997	0	0	0	0	0
88	1̄.9997	1̄.9998	1̄.9998	1̄.9998	1̄.9998	1̄.9999	1̄.9999	1̄.9999	1̄.9999	1̄.9999	0	0	0	0	0
89	1̄.9999	1̄.9999	0.0000	0.0000	0.0000	0.0000	0.0000	0.0000	0.0000	0.0000					
90	0.0000														

Exercise 145 — *All type B*

1) From the tables find the following:

(a) $\log \sin 28° 33'$ (d) $\log \cos 24° 15'$
(b) $\log \sin 74° 24'$ (e) $\log \tan 44° 31'$
(c) $\log \cos 8° 2'$ (f) $\log \tan 7° 5'$

2) From the tables find the following:

(a) If $\log \cos \angle A = \bar{1}.7357$ find $\angle A$
(b) If $\log \sin \angle A = \bar{1}.5813$ find $\angle A$
(c) If $\log \tan \angle B = 0.5755$ find $\angle B$

(d) If $\log \sin \varphi = \bar{1}.3069$ find φ
(e) If $\log \cos \theta = \bar{1}.2381$ find θ
(f) If $\log \tan a = 1.5569$ find a

3) By using logs find the following:

(a) If $\cos \angle A = \dfrac{19.26}{27.58}$ find $\angle A$
(b) If $\sin \angle B = \dfrac{11.23}{35.35}$ find $\angle B$
(c) If $\tan \theta = \dfrac{28.13}{17.57}$ find θ

Logarithms of Cosines

Numbers in difference columns to be *subtracted*, not added.

°	0' 0.0°	6' 0.1°	12' 0.2°	18' 0.3°	24' 0.4°	30' 0.5°	36' 0.6°	42' 0.7°	48' 0.8°	54' 0.9°	1'	2'	3'	4'	5'
0	0.0000	0.0000	0.0000	0.0000	0.0000	0.0000	0.0000	0.0000	0.0000	1̄.9999	0	0	0	0	0
1	1̄.9999	1̄.9999	1̄.9999	1̄.9999	1̄.9999	1̄.9999	1̄.9998	1̄.9998	1̄.9998	1̄.9998	0	0	0	0	0
2	1̄.9997	1̄.9997	1̄.9997	1̄.9996	1̄.9996	1̄.9996	1̄.9996	1̄.9995	1̄.9995	1̄.9994	0	0	0	0	0
3	1̄.9994	1̄.9994	1̄.9993	1̄.9993	1̄.9992	1̄.9992	1̄.9991	1̄.9991	1̄.9990	1̄.9990	0	0	0	0	0
4	1̄.9989	1̄.9989	1̄.9988	1̄.9988	1̄.9987	1̄.9987	1̄.9986	1̄.9985	1̄.9985	1̄.9984	0	0	0	0	0
5	1̄.9983	1̄.9983	1̄.9982	1̄.9981	1̄.9981	1̄.9980	1̄.9979	1̄.9978	1̄.9978	1̄.9977	0	0	0	0	1
6	1̄.9976	1̄.9975	1̄.9975	1̄.9974	1̄.9973	1̄.9972	1̄.9971	1̄.9970	1̄.9969	1̄.9968	0	0	0	1	1
7	1̄.9968	1̄.9967	1̄.9966	1̄.9965	1̄.9964	1̄.9963	1̄.9962	1̄.9961	1̄.9960	1̄.9959	0	0	0	1	1
8	1̄.9958	1̄.9956	1̄.9955	1̄.9954	1̄.9953	1̄.9952	1̄.9951	1̄.9950	1̄.9949	1̄.9947	0	0	1	1	1
9	1̄.9946	1̄.9945	1̄.9944	1̄.9943	1̄.9941	1̄.9940	1̄.9939	1̄.9937	1̄.9936	1̄.9935	0	0	1	1	1
10	1̄.9934	1̄.9932	1̄.9931	1̄.9929	1̄.9928	1̄.9927	1̄.9925	1̄.9924	1̄.9922	1̄.9921	0	0	1	1	1
11	1̄.9919	1̄.9918	1̄.9916	1̄.9915	1̄.9913	1̄.9912	1̄.9910	1̄.9909	1̄.9907	1̄.9906	0	1	1	1	1
12	1̄.9904	1̄.9902	1̄.9901	1̄.9899	1̄.9897	1̄.9896	1̄.9894	1̄.9892	1̄.9891	1̄.9889	0	1	1	1	1
13	1̄.9887	1̄.9885	1̄.9884	1̄.9882	1̄.9880	1̄.9878	1̄.9876	1̄.9875	1̄.9873	1̄.9871	0	1	1	1	2
14	1̄.9869	1̄.9867	1̄.9865	1̄.9863	1̄.9861	1̄.9859	1̄.9857	1̄.9855	1̄.9853	1̄.9851	0	1	1	1	2
15	1̄.9849	1̄.9847	1̄.9845	1̄.9843	1̄.9841	1̄.9839	1̄.9837	1̄.9835	1̄.9833	1̄.9831	0	1	1	1	2
16	1̄.9828	1̄.9826	1̄.9824	1̄.9822	1̄.9820	1̄.9817	1̄.9815	1̄.9813	1̄.9811	1̄.9808	0	1	1	1	2
17	1̄.9806	1̄.9804	1̄.9801	1̄.9799	1̄.9797	1̄.9794	1̄.9792	1̄.9789	1̄.9787	1̄.9785	0	1	1	2	2
18	1̄.9782	1̄.9780	1̄.9777	1̄.9775	1̄.9772	1̄.9770	1̄.9767	1̄.9764	1̄.9762	1̄.9759	0	1	1	2	2
19	1̄.9757	1̄.9754	1̄.9751	1̄.9749	1̄.9746	1̄.9743	1̄.9741	1̄.9738	1̄.9735	1̄.9733	0	1	1	2	2
20	1̄.9730	1̄.9727	1̄.9724	1̄.9722	1̄.9719	1̄.9716	1̄.9713	1̄.9710	1̄.9707	1̄.9704	0	1	1	2	2
21	1̄.9702	1̄.9699	1̄.9696	1̄.9693	1̄.9690	1̄.9687	1̄.9684	1̄.9681	1̄.9678	1̄.9675	1	1	2	2	2
22	1̄.9672	1̄.9669	1̄.9666	1̄.9662	1̄.9659	1̄.9656	1̄.9653	1̄.9650	1̄.9647	1̄.9643	1	1	2	2	3
23	1̄.9640	1̄.9637	1̄.9634	1̄.9631	1̄.9627	1̄.9624	1̄.9621	1̄.9617	1̄.9614	1̄.9611	1	1	2	2	3
24	1̄.9607	1̄.9604	1̄.9601	1̄.9597	1̄.9594	1̄.9590	1̄.9587	1̄.9583	1̄.9580	1̄.9576	1	1	2	2	3
25	1̄.9573	1̄.9569	1̄.9566	1̄.9562	1̄.9558	1̄.9555	1̄.9551	1̄.9548	1̄.9544	1̄.9540	1	1	2	2	3
26	1̄.9537	1̄.9533	1̄.9529	1̄.9525	1̄.9522	1̄.9518	1̄.9514	1̄.9510	1̄.9506	1̄.9503	1	1	2	3	3
27	1̄.9499	1̄.9495	1̄.9491	1̄.9487	1̄.9483	1̄.9479	1̄.9475	1̄.9471	1̄.9467	1̄.9463	1	1	2	3	3
28	1̄.9459	1̄.9455	1̄.9451	1̄.9447	1̄.9443	1̄.9439	1̄.9435	1̄.9431	1̄.9427	1̄.9422	1	1	2	3	3
29	1̄.9418	1̄.9414	1̄.9410	1̄.9406	1̄.9401	1̄.9397	1̄.9393	1̄.9388	1̄.9384	1̄.9380	1	1	2	3	4
30	1̄.9375	1̄.9371	1̄.9367	1̄.9362	1̄.9358	1̄.9353	1̄.9349	1̄.9344	1̄.9340	1̄.9335	1	1	2	3	4
31	1̄.9331	1̄.9326	1̄.9322	1̄.9317	1̄.9312	1̄.9308	1̄.9303	1̄.9298	1̄.9294	1̄.9289	1	2	2	3	4
32	1̄.9284	1̄.9279	1̄.9275	1̄.9270	1̄.9265	1̄.9260	1̄.9255	1̄.9251	1̄.9246	1̄.9241	1	2	2	3	4
33	1̄.9236	1̄.9231	1̄.9226	1̄.9221	1̄.9216	1̄.9211	1̄.9206	1̄.9201	1̄.9196	1̄.9191	1	2	3	3	4
34	1̄.9186	1̄.9181	1̄.9175	1̄.9170	1̄.9165	1̄.9160	1̄.9155	1̄.9149	1̄.9144	1̄.9139	1	2	3	3	4
35	1̄.9134	1̄.9128	1̄.9123	1̄.9118	1̄.9112	1̄.9107	1̄.9101	1̄.9096	1̄.9091	1̄.9085	1	2	3	4	5
36	1̄.9080	1̄.9074	1̄.9069	1̄.9063	1̄.9057	1̄.9052	1̄.9046	1̄.9041	1̄.9035	1̄.9029	1	2	3	4	5
37	1̄.9023	1̄.9018	1̄.9012	1̄.9006	1̄.9000	1̄.8995	1̄.8989	1̄.8983	1̄.8977	1̄.8971	1	2	3	4	5
38	1̄.8965	1̄.8959	1̄.8953	1̄.8947	1̄.8941	1̄.8935	1̄.8929	1̄.8923	1̄.8917	1̄.8911	1	2	3	4	5
39	1̄.8905	1̄.8899	1̄.8893	1̄.8887	1̄.8880	1̄.8874	1̄.8868	1̄.8862	1̄.8855	1̄.8849	1	2	3	4	5
40	1̄.8843	1̄.8836	1̄.8830	1̄.8823	1̄.8817	1̄.8810	1̄.8804	1̄.8797	1̄.8791	1̄.8784	1	2	3	4	5
41	1̄.8778	1̄.8771	1̄.8765	1̄.8758	1̄.8751	1̄.8745	1̄.8738	1̄.8731	1̄.8724	1̄.8718	1	2	3	4	6
42	1̄.8711	1̄.8704	1̄.8697	1̄.8690	1̄.8683	1̄.8676	1̄.8669	1̄.8662	1̄.8655	1̄.8648	1	2	4	5	6
43	1̄.8641	1̄.8634	1̄.8627	1̄.8620	1̄.8613	1̄.8606	1̄.8598	1̄.8591	1̄.8584	1̄.8577	1	2	4	5	6
44	1̄.8569	1̄.8562	1̄.8555	1̄.8547	1̄.8540	1̄.8532	1̄.8525	1̄.8517	1̄.8510	1̄.8502	1	2	4	5	6

4) If $a = \dfrac{b \sin \angle A}{\sin \angle B}$, find, by using logs, the value of a when $b = 8.16$ cm, $\angle A = 43° 27'$ and $\angle B = 37° 11'$.

5) If $\cos A = \dfrac{b^2 + c^2 - a^2}{2bc}$, find, by using logs, the value of $\angle A$ when $b = 11.23$ cm, $c = 9.16$ cm and $a = 8.23$ cm.

6) If $\sin \angle C = \dfrac{c \sin \angle B}{b}$ find, by using logs, the value of C when $c = 0.323$, $\angle B = 29° 8'$ and $b = 0.517$.

7) If $b^2 = a^2 + c^2 - 2ac \cos \angle B$ find the value of b when $a = 11.36$ cm, $c = 8.26$ cm and $\angle B = 29° 25'$.

Logarithms of Cosines

Numbers in difference columns to be *subtracted*, not added.

°	0′ 0.0°	6′ 0.1°	12′ 0.2°	18′ 0.3°	24′ 0.4°	30′ 0.5°	36′ 0.6°	42′ 0.7°	48′ 0.8°	54′ 0.9°	1′	2′	3′	4′	5′
45	1̄.8495	1̄.8487	1̄.8480	1̄.8472	1̄.8464	1̄.8457	1̄.8449	1̄.8441	1̄.8433	1̄.8426	1	3	4	5	6
46	1̄.8418	1̄.8410	1̄.8402	1̄.8394	1̄.8386	1̄.8378	1̄.8370	1̄.8362	1̄.8354	1̄.8346	1	3	4	5	7
47	1̄.8338	1̄.8330	1̄.8322	1̄.8313	1̄.8305	1̄.8297	1̄.8289	1̄.8280	1̄.8272	1̄.8264	1	3	4	6	7
48	1̄.8255	1̄.8247	1̄.8238	1̄.8230	1̄.8221	1̄.8213	1̄.8204	1̄.8195	1̄.8187	1̄.8178	1	3	4	6	7
49	1̄.8169	1̄.8161	1̄.8152	1̄.8143	1̄.8134	1̄.8125	1̄.8117	1̄.8108	1̄.8099	1̄.8090	1	3	4	6	7
50	1̄.8081	1̄.8072	1̄.8063	1̄.8053	1̄.8044	1̄.8035	1̄.8026	1̄.8017	1̄.8007	1̄.7998	2	3	5	6	8
51	1̄.7989	1̄.7979	1̄.7970	1̄.7960	1̄.7951	1̄.7941	1̄.7932	1̄.7922	1̄.7913	1̄.7903	2	3	5	6	8
52	1̄.7893	1̄.7884	1̄.7874	1̄.7864	1̄.7854	1̄.7844	1̄.7835	1̄.7825	1̄.7815	1̄.7805	2	3	5	7	8
53	1̄.7795	1̄.7785	1̄.7774	1̄.7764	1̄.7754	1̄.7744	1̄.7734	1̄.7723	1̄.7713	1̄.7703	2	3	5	7	9
54	1̄.7692	1̄.7682	1̄.7671	1̄.7661	1̄.7650	1̄.7640	1̄.7629	1̄.7618	1̄.7607	1̄.7597	2	4	5	7	9
55	1̄.7586	1̄.7575	1̄.7564	1̄.7553	1̄.7542	1̄.7531	1̄.7520	1̄.7509	1̄.7498	1̄.7487	2	4	6	7	9
56	1̄.7476	1̄.7464	1̄.7453	1̄.7442	1̄.7430	1̄.7419	1̄.7407	1̄.7396	1̄.7384	1̄.7373	2	4	6	8	10
57	1̄.7361	1̄.7349	1̄.7338	1̄.7326	1̄.7314	1̄.7302	1̄.7290	1̄.7278	1̄.7266	1̄.7254	2	4	6	8	10
58	1̄.7242	1̄.7230	1̄.7218	1̄.7205	1̄.7193	1̄.7181	1̄.7168	1̄.7156	1̄.7144	1̄.7131	2	4	6	8	10
59	1̄.7118	1̄.7106	1̄.7093	1̄.7080	1̄.7068	1̄.7055	1̄.7042	1̄.7029	1̄.7016	1̄.7003	2	4	6	9	11
60	1̄.6990	1̄.6977	1̄.6963	1̄.6950	1̄.6937	1̄.6923	1̄.6910	1̄.6896	1̄.6883	1̄.6869	2	4	7	9	11
61	1̄.6856	1̄.6842	1̄.6828	1̄.6814	1̄.6801	1̄.6787	1̄.6773	1̄.6759	1̄.6744	1̄.6730	2	5	7	9	12
62	1̄.6716	1̄.6702	1̄.6687	1̄.6673	1̄.6659	1̄.6644	1̄.6629	1̄.6615	1̄.6600	1̄.6585	2	5	7	10	12
63	1̄.6570	1̄.6556	1̄.6541	1̄.6526	1̄.6510	1̄.6495	1̄.6480	1̄.6465	1̄.6449	1̄.6434	3	5	8	10	13
64	1̄.6418	1̄.6403	1̄.6387	1̄.6371	1̄.6356	1̄.6340	1̄.6324	1̄.6308	1̄.6292	1̄.6276	3	5	8	11	13
65	1̄.6259	1̄.6243	1̄.6227	1̄.6210	1̄.6194	1̄.6177	1̄.6161	1̄.6144	1̄.6127	1̄.6110	3	6	8	11	14
66	1̄.6093	1̄.6076	1̄.6059	1̄.6042	1̄.6024	1̄.6007	1̄.5990	1̄.5972	1̄.5954	1̄.5937	3	6	9	12	14
67	1̄.5919	1̄.5901	1̄.5883	1̄.5865	1̄.5847	1̄.5828	1̄.5810	1̄.5792	1̄.5773	1̄.5754	3	6	9	12	15
68	1̄.5736	1̄.5717	1̄.5698	1̄.5679	1̄.5660	1̄.5641	1̄.5621	1̄.5602	1̄.5583	1̄.5563	3	6	10	13	16
69	1̄.5543	1̄.5523	1̄.5504	1̄.5484	1̄.5463	1̄.5443	1̄.5423	1̄.5402	1̄.5382	1̄.5361	3	7	10	13	17
70	1̄.5341	1̄.5320	1̄.5299	1̄.5278	1̄.5256	1̄.5235	1̄.5213	1̄.5192	1̄.5170	1̄.5148	4	7	11	14	18
71	1̄.5126	1̄.5104	1̄.5082	1̄.5060	1̄.5037	1̄.5015	1̄.4992	1̄.4969	1̄.4946	1̄.4923	4	8	11	15	19
72	1̄.4900	1̄.4876	1̄.4853	1̄.4829	1̄.4805	1̄.4781	1̄.4757	1̄.4733	1̄.4709	1̄.4684	4	8	12	16	20
73	1̄.4659	1̄.4634	1̄.4609	1̄.4584	1̄.4559	1̄.4533	1̄.4508	1̄.4482	1̄.4456	1̄.4430	4	9	13	17	21
74	1̄.4403	1̄.4377	1̄.4350	1̄.4323	1̄.4296	1̄.4269	1̄.4242	1̄.4214	1̄.4186	1̄.4158	5	9	14	18	23
75	1̄.4130	1̄.4102	1̄.4073	1̄.4044	1̄.4015	1̄.3986	1̄.3957	1̄.3927	1̄.3897	1̄.3867	5	10	15	20	24
76	1̄.3837	1̄.3806	1̄.3775	1̄.3745	1̄.3713	1̄.3682	1̄.3650	1̄.3618	1̄.3586	1̄.3554	5	11	16	21	26
77	1̄.3521	1̄.3488	1̄.3455	1̄.3421	1̄.3387	1̄.3353	1̄.3319	1̄.3284	1̄.3250	1̄.3214	6	11	17	23	28
78	1̄.3179	1̄.3143	1̄.3107	1̄.3070	1̄.3034	1̄.2997	1̄.2959	1̄.2921	1̄.2883	1̄.2845	6	12	19	25	31
79	1̄.2806	1̄.2767	1̄.2727	1̄.2687	1̄.2647	1̄.2606	1̄.2565	1̄.2524	1̄.2482	1̄.2439	7	14	20	27	34
80	1̄.2397	1̄.2353	1̄.2310	1̄.2266	1̄.2221	1̄.2176	1̄.2131	1̄.2085	1̄.2038	1̄.1991	8	15	23	30	38
81	1̄.1943	1̄.1895	1̄.1847	1̄.1797	1̄.1747	1̄.1697	1̄.1646	1̄.1594	1̄.1542	1̄.1489	8	17	25	34	42
82	1̄.1436	1̄.1381	1̄.1326	1̄.1271	1̄.1214	1̄.1157	1̄.1099	1̄.1040	1̄.0981	1̄.0920	10	19	29	38	48
83	1̄.0859	1̄.0797	1̄.0734	1̄.0670	1̄.0605	1̄.0539	1̄.0472	1̄.0403	1̄.0334	1̄.0264	11	22	33	44	55
84	1̄.0192	1̄.0120	1̄.0046	2̄.9970	2̄.9894	2̄.9816	2̄.9736	2̄.9655	2̄.9573	2̄.9489	13	26	39	52	65
85	2̄.9403	2̄.9315	2̄.9226	2̄.9135	2̄.9042	2̄.8946	2̄.8849	2̄.8749	2̄.8647	2̄.8543	16	32	48	64	80
86	2̄.8436	2̄.8326	2̄.8213	2̄.8098	2̄.7979	2̄.7857	2̄.7731	2̄.7602	2̄.7468	2̄.7330					
87	2̄.7188	2̄.7041	2̄.6889	2̄.6731	2̄.6567	2̄.6397	2̄.6220	2̄.6035	2̄.5842	2̄.5640					
88	2̄.5428	2̄.5206	2̄.4971	2̄.4723	2̄.4459	2̄.4179	2̄.3880	2̄.3558	2̄.3210	2̄.2832			Differences		
89	2̄.2419	2̄.1961	2̄.1450	2̄.0870	2̄.0200	3̄.9408	3̄.8439	3̄.7190	3̄.5429	3̄.2419			untrustworthy		
90	$-\infty$												here		

Trigonometrical Ratios for 30°, 60° and 45°

Ratios for 30° and 60°

Fig. 25.26 shows an equilateral triangle ABC with each of the sides equal to 2 units. From C draw the perpendicular CD which bisects the base AB and also bisects ∠C.

therefore

$$CD = \sqrt{3}$$

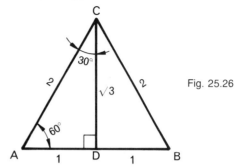

Fig. 25.26

In △ACD,

$$CD^2 = AC^2 - AD^2 = 2^2 - 1^2 = 3$$

Logarithms of Tangents

°	0' 0.0°	6' 0.1°	12' 0.2°	18' 0.3°	24' 0.4°	30' 0.5°	36' 0.6°	42' 0.7°	48' 0.8°	54' 0.9°	1'	2'	3'	4'	5'
0	−∞	3.2419	3.5429	3.7190	3.8439	3.9409	2.0200	2.0870	2.1450	2.1962	Differences			
1	2.2419	2.2833	2.3211	2.3559	2.3881	2.4181	2.4461	2.4725	2.4973	2.5208	untrustworthy			
2	2.5431	2.5643	2.5845	2.6038	2.6223	2.6401	2.6571	2.6736	2.6894	2.7046	here			
3	2.7194	2.7337	2.7475	2.7609	2.7739	2.7865	2.7988	2.8107	2.8223	2.8336					
4	2.8446	2.8554	2.8659	2.8762	2.8862	2.8960	2.9056	2.9150	2.9241	2.9331	16	32	48	64	81
5	2.9420	2.9506	2.9591	2.9674	2.9756	2.9836	2.9915	2.9992	1.0068	1.0143	13	26	40	53	66
6	1.0216	1.0289	1.0360	1.0430	1.0499	1.0567	1.0633	1.0699	1.0764	1.0828	11	22	34	45	56
7	1.0891	1.0954	1.1015	1.1076	1.1135	1.1194	1.1252	1.1310	1.1367	1.1423	10	20	29	39	49
8	1.1478	1.1533	1.1587	1.1640	1.1693	1.1745	1.1797	1.1848	1.1898	1.1948	9	17	26	35	43
9	1.1997	1.2046	1.2094	1.2142	1.2189	1.2236	1.2282	1.2328	1.2374	1.2419	8	16	23	31	39
10	1.2463	1.2507	1.2551	1.2594	1.2637	1.2680	1.2722	1.2764	1.2805	1.2846	7	14	21	28	35
11	1.2887	1.2927	1.2967	1.3006	1.3046	1.3085	1.3123	1.3162	1.3200	1.3237	6	13	19	26	32
12	1.3275	1.3312	1.3349	1.3385	1.3422	1.3458	1.3493	1.3529	1.3564	1.3599	6	12	18	24	30
13	1.3634	1.3668	1.3702	1.3736	1.3770	1.3804	1.3837	1.3870	1.3903	1.3935	6	11	17	22	28
14	1.3968	1.4000	1.4032	1.4064	1.4095	1.4127	1.4158	1.4189	1.4220	1.4250	5	10	16	21	26
15	1.4281	1.4311	1.4341	1.4371	1.4400	1.4430	1.4459	1.4488	1.4517	1.4546	5	10	15	20	24
16	1.4575	1.4603	1.4632	1.4660	1.4688	1.4716	1.4744	1.4771	1.4799	1.4826	5	9	14	19	23
17	1.4853	1.4880	1.4907	1.4934	1.4961	1.4987	1.5014	1.5040	1.5066	1.5092	4	9	13	18	22
18	1.5118	1.5143	1.5169	1.5195	1.5220	1.5245	1.5270	1.5295	1.5320	1.5345	4	8	13	17	21
19	1.5370	1.5394	1.5419	1.5443	1.5467	1.5491	1.5516	1.5539	1.5563	1.5587	4	8	12	16	20
20	1.5611	1.5634	1.5658	1.5681	1.5704	1.5727	1.5750	1.5773	1.5796	1.5819	4	8	12	15	19
21	1.5842	1.5864	1.5887	1.5909	1.5932	1.5954	1.5976	1.5998	1.6020	1.6042	4	7	11	15	18
22	1.6064	1.6086	1.6108	1.6129	1.6151	1.6172	1.6194	1.6215	1.6236	1.6257	4	7	11	14	18
23	1.6279	1.6300	1.6321	1.6341	1.6362	1.6383	1.6404	1.6424	1.6445	1.6465	3	7	10	14	17
24	1.6486	1.6506	1.6527	1.6547	1.6567	1.6587	1.6607	1.6627	1.6647	1.6667	3	7	10	13	17
25	1.6687	1.6706	1.6726	1.6746	1.6765	1.6785	1.6804	1.6824	1.6843	1.6863	3	6	10	13	16
26	1.6882	1.6901	1.6920	1.6939	1.6958	1.6977	1.6996	1.7015	1.7034	1.7053	3	6	10	13	16
27	1.7072	1.7090	1.7109	1.7128	1.7146	1.7165	1.7183	1.7202	1.7220	1.7238	3	6	9	12	15
28	1.7257	1.7275	1.7293	1.7311	1.7330	1.7348	1.7366	1.7384	1.7402	1.7420	3	6	9	12	15
29	1.7438	1.7455	1.7473	1.7491	1.7509	1.7526	1.7544	1.7562	1.7579	1.7597	3	6	9	12	15
30	1.7614	1.7632	1.7649	1.7667	1.7684	1.7701	1.7719	1.7736	1.7753	1.7771	3	6	9	12	15
31	1.7788	1.7805	1.7822	1.7839	1.7856	1.7873	1.7890	1.7907	1.7924	1.7941	3	6	9	11	14
32	1.7958	1.7975	1.7992	1.8008	1.8025	1.8042	1.8059	1.8075	1.8092	1.8109	3	6	8	11	14
33	1.8125	1.8142	1.8158	1.8175	1.8191	1.8208	1.8224	1.8241	1.8257	1.8274	3	6	8	11	14
34	1.8290	1.8306	1.8323	1.8339	1.8355	1.8371	1.8388	1.8404	1.8420	1.8436	3	5	8	11	14
35	1.8452	1.8468	1.8484	1.8501	1.8517	1.8533	1.8549	1.8565	1.8581	1.8597	3	5	8	11	13
36	1.8613	1.8629	1.8644	1.8660	1.8676	1.8692	1.8708	1.8724	1.8740	1.8755	3	5	8	11	13
37	1.8771	1.8787	1.8803	1.8818	1.8834	1.8850	1.8865	1.8881	1.8897	1.8912	3	5	8	10	13
38	1.8928	1.8944	1.8959	1.8975	1.8990	1.9006	1.9022	1.9037	1.9053	1.9068	3	5	8	10	13
39	1.9084	1.9099	1.9115	1.9130	1.9146	1.9161	1.9176	1.9192	1.9207	1.9223	3	5	8	10	13
40	1.9238	1.9254	1.9269	1.9284	1.9300	1.9315	1.9330	1.9346	1.9361	1.9376	3	5	8	10	13
41	1.9392	1.9407	1.9422	1.9438	1.9453	1.9468	1.9483	1.9499	1.9514	1.9529	3	5	8	10	13
42	1.9544	1.9560	1.9575	1.9590	1.9605	1.9621	1.9636	1.9651	1.9666	1.9681	3	5	8	10	13
43	1.9697	1.9712	1.9727	1.9742	1.9757	1.9772	1.9788	1.9803	1.9818	1.9833	3	5	8	10	13
44	1.9848	1.9864	1.9879	1.9894	1.9909	1.9924	1.9939	1.9955	1.9970	1.9985	3	5	8	10	13

197

Since all the angles of $\triangle ABC$ are 60° and $\angle ACD = 30°$,

isosceles triangle ABC with the equal sides each 1 unit in length. The equal angles are each 45°.

$$\sin 60° = \frac{\sqrt{3}}{2} \qquad \sin 30° = \frac{1}{2}$$

$$\tan 60° = \frac{\sqrt{3}}{1} = \sqrt{3} \qquad \tan 30° = \frac{1}{\sqrt{3}} = \frac{\sqrt{3}}{3}$$

$$\cos 60° = \frac{1}{2} \qquad \cos 30° = \frac{\sqrt{3}}{2}$$

Ratios for 45°

Figure 25.27 shows a right-angled

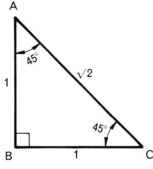

Fig. 25.27

Logarithms of Tangents

°	0' 0.0°	6' 0.1°	12' 0.2°	18' 0.3°	24' 0.4°	30' 0.5°	36' 0.6°	42' 0.7°	48' 0.8°	54' 0.9°	1'	2'	3'	4'	5'
45	0.0000	0.0015	0.0030	0.0045	0.0061	0.0076	0.0091	0.0106	0.0121	0.0136	3	5	8	10	13
46	0.0152	0.0167	0.0182	0.0197	0.0212	0.0228	0.0243	0.0258	0.0273	0.0288	3	5	8	10	13
47	0.0303	0.0319	0.0334	0.0349	0.0364	0.0379	0.0395	0.0410	0.0425	0.0440	3	5	8	10	13
48	0.0456	0.0471	0.0486	0.0501	0.0517	0.0532	0.0547	0.0562	0.0578	0.0593	3	5	8	10	13
49	0.0608	0.0624	0.0639	0.0654	0.0670	0.0685	0.0700	0.0716	0.0731	0.0746	3	5	8	10	13
50	0.0762	0.0777	0.0793	0.0808	0.0824	0.0839	0.0854	0.0870	0.0885	0.0901	3	5	8	10	13
51	0.0916	0.0932	0.0947	0.0963	0.0978	0.0994	0.1010	0.1025	0.1041	0.1056	3	5	8	10	13
52	0.1072	0.1088	0.1103	0.1119	0.1135	0.1150	0.1166	0.1182	0.1197	0.1213	3	5	8	10	13
53	0.1229	0.1245	0.1260	0.1276	0.1292	0.1308	0.1324	0.1340	0.1356	0.1371	3	5	8	11	13
54	0.1387	0.1403	0.1419	0.1435	0.1451	0.1467	0.1483	0.1499	0.1516	0.1532	3	5	8	11	13
55	0.1548	0.1564	0.1580	0.1596	0.1612	0.1629	0.1645	0.1661	0.1677	0.1694	3	5	8	11	14
56	0.1710	0.1726	0.1743	0.1759	0.1776	0.1792	0.1809	0.1825	0.1842	0.1858	3	6	8	11	14
57	0.1875	0.1891	0.1908	0.1925	0.1941	0.1958	0.1975	0.1992	0.2008	0.2025	3	6	8	11	14
58	0.2042	0.2059	0.2076	0.2093	0.2110	0.2127	0.2144	0.2161	0.2178	0.2195	3	6	9	11	14
59	0.2212	0.2229	0.2247	0.2264	0.2281	0.2299	0.2316	0.2333	0.2351	0.2368	3	6	9	12	15
60	0.2386	0.2403	0.2421	0.2438	0.2456	0.2474	0.2491	0.2509	0.2527	0.2545	3	6	9	12	15
61	0.2562	0.2580	0.2598	0.2616	0.2634	0.2652	0.2670	0.2689	0.2707	0.2725	3	6	9	12	15
62	0.2743	0.2762	0.2780	0.2798	0.2817	0.2835	0.2854	0.2872	0.2891	0.2910	3	6	9	12	15
63	0.2928	0.2947	0.2966	0.2985	0.3004	0.3023	0.3042	0.3061	0.3080	0.3099	3	6	9	13	16
64	0.3118	0.3137	0.3157	0.3176	0.3196	0.3215	0.3235	0.3254	0.3274	0.3294	3	6	10	13	16
65	0.3313	0.3333	0.3353	0.3373	0.3393	0.3413	0.3433	0.3453	0.3473	0.3494	3	7	10	13	17
66	0.3514	0.3535	0.3555	0.3576	0.3596	0.3617	0.3638	0.3659	0.3679	0.3700	3	7	10	14	17
67	0.3721	0.3743	0.3764	0.3785	0.3806	0.3828	0.3849	0.3871	0.3892	0.3914	4	7	11	14	18
68	0.3936	0.3958	0.3980	0.4002	0.4024	0.4046	0.4068	0.4091	0.4113	0.4136	4	7	11	15	18
69	0.4158	0.4181	0.4204	0.4227	0.4250	0.4273	0.4296	0.4319	0.4342	0.4366	4	8	12	15	19
70	0.4389	0.4413	0.4437	0.4461	0.4484	0.4509	0.4533	0.4557	0.4581	0.4606	4	8	12	16	20
71	0.4630	0.4655	0.4680	0.4705	0.4730	0.4755	0.4780	0.4805	0.4831	0.4857	4	8	13	17	21
72	0.4882	0.4908	0.4934	0.4960	0.4986	0.5013	0.5039	0.5066	0.5093	0.5120	4	9	13	18	22
73	0.5147	0.5174	0.5201	0.5229	0.5256	0.5284	0.5312	0.5340	0.5368	0.5397	5	9	14	19	23
74	0.5425	0.5454	0.5483	0.5512	0.5541	0.5570	0.5600	0.5629	0.5659	0.5689	5	10	15	20	24
75	0.5719	0.5750	0.5780	0.5811	0.5842	0.5873	0.5905	0.5936	0.5968	0.6000	5	10	16	21	26
76	0.6032	0.6065	0.6097	0.6130	0.6163	0.6196	0.6230	0.6264	0.6298	0.6332	6	11	17	22	28
77	0.6366	0.6401	0.6436	0.6471	0.6507	0.6542	0.6578	0.6615	0.6651	0.6688	6	12	18	24	30
78	0.6725	0.6763	0.6800	0.6838	0.6877	0.6915	0.6954	0.6994	0.7033	0.7073	6	13	19	26	32
79	0.7113	0.7154	0.7195	0.7236	0.7278	0.7320	0.7363	0.7406	0.7449	0.7493	7	14	21	28	35
80	0.7537	0.7581	0.7626	0.7672	0.7718	0.7764	0.7811	0.7858	0.7906	0.7954	8	16	23	31	39
81	0.8003	0.8052	0.8102	0.8152	0.8203	0.8255	0.8307	0.8360	0.8413	0.8467	9	17	26	35	43
82	0.8522	0.8577	0.8633	0.8690	0.8748	0.8806	0.8865	0.8924	0.8985	0.9046	10	20	29	39	49
83	0.9109	0.9172	0.9236	0.9301	0.9367	0.9433	0.9501	0.9570	0.9640	0.9711	11	22	34	45	56
84	0.9784	0.9857	0.9932	1.0008	1.0085	1.0164	1.0244	1.0326	1.0409	1.0494	13	26	40	53	66
85	1.0580	1.0669	1.0759	1.0850	1.0944	1.1040	1.1138	1.1238	1.1341	1.1446	16	32	48	64	81
86	1.1554	1.1664	1.1777	1.1893	1.2012	1.2135	1.2261	1.2391	1.2525	1.2663					
87	1.2806	1.2954	1.3106	1.3264	1.3429	1.3599	1.3777	1.3962	1.4155	1.4357	Differences				
88	1.4569	1.4792	1.5027	1.5275	1.5539	1.5819	1.6119	1.6441	1.6789	1.7167	untrustworthy				
89	1.7581	1.8038	1.8550	1.9130	1.9800	2.0591	2.1561	2.2810	2.4571	2.7581	here				

Now, $AC^2 = AB^2 + BC^2 = 1^2 + 1^2 = 2$

therefore

$$AC = \sqrt{2}$$

$$\sin 45° = \frac{1}{\sqrt{2}} = \frac{\sqrt{2}}{2} \qquad \cos 45° = \frac{1}{\sqrt{2}} = \frac{\sqrt{2}}{2}$$

$$\tan 45° = \frac{1}{1} = 1$$

Given One Ratio to Find the Others

The method is shown in the following example.

Example 6

If $\cos \angle A = 0.7$, find, without using tables, the values of $\sin \angle A$ and $\tan \angle A$.

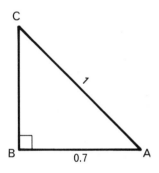

Fig. 25.28

In Fig. 25.28 if we make $AB = 0.7$ units and $AC = 1$ unit, then

$$\cos \angle A = \frac{0.7}{1} = 0.7$$

By Pythagoras' theorem,

$$BC^2 = AC^2 - AB^2 = 1^2 - 0.7^2 = 0.51$$

$$BC = \sqrt{0.51} = 0.7141$$

$$\sin \angle A = \frac{BC}{AC} = \frac{0.7141}{1} = 0.7141$$

$$\tan \angle A = \frac{BC}{AB} = \frac{0.7141}{0.7} = 1.020$$

Complementary Angles

Complementary angles are angles whose sum is 90°.

Consider the triangle ABC shown in Fig. 25.29.

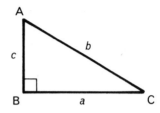

Fig. 25.29

$$\sin A = \frac{a}{b} \qquad \cos C = \frac{a}{b}$$

Hence,

$$\sin A = \cos C = \cos (90° - A)$$

Similarly,

$$\cos A = \sin (90° - A)$$

Therefore, *the sine of an angle is equal to the cosine of its complementary angle and vice versa.*

$$\sin 26° = \cos 64° = 0.4384$$

$$\cos 70° = \sin 20° = 0.3420$$

Exercise 146 — *All type B*

1) If $\sin A = 0.3171$ find the values of $\cos A$ and $\tan A$ without using tables.

2) If $\tan A = \frac{3}{4}$, find the values of $\sin A$ and $\cos A$ without using tables.

3) If $\cos A = \frac{12}{13}$, find without using tables the values of $\sin A$ and $\tan A$.

4) Show that $\cos 60° + \cos 30° = \frac{1 + \sqrt{3}}{2}$

5) Show that $\sin 60° + \cos 30° = \sqrt{3}$

6) Show that
$$\cos 45° + \sin 60° + \sin 30° = \frac{\sqrt{2}+\sqrt{3}+1}{2}$$

7) Given that $\sin 48° = 0.7431$ find the values of $\cos 42°$, without using tables.

8) If $\cos 63° = 0.4540$, what is the value of $\sin 27°$?

Exercise 147 — *Questions 1–6 type A, remainder B*

All the questions in this exercise have been taken from past C.S.E. examination papers.

1) What is the length of QR (Fig. 25.30) in metres.

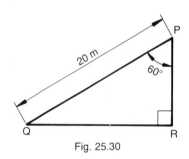
Fig. 25.30

$\sin 60° = 0.866$ $\cos 60° = 0.500$ $\tan 60° = 1.732$

   a 3.464   **b** 8.66   **c** 10
   d 17.32   **e** 34.64   (*S.E.*)

2) In Fig. 25.31, tan C as a vulgar fraction is:

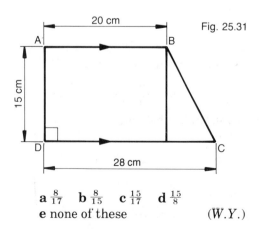
Fig. 25.31

  a $\frac{8}{17}$ **b** $\frac{8}{15}$ **c** $\frac{15}{17}$ **d** $\frac{15}{8}$
  e none of these   (*W.Y.*)

3) Calculate the length of the side marked x in Fig. 25.32.   (*Y.R.*)

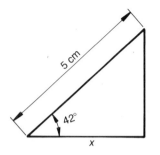
Fig. 25.32

4) In Fig. 25.33, calculate the angle ABC, giving your answer to the nearest minute.   (*Y.R.*)

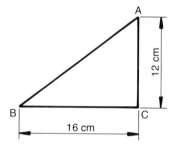
Fig. 25.33

5) From the information in Fig. 25.34, write down, as a single fraction:

  (a) $\sin A$ (c) $\tan C$
  (b) $\cos A$ (*M*)

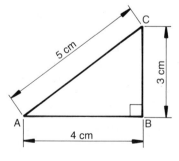
Fig. 25.34

6) Use tables to find, as accurately as you can, the values of:

  (a) 6.75^2 (d) $\cos 53° 10'$
  (b) $\sqrt{6.75}$ (e) $\log \sin 5° 48'$
  (c) $\tan 71° 35'$ (*M*)

7) In Fig. 25.35, ABMQ is a square and AKC is an equilateral triangle.

(a) Calculate the length of BC.

(b) Calculate the size of the angle BAC.

(c) Calculate the size of the reflex angle QAK.

(d) Find the area of the quadrilateral BQAC.

(e) Find the perpendicular distance of C from the line MQ. *(S)*

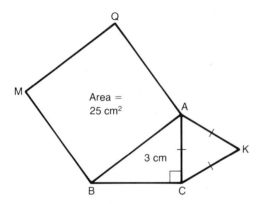

Fig. 25.35

8) Given that $\sin A = 0.28$ and A is an acute angle, find, without using trigonometrical tables the value of $\cos A$.

Given that $\tan B = \frac{4}{3}$ and B is an acute angle, find, without using trigonometrical tables, the exact value of $\tan (90° - B)$. *(M)*

9) If $\tan x = \frac{3}{4}$, what is the value of $\sin z$ (Fig. 25.36)?

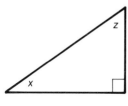

Fig. 25.36

a $\frac{3}{5}$ **b** $\frac{3}{4}$ **c** $\frac{4}{5}$ **d** $\frac{4}{3}$ **e** $\frac{5}{3}$ *(S.E.)*

10) In Fig. 25.37, calculate:

(a) The length of AM in centimetres.

(b) The cosine of angle MAC, leaving your answer as a vulgar fraction in its simplest form.

(c) The size of angle ABC, giving your answer to the nearest degree. *(Y.R.)*

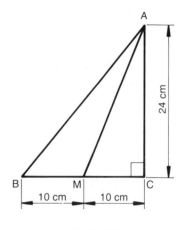

Fig. 25.37

11) In Fig. 25.38, AB = 25 m, $\angle$ ABC = 90°, $\angle$ BDC = 90° and $\tan C = 1.25$.

(a) Calculate the length of BC.

(b) Find the size of C in degrees and minutes.

(c) Calculate the length DC correct to the nearest metre. *(W)*

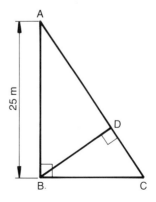

Fig. 25.38

201

12) In Fig. 25.39, calculate:

(a) the length AE

(b) the length ED

(c) the tangent of angle DAE

(d) the size of angle DAE

(e) the length of the diagonal BD, correct to one place of decimals.

(*N.W.*)

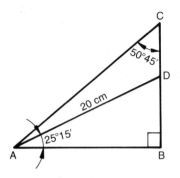

Fig. 25.40

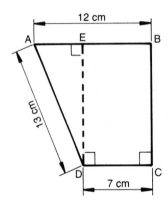

Fig. 25.39

13) In Fig. 25.40, calculate:

(a) the length AB

(b) the length CB

(c) the area of the triangle ADC. (*W*)

14) On the axes O*x* and O*y* (Fig. 25.41), P is the point (0, 4) and Q is the point (3, 0).

(a) What is the length PQ?

(b) Calculate the size of angle PQO.

(c) If angle PQO = angle PRQ and angle RPQ = 90°, use similar triangles to find the length QR. (*S*)

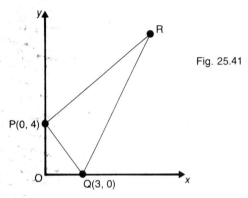

Fig. 25.41

Chapter 26 Road Maps

Road Maps

These maps which are extensively used by motorists and others allow the route from one town to another to be planned. On some road maps the distances between one point and another is given on the map. On other maps distances are not given, but these may be obtained by scaling the map. In either case it is possible to find the length of a journey by adding distances.

Example 1

Fig. 26.1 shows a simplified road map. The figures alongside the roads are given in kilometres and represent the distances between the towns.

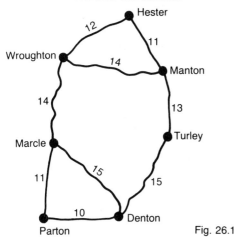

Fig. 26.1

(a) How far is it between Denton and Hester

(i) via Turley and Manton,

(ii) via Marcle and Wroughton,

(iii) via Parton, Marcle and Wroughton.

(b) Which is the shorter journey and by how many kilometres?

(a) (i) Denton to Turley   15 km
       Turley to Manton   13 km
       Manton to Hester   11 km
       Total distance   39 km

(ii) Denton to Marcle   15 km
       Marcle to
           Wroughton   14 km
       Wroughton to
           Hester   12 km
       Total distance   41 km

(iii) Denton to Parton   10 km
       Parton to Marcle   11 km
       Marcle to
           Wroughton   14 km
       Wroughton to
           Hester   12 km
       Total distance   47 km

(b) The shortest journey is via Turley and Manton. It is 2 km shorter than the journey via Marcle and Wroughton and 8 km shorter than the journey via Parton, Marcle and Wroughton.

Exercise 148 — *All type A*

The maps below give the distances in kilometres between the various towns and places.

1) In Fig. 26.2 find:

(a) the distance between Launceston and Torrington through Holsworthy;

(b) the distance between Launceston and Torrington via Okehampton and Hatherleigh;

(c)   the distance between Launceston
and Holsworthy via Okehampton
and Hatherleigh.

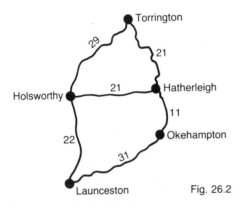

Fig. 26.2

2) Fig. 26.3 shows a simplified road
map of part of Yorkshire. The figures
alongside the roads are the distances
in kilometres between the towns.

(a)   Find the distance between Pickering and Gaisborough:
(i)   via Whitby
(ii)   via Castleton.

(b)   The distance between Malton and
Gaisborough:
(i)   via Horingham, Kirby-
moorside and Castleton
(ii)   via Pickering and Castleton
(iii)   via Pickering and Whitby.

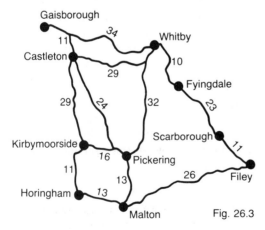

Fig. 26.3

3) Fig. 26.4 is a road map of East
Lancashire. All the distances between
the towns are stated in kilometres.
Find:

(a)   the distances between Farnworth
and Blackburn:
(i)   via Bolton
(ii)   via Radcliff, Whitfield and
Rawtenstall
(iii)   via Chorley.

(b)   Which is the shorter journey?
How much shorter is it than the
other two journeys?

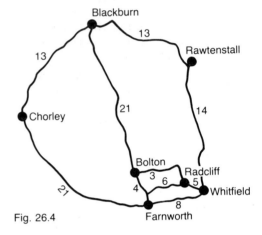

Fig. 26.4

4) According to the road map of Fig.
26.5, there are four ways of going from
Telford to Chester. They are:

(a)   via Shrewsbury, Ellsmere and
Wrexham;

(b)   via Whitchurch, Ellsmere and
Wrexham;

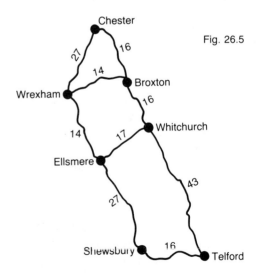

Fig. 26.5

204

(c) via Whitchurch, Broxton and Wrexham;

(d) via Whitchurch and Broxton.

Find the length of each of these journeys in kilometres. Which is the shorter journey? How much shorter is it than each of the others?

5) Fig. 26.6 shows a simplified road map of part of the East Midlands. The figures alongside the roads are the distance in kilometres between the towns. How far is it from Chesterfield to Leicester through:

(a) Derby   (b) Nottingham.

Which is the shorter journey and by how many kilometres?   (*E.M.*)

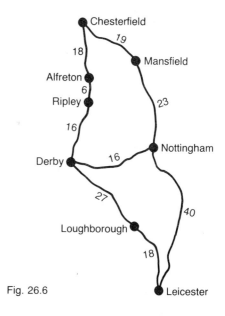

Fig. 26.6

Chapter 27 Sets

Collections

A set is a word for a collection of objects, numbers, ideas, etc. Some sets have special names such as a *pack* of cards, a *fleet* of ships, a *pride* of lions and so on. However many sets do not have special names because the objects in the set are seldom considered collectively, for example, the objects in a girl's handbag.

Elements

The different objects, numbers, etc. which form a set are called the *members* or *elements* of the set, just as the people who belong to a club are called members of the club.

The elements of a set may be specified in two ways:

(i) by listing the elements,

(ii) by description.

Some examples are:

Listing	Description
{2, 4, 6, 8, 10}	the set of even numbers between 1 and 11
{a, e, i, o, u}	the set of vowels in the alphabet

The elements making up the set are enclosed in curly brackets or braces { }. The braces stand for the words 'the set of' or 'the set'. Braces can also be used with descriptions. Thus the second set above could be written

{vowels in the alphabet}

Naming Sets

When a set is to be used more than once a capital letter is used to denote it. Thus we might write

$$A = \{1, 3, 5, 7, 9, 11\}$$

Now consider

$$B = \{\text{all the even numbers}\}$$

It is not possible to list all of the elements of B and so we write

$$B = \{2, 4, 6, 8, \ldots\}$$

where the dots mean 'and so on'.

Exercise 149 — *All type A*

Write down the members of the following sets:

1) $A = \{\text{odd numbers from 5 to 15 inclusive}\}$

2) $X = \{\text{days of the week beginning with T}\}$

3) $B = \{\text{even numbers less than 12}\}$

4) $P = \{\text{prime numbers less than 25}\}$

5) $Q = \{\text{multiples of 3 up to 33}\}$

Name each of the following sets:

6) $A = \{5, 10, 15, 20, 25\}$

7) $B = \{\text{brothers, sisters, mother, father}\}$

8) $C = \{3, 5, 7, 11, 13, 17\}$

Types of Sets

A set in which all of the elements can be listed is called a *finite* set. Thus the set of coins which a collector possesses is a finite set and so is the set of even numbers between 0 and 50.

In some cases it is impossible to list all the members of a set. Such sets are called *infinite* sets. Thus the set of natural numbers is an infinite set. If $A = \{1, 2, 3, 4, \ldots\}$ then A is an infinite set because no matter which is the last number we write, we can always go one larger.

The number of elements in a set A is denoted by n(A). Thus if $A = \{2, 4, 6, 8, 10\}$, n(A) = 5 because there are 5 elements in the set A.

A set containing no elements is called a *null* set. It is represented by { } or by ø (the Danish letter oe). The set of whole numbers between 0.5 and 0.9 is null and so is the set of prime numbers between 8 and 11.

Exercise 150 — *All type A*

Say which of the following sets are finite, infinite or null:

1) $A = \{1, 3, 5, 7, 9, \ldots\}$

2) $B = \{2, 4, 6, 8, 10, 12\}$

3) The set of points on the circumference of a circle.

4) The set of letters in the alphabet.

5) The set of even numbers which can be divided exactly by 3.

6) The set of odd numbers which can be exactly divided by 2.

7) The set of planets in the solar system.

8) The number of people that have swam the Atlantic Ocean.

9) If $A = \{d, b, c, d\}$, what is n (A)?

10) $B = \{2, 4, 6, 8, 10, 12, 14, 16, 18, 20\}$, find n ($B$)

Membership of a Set

The symbol $\in$ means 'is a member of'. Thus if

$$A = \{3, 5, 7, 9\}$$

the fact that 5 is a member of A is written $5 \in A$.

The symbol $\notin$ means is not a member of. Because 4 is not a member of A we write $4 \notin A$.

Example 1

In the following set, one of the elements is incorrect. Rewrite the set correctly and, using set notation, state which element is not a member of the corrected set.

$$P = \{1, 6, 11, 17, 21, 26\}$$

The sequence of numbers in the set should all differ by 5. Hence the corrected set is:

$$P = \{1, 6, 11, 16, 21, 26\}$$

In the corrected set 17, which appeared in the original set, is not a member and we write

$$17 \notin P$$

Exercise 151 — *All type A*

In the following sets one of the elements is incorrect. Rewrite the set correctly and state, using set notation, the element which is not a member of the corrected set.

1) $P = \{2, 4, 7, 8, 10\}$

2) $Q = \{1, 4, 9, 18, 25, 36\}$

3) $R = \{17, 14, 11, 9, 5, 2\}$

4) $S = \{a, b, c, \emptyset, e, f\}$

5) $T = \{5, 9, 11, 13, 17, 19, 23, 29\}$

State which of the following statements are true:

6) $7 \in \{\text{prime factors of } 63\}$

7) Cod $\in \{\text{fish}\}$

8) $24 \notin \{\text{multiples of } 5\}$

9) hexagon $\in \{\text{quadrilaterals}\}$

10) octagon $\notin \{\text{polygons}\}$

Subsets

Four groups of people belonging to a youth club are taking part in different activities. The first group is listening to records, the second is playing table tennis, the third is preparing for a concert and the fourth group is listening to a talk.

All the people in the four groups are contained in the set of members of the youth club but each of the groups form a set in their own right. Each of the groups forms a subset of the set of members of the youth club. A subset can be the set of all the members of the club because the leader of the club might want to talk to all the members of the club as well as to each individual group. The leader may choose not to talk to any of the groups and hence the null set is also a subset of the set of members of the club.

$\{1, 3, 5\}$ is a subset of $\{1, 3, 5, 7, 9\}$ because each of the three elements of $\{1, 3, 5\}$ is also an element of $\{1, 3, 5, 7, 9\}$. To indicate that one set is a subset of another we use the symbol $\subset$, which means 'is contained in'. Thus $\{3\} \subset \{1, 3, 5\}$ and $\{1, 3, 5\} \subset \{1, 3, 5, 7, 9\}$. These two statements could be written

$$\{3\} \subset \{1, 3, 5\} \subset \{1, 3, 5, 7, 9\}$$

Out of the set $\{7, 8, 9\}$ we can select either 0 elements, 1 element, 2 elements or 3 elements as follows:

(i) $\{\ \}$ (ii) $\{7\}$ (iii) $\{8\}$ (iv) $\{9\}$ (v) $\{7, 8\}$ (vi) $\{7, 9\}$ (vii) $\{8, 9\}$ (viii) $\{7, 8, 9\}$.

The two extremes, the null set and the original set are regarded as subsets of the original set as pointed out above. Thus every set is a subset of itself and the null set is a subset of every set. The sets numbered (ii) to (vii) inclusive are called *proper* subsets.

The symbol $\subset$ can be used the other way round. Thus if $C = \{2, 4, 6, 8\}$ and $D = \{4, 6\}$ we can write $C \supset D$, i.e. C contains D.

Exercise 152 — *All type B*

1) $A = \{3, 5, 6, 8, 9, 11, 12, 13, 15\}$. List the subsets whose members are:

(a) all the odd numbers of A;
(b) all the even numbers of A;
(c) all the prime numbers in A;
(d) all the numbers in A divisible by 2.

2) $B = \{5, 10, 15, 20\}$. Form *all* the subsets of B. How many are there?

3) If $A = \{3, 6, 9, 12, 15\}$, $B = \{3, 6, 7, 12\}$ and $C = \{3, 12\}$, state which of the following statements are correct:

    a $A \subset B$ **b** $B \subset A$ **c** $C \subset A$
    d $C \subset B$ **e** $C \subset B \subset A$.

4) If $A = \{1, 3\}$, $B = \{1, 3, 5, 7\}$ and $C = \{1, 3, 5\}$ is the statement $A \subset B \subset C$ correct? If not write down the correct statement.

5) Write down all the proper subsets of $\{a, b, c, d\}$.

6) Below are given eight sets. Connect appropriate sets by the symbol $\subset$.

(a) {natural numbers between 1 and 24}
(b) {all cutlery}
(c) {all footwear}
(d) {letters of the alphabet}
(e) {boot, shoe}
(f) {a, e, i, o, u}
(g) {2, 4, 6, 8}
(h) {knife, fork, spoon}.

7) A = {all sports}. List:

(a) a subset of A containing three sports played with a ball

(b) a subset of A containing three sports generally played by girls

(c) four sports not played with a ball.

8) If A = {2, 4, 6, 8, 10} say which of the following statements are correct:

a $2 \in A$	**b** $8 \notin A$
c $7 \in A$	**d** $\{6, 8\} \subset A$
e $\{3, 4\} \subset A$	**f** $\{2, 6, 8\} \supset A$
g $A \supset \{4, 6\}$	**h** $A \subset \{3, 8\}$

Equality

The order in which the elements of a set are written does not matter. Thus {1, 3, 5, 7} is the same as {5, 3, 7, 1} and {3, 1, 7, 5}.

Two sets are said to be equal if their elements are identical. Thus if A = {2, 4, 6, 8} and B = {8, 6, 2, 4} then, because the elements in A are the same as those in B, A = B.

If two sets are not equal we use the symbol $\neq$ (meaning not equal to). Thus if A = {3, 5, 7, 9} and B = {2, 4, 6, 8} then $A \neq B$.

The Universal Set

Frequently we use sets which are subsets of much larger sets. Thus suppose that in a class in a school we are asked to form sets (i) of those who like playing hockey, (ii) of those who wear spectacles and (iii) of those who cycle to school. Each of these sets are subsets of {class}. The class in this case is the universal set.

The universal set is represented by the symbol $\mathscr{E}$, an abbreviation for ensemble, which is the French word for set.

If $\mathscr{E}$ = {natural numbers} then if A = {even numbers} and B = {odd numbers} then $A \subset \mathscr{E}$ and $B \subset \mathscr{E}$.

Exercise 153 — *All type B*

1) $\mathscr{E}$ = {letters of the alphabet}. Give the subsets:

(a) of vowels
(b) of letters after t
(c) of consonants.

2) $\mathscr{E}$ = {all polygons}. Write down the subsets of polygons with less than nine sides.

3) $\mathscr{E}$ = {natural numbers}. Give the subsets of:

(a) prime numbers less than 20
(b) numbers less than 20 which are multiples of 3
(c) all the prime factors of 210.

4) $\mathscr{E}$ = {months of the year}. Write down the subsets of:

(a) the winter months
(b) the autumn months.

5) $\mathscr{E}$ = {squares of natural numbers}. Write down the subset of the squares of the first five natural numbers (i.e. 1, 2, 3, 4, 5).

Such That

Rather than write B = {x such that x lies between 0 and 8} we write $B = \{x : 0 \leqslant x \leqslant 8\}$. Thus $C = \{x : x^2 = 9\}$ is read as 'the set of numbers such that x^2 is equal to 9.

Example 2

Show that
$$\{x : 2 \leqslant x \leqslant 4\} \subset \{x : 1 \leqslant x \leqslant 7\},$$
$$\{x : 1 \leqslant x \leqslant 7\} = \{1, 2, 3, 4, 5, 6, 7\}$$
and
$$\{x : 2 \leqslant x \leqslant 4\} = \{2, 3, 4\}.$$

Hence
$$\{x : 2 \leqslant x \leqslant 4\} \subset \{x : 1 \leqslant x \leqslant 7\}.$$

Venn Diagrams

Sets and set problems may be represented by diagrams called Venn diagrams, after mathematician Joseph Venn who lived in the nineteenth century and who first represented sets diagrammatically.

A universal set is represented by a rectangle (Fig. 27.1). If the universal set is $\mathscr{E} = \{\text{class}\}$ then all the children in the class would be represented by all the points inside the rectangle or on its perimeter. All the children in the class who cycled to school would be a subset to the universal set. If we use the letter C to represent this subset, then a circle drawn within the rectangle shows that C is a subset of $\mathscr{E}$ or $C \subset \mathscr{E}$ (Fig. 27.2).

Fig. 27.1

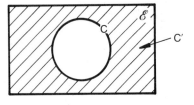

Fig. 27.2

Complement

The shaded part of the rectangle in Fig. 27.2, is called the *complement* of the set C and is written C'. It represents all the children in the class who do not cycle to school.

Example 3

The universal set is $\mathscr{E} = \{1, 2, 3, 4, 5, 6\}$. If $A = \{1, 3, 5\}$ find the complement of A.

The Venn diagram is shown in Fig. 27.3. The subset A is represented by the circle which contains the numbers 1, 3 and 5 which are the elements of A. The numbers outside the circle, 2, 4 and 6 form the complement of A and hence $A' = \{2, 4, 6\}$.

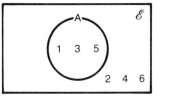

Fig. 27.3

Subsets of a given set are represented by a circle within a circle as shown in Fig. 27.4. If $\mathscr{E} = \{1, 2, 3, 4, 5, 6, 7, 8\}$ and $A = \{2, 3, 4, 5, 6\}$ then $A \subset \mathscr{E}$. If $B = \{3, 4\}$ then $B \subset A \subset \mathscr{E}$. This is represented as shown in Fig. 27.5.

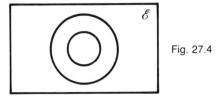

Fig. 27.4

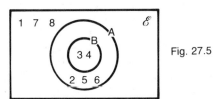

Fig. 27.5

Intersection

The intersection of two sets A and B is the set of elements which are members of both A and B. The shaded portion of Fig. 27.6 represents the intersection of A and B.

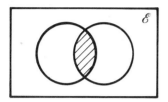

Fig. 27.6

The intersection of A and B is written, in set notation, as $A \cap B$, which is read as 'A cap B' or 'A intersection B'.

Example 4

If $A = \{1, 3, 5, 7, 9\}$ and $B = \{7, 9, 11\}$ find $A \cap B$.

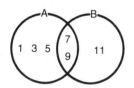

Fig. 27.7

As shown in Fig. 27.7, $A \cap B = \{7, 9\}$. Note that the intersection of A and B is the set which contains all the elements which are common to both A and B. If there are no common elements in two sets the Venn diagram would look like Fig. 27.8. Thus if $A = \{1, 3, 5, 7\}$ and $B = \{2, 4, 6, 8\}$ then $A \cap B = \emptyset$, $\emptyset$ being the null set. When there is no intersection between two or more sets the sets are said to be *disjoint*. Thus in Fig. 27.8, the sets A and B are disjoint.

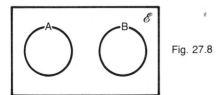

Fig. 27.8

Union

The union of sets A and B are all of the elements contained in A and B. Thus if $A = \{3, 4, 5\}$ and $B = \{6, 7, 8\}$ then the union of A and B is $\{3, 4, 5, 6, 7, 8\}$.

If this set is called C then we write $C = A \cup B$, which is read as 'A cup B', the symbol $\cup$ standing for 'union'. The Venn diagram (Fig. 27.9) shows $C = A \cup B$, the shaded portion representing C.

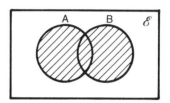

Fig. 27.9

Example 5

If $S = \{1, 3, 5, 7\}$ and $R = \{7, 9, 11\}$, write down $S \cup R$.

As shown in Fig. 27.10,

$$S \cup R = \{1, 3, 5, 7, 9, 11\}$$

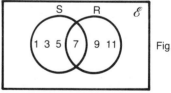

Fig. 27.10

Note that the element 7, which is contained in both S and R, appears only once in the union of S and R.

Exercise 154 — *All type B*

Fig. 27.11 shows the universal set $\mathcal{E}$ and the two subsets A and B. For each of the following write down the answer in the way suggested.

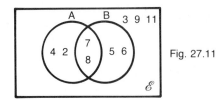

Fig. 27.11

The Venn diagram (Fig. 27.12), shows two sets A and B. Copy and complete:

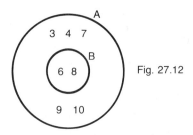

Fig. 27.12

1) Write down all the elements of the universal set. $\mathscr{E} = \{\qquad\}$.

2) Write down all the elements of set A. $A = \{\qquad\}$.

3) Write down all the elements of set B. $B = \{\qquad\}$.

4) Write down the complement of A. $A' = \{\qquad\}$.

5) Write down the complement of B. $B' = \{\qquad\}$.

6) Write down $A \cap B$. $A \cap B = \{\qquad\}$.

7) Write down $A \cup B$. $A \cup B = \{\qquad\}$.

8) Write down the complement of $(A \cup B)$. $(A \cup B)' = \{\qquad\}$.

Link each of the following with one of the symbols $\in, \notin, =, \neq, \subset, \supset, \cup$ or $\cap$.

9) 7 $\{2, 4, 6, 8\}$.

10) $\{1, 3, 5, 7\}$ $\{2, 3, 5, 6\}$ $\{3, 5\}$.

11) 8 $\{4, 8, 16, 32\}$.

12) $\{3, 4, 6\}$ $\{6, 3, 4\}$.

13) $\{$rectangles, triangles$\}$ $\{$all plane figures$\}$.

14) $\{1, 3, 5, 7, 9\}$ $\{5, 7\}$.

15) $\{2, 4, 6, 8\}$ $\{3, 5, 7, 9, 11\}$.

16) $\{2, 4\}$ $\{2, 4, 8, 9\}$ $\{1, 2, 4, 8, 9\}$.

17) $\{$John$\}$ $\{$all girl's names$\}$.

18) $\{7, 14, 21, 28\}$ $\{$multiples of 7$\}$.

19) $\{x : 1 \leqslant x \leqslant 7\}$ $\{1, 2, 3, 4, 5, 7\}$.

20) $\{x : 3 \leqslant x \leqslant 5\}$ $\{x : 1 \leqslant x \leqslant 10\}$.

21) $A = \{\qquad\}$.

22) $B = \{\qquad\}$.

23) $A \cup B = \{\qquad\}$.

24) $A \cap B = \{\qquad\}$.

25) A B.

The Venn diagram (Fig. 27.13) shows two sets A and B which are subsets of the universal set $\mathscr{E}$. Copy and complete the following:

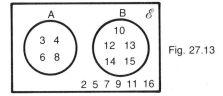

Fig. 27.13

26) $\mathscr{E} = \{\qquad\}$.

27) $A = \{\qquad\}$.

28) $B = \{\qquad\}$.

29) $A \cap B = \{\qquad\}$.

30) $A \cup B = \{\qquad\}$.

Fig. 27.14 shows a Venn diagram representing the universal set and two subsets. Draw a similar diagram, inserting the elements, to represent each of the following:

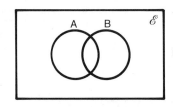

Fig. 27.14

31) $\mathcal{E} = \{1, 2, 3, 4, 5, 6, 7, 8, 9, 10\}$, $A = \{1, 2, 3, 4\}$, $B = \{4, 5, 6, 7, 8\}$.

32) $\mathcal{E} = \{a, b, c, d, e, f, g, h\}$, $A = \{a, b, c, d\}$, $A \cap B = \{c, d\}$, $A \cup B = \{a, b, c, d, g, h\}$.

Fig. 27.15 shows three Venn diagrams. Using diagrams similar to these, represent the following:

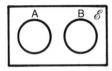
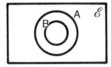

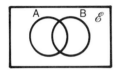

Fig. 27.15

33) $\mathcal{E} = \{x : 5 \leqslant x \leqslant 12\}$, $X = \{6, 7, 9, 10, 11\}$, $Y = \{6, 7\}$.

34) $\mathcal{E} = \{x : 3 \leqslant x \leqslant 10\}$, $A = \{4, 5\}$, $B = \{6, 7\}$.

35) $\mathcal{E} = \{$natural numbers between 1 and 9 inclusive$\}$, $P = \{3, 4, 5, 6\}$, $Q = \{5, 6, 7, 8, 9\}$.

36) Use set notation to describe the shaded portions of the Venn diagrams shown in Fig. 27.16.

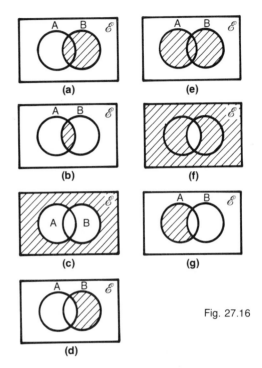

Fig. 27.16

37) Draw a Venn diagram to represent the following information.

$\mathcal{E} = \{A, B, C, D, E, F, G, H\}$,
$X = \{A, B, C, D\}$,
$Y = \{C, D, E, F, G\}$.

213

Chapter 28   Number Scales

The Binary System

In the ordinary decimal system (sometimes known as the denary system) the digits 0 to 9 are used.

Consider the number 5623. It means

$$5\times1000+6\times100+2\times10+3\times1$$

Remembering that $10^0 = 1$, we may write

$$5623 = 5\times10^3+6\times10^2$$
$$+2\times10^1+3\times10^0$$

Thus

$$80\,321 = 8\times10^4+0\times10^3$$
$$+3\times10^2+2\times10^1+1\times10^0$$

Now consider the decimal fraction 0.3813. It means

$$\frac{3}{10}+\frac{8}{100}+\frac{1}{1000}+\frac{3}{10\,000}$$

Therefore,

$$0.3813 = 3\times10^{-1}+8\times10^{-2}$$
$$+1\times10^{-3}+3\times10^{-4}$$

Now consider the number 736.58

$$736.58 = 7\times10^2+3\times10^1$$
$$+6\times10^0+5\times10^{-1}+8\times10^{-2}$$

Note that the decimal point indicates the change from positive powers of 10 to negative powers of 10.

It is perfectly possible to have a number system which works on the powers of any number. The most popular of these systems is the binary (bi meaning two) which operates with powers of 2.

It will be noticed in the decimal system that the greatest digit used is 9 which is one less than 10. Thus, in the binary system the greatest digit that can be used is 1 which is one less than 2. A number written in binary consists only of the digits 0 and 1 and a typical binary number is 1010111.

The number 1010111 means.

$$1\times2^6+0\times2^5+1\times2^4+0\times2^3$$
$$+1\times2^2+1\times2^1+1\times2^0$$

The number .11011 means:

$$1\times2^{-1}+1\times2^{-2}+0\times2^{-3}$$
$$+1\times2^{-4}+1\times2^{-5}$$

The number 101.11 means:

$$1\times2^2+0\times2^1+1\times2^0$$
$$+1\times2^{-1}+1\times2^{-2}$$

The *binary point* separates the positive powers of 2 from the negative powers of 2. Numbers containing a binary point are sometimes called *bicimals*.

Conversion from Binary to Decimal and Vice Versa

There are several ways of converting decimal numbers to binary numbers. A simple method is shown in the Example 1.

Example 1

(a)   Convert 59 to a binary number.

Remainder	Power of 2		Explanation
59	1	0	$59 \div 2 = 29$ remainder 1
29	1	1	$29 \div 2 = 14$ remainder 1
14	0	2	$14 \div 2 = 7$ remainder 0
7	1	3	$7 \div 2 = 3$ remainder 1
3	1	4	$3 \div 2 = 1$ remainder 1
1	1	5	$1 \div 2 = 0$ remainder 1

Therefore,

$$59 \text{ (decimal)} = 1\,1\,1\,0\,1\,1 \text{ (binary)}$$

(b) Convert 0.378 to binary.

0.378	Whole Number	Power of 2	Explanation
0.756	0	2^{-1}	$2 \times 0.378 = 0.756.$ Whole number $= 0$
1.512	1	2^{-2}	$2 \times 0.756 = 1.512.$ Whole number $= 1$ Remove the whole number 1. Then,
1.024	1	2^{-3}	$2 \times 0.512 = 1.024.$ Whole number $= 1$ Remove the whole number 1. Then,
0.048	0	2^{-4}	$2 \times 0.024 = 0.048.$ Whole number $= 0$
0.096	0	2^{-5}	$2 \times 0.048 = 0.096.$ Whole number $= 0$
0.192	0	2^{-6}	$2 \times 0.096 = 0.192.$ Whole number $= 0$
0.384	0	2^{-7}	$2 \times 0.192 = 0.384.$ Whole number $= 0$
0.768	0	2^{-8}	$2 \times 0.384 = 0.768.$ Whole number $= 0$
1.536	1	2^{-9}	$2 \times 0.768 = 1.536.$ Whole number $= 1$ Remove the whole number 1. Then,
1.072	1 etc.	2^{-10}	$2 \times 0.536 = 1.072.$ Whole number $= 1$

Therefore, $0.378 = .0\,1\,1\,0\,0\,0\,0\,0\,1\,1$ (correct to 10 binary places).

Most decimal fractions do not have an exact equivalent in binary. When converting these all we can do is to work to a specified number of binary places as in the example above. When converting numbers which have a whole number and a decimal part we convert the whole number part as shown in the first example and the decimal part as shown in the second example. Thus,

$$59.378 = 1\,1\,1\,0\,1\,1.0\,1\,1\,0\,0\,0\,0\,0\,1\,1$$
(correct to 10 binary places).

To convert a binary number into its decimal equivalent we make use of a table similar to the one shown below. The table may be extended in either direction as required.

2^6	2^5	2^4	2^3	2^2
64	32	16	8	4

2^1	2^0	2^{-1}	2^{-2}	2^{-3}
2	1	0.5	0.25	0.125

Example 2

Convert $1\,1\,0\,1.1\,0\,1$ to decimal.

$1\,1\,0\,1.1\,0\,1$ (binary)
$$= 1 \times 2^3 + 1 \times 2^2 + 0 \times 2^1 + 1 \times 2^0$$
$$+ 1 \times 2^{-1} + 0 \times 2^{-2} + 1 \times 2^{-3}$$
$$= 8 + 4 + 0 + 1 + 0.5 + 0 + 0.125$$
$$= 13.625 \text{ (decimal)}$$

The binary system is used in computers and other calculating machines. Since only the digits 0 and 1 are used in the system this is equivalent to a two-state system. For instance if a device is *off* it represents a 0—if it is *on* a 1 is represented. Fig. 28.1 shows how the number $1\,0\,1\,1\,0$ can be represented by 5 electric light bulbs.

215

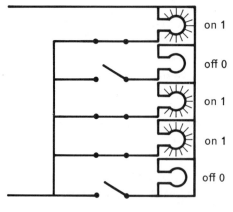

Fig. 28.1

Addition of Binary Numbers

When adding binary numbers the following rules apply:

$$1+0 = 1$$

$$0+1 = 1$$

$$1+1 = 10$$

Note that $1+1 = 2$ in the decimal system but it is 10 in binary, i.e. one two and no units.

Example 3

(a)
```
   11
    1      numbers
  11   ←   carried
 ────
  100
```

(b)
```
  10111
   1011
   1101      numbers
  11111  ←   carried
 ──────
 101111
```

(c)
```
 110101
  11111      numbers
 111111  ←   carried
 ──────
1010100
```

Subtraction of Binary Numbers

In decimal subtraction we borrow' and 'pay back' in tens. Similarly, in binary subtraction we 'borrow' and 'pay back' in twos. In Example 4, decimal numbers are used to show the result of 'borrowing' and 'paying back'.

Example 4

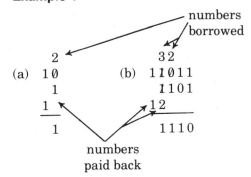

Multiplication of Binary Numbers

The multiplication table in binary is as follows:

$$0\times0 = 0 \qquad 0\times1 = 1$$

$$1\times0 = 0 \qquad 1\times1 = 1$$

When multiplying, remember the importance of starting each line of the multiplication under the number we are multiplying by.

Example 5

Multiply 1101 by 101

```
    1101
     101
   ─────
    1101
    0000
    1101
    1111  ←────── numbers carried
   ─────
 1000001
```

216

A check may be made by converting into decimal.

$$1101 \text{ (binary)} = 13 \text{ (decimal)}$$

$$101 \text{ (binary)} = 5 \text{ (decimal)}$$

$$13 \times 5 \text{ (decimal)} = 65 \text{ (decimal)}$$

$$= 1000001$$
$$\text{(binary)}$$

Hence the binary product 1000001 is correct and

$$1101 \times 101 = 1000001$$

Division of Binary Numbers

Division is really repeated subtraction as shown in Example 6.

Example 6

Divide 1000001 by 1101

```
1101)1000001(101
     1101
     ────
      1101
      1101
      ────
      . . . .
```

$1101 \times 1 = 1101$. Place 1 in the answer. $10000 - 1101 = 11$. Bring down next figure which is 0. 1101 will not go into 110 so place 0 in answer and bring down the next figure, which is 1. 1101 goes into 1101 exactly 1. Hence the answer is 101.

A check can be made by converting the binary numbers into decimal. Thus 1101 (binary) = 13 (decimal) and 1000001 (binary) = 65 (decimal). $65 + 13 = 5$ (decimal) = 101 (binary). Hence

$$1000001 \div 1101 = 101$$

Operations with Bicimals

Example 7

Multiply 101.1 by 11.1.

First disregard the binary point and multiply 1011 by 111.

```
   1011
    111
   ────
   1011
  1011
 1011
 ───────
 1001101
```

Now count up the number of digits following the binary point in each number, i.e. $1 + 1 = 2$. In the answer to the multiplication (the product), count this total number of digits from the right and insert the binary point. The product then becomes 10011.01.

To check the product, convert each of the original numbers to decimal. Thus

$$101.1 = 5\tfrac{1}{2} \quad \text{and} \quad 11.1 = 3\tfrac{1}{2}$$

$$5\tfrac{1}{2} \times 3\tfrac{1}{2} = 19\tfrac{1}{4} = 10011.01$$

Hence

$$101.1 \times 11.1 = 10011.01$$

Example 8

Divide 101.1 by 11 giving the answer to 4 places after the binary point.

```
11)101.1(1.1101
   11
   ──
   101
    11
    ──
    100
     11
     ──
     100
      11
      ──
       1
```

The first line $11 \times 1 = 11$.
$101 - 11 = 10$. Bring down 1. Since this figure lies behind the binary point insert a point in the answer.
$101 - 11 = 10$. Since all the figures in the dividend have been used up bring down a zero. 11 will not go into 10 so place a zero in the answer and bring down a second zero. Now divide 11 into 100. It goes 1 remainder 1. We now have the answer to 4 places after the binary point.
$101 \div 11 = 1.1101$ correct to 4 figures after the binary point.

Exercise 155 — *Questions 1–5 type A, 6–8 type B, 9–10 type C*

1) Convert to binary:

(a) 23 (b) 42 (c) 61 (d) 57

2) Convert to denary:

(a) 10110   (c) 1011010
(b) 111001   (d) 110111

3) Convert to denary:

(a) 0.1101   (c) 0.0011
(b) 0.0111

4) Convert to binary:

(a) $\frac{3}{8}$ (b) $\frac{5}{16}$ (c) $\frac{7}{8}$

5) Convert to binary and correct to 7 places of binary:

(a) 0.169   (c) 108.710
(b) 18.467

6) Add the following binary numbers:

(a) $1011 + 11$
(b) $11011 + 1011$
(c) $10111 + 11010 + 111$
(d) $101101 + 1010 + 101101$
(e) $0.1101 + 0.0110$
(f) $0.11101 + 0.11011$
(g) $11.1101 + 111.1001 + 1.1100$
(h) $101.11 + 111.10 + 100.11$

7) Subtract the following binary numbers:

(a) $111 - 10$
(b) $1011 - 111$
(c) $11011 - 1101$
(d) $11.011 - 1.101$
(e) $101.110 - 11.101$

8) Multiply together the following binary numbers:

(a) 11×10
(b) 101×111
(c) 1011×1010
(d) 11011×1101
(e) 11010×1011

9) Divide the following binary numbers:

(a) $1001 \div 11$
(b) $1100 \div 11$
(c) $1001011 \div 1111$
(d) $1100100 \div 1010$
(e) $101011111 \div 11011$

10) Find the values of the following giving your answer in binary:

(a) 1101.1×1.11
(b) 101.01×11.101
(c) $1010.1 \div 101$ giving the answer to 4 figures after the binary point.
(d) $1111.01 \div 1101$ giving the answer to 5 figures after the binary point.

Other Number Scales

In the scale of 5, powers of 5 are used. Only the digits 0, 1, 2, 3 and 4 are available because the greatest digit used must be one less than 5. If you are told that the number 3412 is in the scale of 5 it means that the number is *based* upon powers of 5. To show that this is so we write 3412_5. The suffix 5 indicates that the number scale of 5 is being used. The number scale is usually called the *base*. We say that the number 3412_5 is to the base 5. Similarly 463_8 is a number to the base 8.

218

$$3412_5 = 3\times5^3 + 4\times5^2 + 1\times5^1 + 2\times5^0$$
$$= 3\times125 + 4\times25$$
$$+ 1\times5 + 2\times1 = 482_{10}$$
$$463_8 = 4\times8^2 + 6\times8^1 + 3\times8^0$$
$$= 4\times64 + 6\times8 + 3\times1 = 307_{10}$$

Addition and Subtraction

The addition table for the base 6 is shown below.

+	0	1	2	3	4	5
0	0	1	2	3	4	5
1	1	2	3	4	5	10
2	2	3	4	5	10	11
3	3	4	5	10	11	12
4	4	5	10	11	12	13
5	5	10	11	12	13	14

Note that $1+5 = 6$ in the decimal system but it is 10 in the base 6, i.e., one six and no units. Similarly, $4+5 = 13$ in the base 6, i.e., one six and three units.

Example 9

Add (a) $322_4 + 31_4$
     (b) $637_8 + 56_8$
     (c) $112_3 + 112_3 + 212_3$

(a) 322
     31
     1   ←— numbers carried
     ____
     1013

(b) 637
     56
     11   ←— numbers carried
     ____
     715

(c) 122
     112
     212
     222   ←— numbers carried
     ____
     2000

In decimal subtraction we 'borrow' and 'pay back' in tens. In binary subtraction we 'borrow' and 'pay back' in twos. Therefore, for example, when subtracting in the base 3, we 'borrow' and 'pay back' in threes. In Example 10, decimal numbers are used to show the effects of 'borrowing' and 'paying back'.

Example 10

Subtract (a) $321_5 - 232_5$
          (b) $4374_8 - 2537_8$

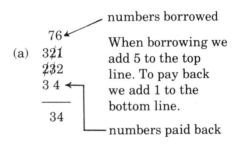

                    numbers borrowed
        76←
(a)   321   When borrowing we
        232   add 5 to the top
        3 4 ←   line. To pay back
        ____   we add 1 to the
        34   bottom line.
                    numbers paid back

        11 12 ←—— numbers borrowed
(b)   4374
        2537   To borrow, 8 is
        3 4 ←   added to the top
        ____   line and to pay
        1635   back 1 is added to
                    the bottom line.
                    numbers paid back

Multiplication and Division

The multiplication table for the base 5 is shown below.

×	0	1	2	3	4
0	0	0	0	0	0
1	0	1	2	3	4
2	0	2	4	11	13
3	0	3	11	14	22
4	0	4	13	22	31

Note that $2\times3 = 6$ in decimal but it is 11 in base 5, i.e., one five and one unit. $4\times3 = 12$ in the decimal system but it is 22 in base 5, i.e., two fives and two units.

Remember, when multiplying, start each line under the number you are multiplying by.

Example 11

Multiply   (a) 212_3 by 21_3
　　　　　(b) 423_5 by 34_5

(a)　　212
　　　　21

　　　212
　　　1201

　　　12222

(b)　　423
　　　　34

　　　3302
　　　2324
　　　11 ◄——numbers carried

　　　32042

To check the answers we can convert each number to decimal. Thus in (a),

$$212_3 = 23_{10} \quad \text{and} \quad 21_3 = 7_{10}$$

$$23_{10} \times 7_{10} = 161_{10} = 12222_3$$

Hence,　$212_3 \times 21_3 = 12222_3$

Example 12

Divide 10211_8 by 123_8

123)10211(63
　762

　371
　371
　...

$123_8 \times 6_8 = 762_8$.　Place 6 in the answer.　$1021_8 - 762_8 = 37_8$.　Bring down the next figure which is 1.
$123_8 \times 3_8 = 371_8$.　$371_8 - 371_8 = 0$.
Since there is no remainder the division is complete. Hence
$10211_8 \div 123_8 = 63_8$.

220

In decimal and binary we discovered that the decimal point and the binary point separated the whole numbers from the fractional part of a number. In any other base the same rule applies. Thus:

$$312.13_4 = 3 \times 4^2 + 1 \times 4^1$$
$$+ 2 \times 4^0 + 1 \times 4^{-1} + 3 \times 4^{-2}$$

$$= 3 \times 16 + 1 \times 4$$
$$+ 2 \times 1 + \tfrac{1}{4} + \tfrac{3}{16} = 54\tfrac{7}{16}$$

Example 13

Multiply 43.2_5 by 4.3_5

First disregard the point and multiply $432_5 \times 43_5$.

　　　432
　　　43

　　　2401
　　　3333

　　　41231

The total number of digits following the point in both the original numbers is $1 + 1 = 2$. In the product the point is inserted between the second and third digits giving
$43.2_5 \times 4.3_5 = 412.31_5$.

Conversion from One Base to Another

It is difficult to change directly from one base to another without going through 10 first because the calculation would have to be done in a strange system. A simple method of converting a number in base 10 to a number in any other base is shown in the Example 14.

Example 14

(a)   Convert 413_{10} into its equivalent in base 8.

	Remain-der	Power of 8	Explanation
413			
51	5	8^0	$413 \div 8 = 51$ remainder 5
6	3	8^1	$51 \div 8 = 6$ remainder 3
0	6	8^2	$6 \div 8 = 1$ remainder 6

Hence $413_{10} = 635_8$

(b) Express $(101_8 - 101_2)$ as a number in base eight.

$$101_2 = (1 \times 2^2 + 0 \times 2^1 + \times 2^0)_{10} = 5_{10}$$

$$5_{10} = 5_8$$

$\therefore \quad (101_8 - 101_2) = 101_8 - 5_8 = 74_8$

Exercise 156 — *Questions 1–3 type B, 4–5 type C, 6–7 type D*

1) Perform the following additions:

(a) $12_3 + 22_3$
(b) $201_3 + 212_3$
(c) $2222_3 + 1212_3$
(d) $413_5 + 324_5$
(e) $315_6 + 24_6 + 52_6$
(f) $31_4 + 303_4 + 213_4$
(g) $36_8 + 44_8 + 57_8$
(h) $514_6 + 325_6 + 14_6 + 3_6$

2) Perform the following subtractions:

(a) $212_3 - 112_3$ (d) $311_4 - 232_4$
(b) $32_4 - 23_4$ (e) $5321_8 - 677_8$
(c) $2122_3 - 1022_3$ (f) $403_5 - 214_5$

3) Convert the following numbers to decimal:

(a) 326_8 (d) 625_7
(b) 2120_3 (e) 2323_4
(c) 345_6

4) Perform the following multiplications:

(a) $5_8 \times 6_8$ (d) $564_7 \times 65_7$
(b) $22_3 \times 2_3$ (e) $177_8 \times 27_8$
(c) $53_6 \times 31_6$ (f) $443_5 \times 324_5$

5)
(a) Express $325_{10} + 325_8$ as a number in base 8.
(b) Express $212_3 - 110_2$ as a number in base 3.
(c) Express $222_8 - 222_3$ as a number in base 3.
(d) Express $111_8 + 111_2$ as a number in base 8.
(e) Express $332_4 \times 43_5$ as a number in base 5.
(f) Express $76_8 \times 202_3$ as a number in base 8.
(g) Express $26_7 \times 101_2$ as a binary number.

6) Perform the following divisions:

(a) $101_3 \div 2_3$
(b) $143_5 \div 31_5$
(c) $333_4 \div 111_4$
(d) $15311_6 \div 125_6$
(e) $4026_8 \div 212_8$
(f) $44341_7 \div 145_7$

7) Find the values of the following:

(a) $13.2_4 \times 11.3_4$ (d) $5.43_6 \times 1.2_6$
(b) $3.12_5 \times 0.43_5$ (e) $2.212_3 \times 11.01_3$
(c) $8.72_9 \times 3.41_9$

Exercise 157 — *Questions 1–4 type A, 5–14 type B, 15–18 type C, remainder D*

All the questions in this exercise have been taken from past C.S.E. examination papers.

1) Convert 10111 base 2 to base 10. (S)

2) $101 \times 101 = 10201$. In what base is this not true? (S)

3) Write the binary number 10110_2 as a dernary number. (Y.R.)

4) Write $\frac{3}{4}$ as bicimal. (S.W.)

5) Add the numbers 121_3, 20_3 and 212_3 giving your answer in base 3. (S)

6) Convert 34 base 5 to base 6. (S)

221

7) The dernary number 94 is the same as the three figure number 2*4 in another base. Find the value of *.
(S)

8) Find the value of $32_4 - 13_4$. (W.M.)

9) Calculate, in base 2, 111×101.
(S.W.)

10) Decide which base has been used for the calculation: $12 + 31 + 23 = 1*1$ and find the missing number. (S.W.)

11) Change 123.3_4 to base 10. (W)

12) Change 14.5_{10} to base 4. (W)

13) What is the value, in dernary, of the underlined figures?

(a) $(3\underline{4}5)_6$ (b) $(1.1\underline{3})_5$ (W)

14) Using the binary scale only calculate:

(a) 1011×1011
(b) $10001111 \div 1101$. (W)

15) Carry out the following calculation leaving your answer in base 3:
$10_3(21_3 + 10_3)$. (Y.R.)

16) If $123_4 = 33_x$, find the value of x. (W)

17) Express the following numbers in order of size, smallest first: 101100_2, 41_5, 212_3 and 102_4. (Y.R.)

18) Find the value of the following in the given base:

(a) $(535.2 + 25.5)_6$
(b) $(535.2 - 25.5)_6$ (W)

19) Work out the following to the bases stated:

(a) $(42.3 \times 25.3)_6$
(b) $(16.313 \div 2.34)_8$

giving your answer to 2 places after the point. (W)

20) Find the value of the following in the given base:

(a) $(2.3 \times 3.2)_4$
(b) $(110.22 \div 2.3)_4$. (W)

222

Chapter 29 Matrices

When a large amount of numerical data has to be used it is often convenient to arrange the numbers in the form of a matrix.

Suppose that a nurseryman offers collections of fruit trees in three separate collections. The table below shows the name of each collection and the number of each type of tree included in it.

	Apple	Pear	Plum	Cherry
Collection				
A	6	2	1	1
B	3	2	2	1
C	3	1	1	0

After a time the headings and titles could be removed because those concerned with the packing of the collections would know what the various numbers meant. The table could then look like this

$$\begin{pmatrix} 6 & 2 & 1 & 1 \\ 3 & 2 & 2 & 1 \\ 3 & 1 & 1 & 0 \end{pmatrix}$$

The information has now been arranged in the form of a *matrix*, that is, in the form of an array of numbers.

A matrix is always enclosed in curved brackets. The above matrix has 3 rows and 4 columns. It is called a matrix of order 3×4. In defining the order of a matrix the number of rows is always stated first and then the number of columns. The matrix shown below is of order 2×5 because it has 2 rows and 5 columns.

$$\begin{pmatrix} 1 & 2 & 5 & 2 & 4 \\ 3 & 0 & 3 & 1 & 2 \end{pmatrix}$$

Types of Matrices

1) *Row matrix*. This is a matrix having only one row. Thus (3 5) is a row matrix.

2) *Column matrix*. This is a matrix having only one column. Thus $\begin{pmatrix} 1 \\ 6 \end{pmatrix}$ is a column matrix.

3) *Null matrix*. This is a matrix with all its elements zero. Thus $\begin{pmatrix} 0 & 0 \\ 0 & 0 \end{pmatrix}$ is a null matrix.

4) *Square matrix*. This is a matrix having the same number of rows and columns. Thus $\begin{pmatrix} 2 & 1 \\ 6 & 3 \end{pmatrix}$ is a square matrix.

5) *Diagonal matrix*. This is a square matrix in which all the elements are zero except the diagonal elements. Thus $\begin{pmatrix} 2 & 0 \\ 0 & 3 \end{pmatrix}$ is a diagonal matrix. Note that the diagonal in a matrix always runs from upper left to lower right.

6) *Unit matrix*. This is a diagonal matrix in which the diagonal elements equal 1. A unit matrix is usually denoted by the symbol I. Thus

$$I = \begin{pmatrix} 1 & 0 \\ 0 & 1 \end{pmatrix}$$

Addition and Subtraction of Matrices

Two matrices may be added or subtracted provided they are of the *same order*. Addition is done by adding together the corresponding elements of each of the two matrices. Thus

$$\begin{pmatrix} 3 & 5 \\ 6 & 2 \end{pmatrix} + \begin{pmatrix} 4 & 7 \\ 8 & 1 \end{pmatrix} = \begin{pmatrix} 3+4 & 5+7 \\ 6+8 & 2+1 \end{pmatrix}$$

$$= \begin{pmatrix} 7 & 12 \\ 14 & 3 \end{pmatrix}$$

Subtraction is done in a similar fashion except the corresponding elements are subtracted. Thus

$$\begin{pmatrix} 6 & 2 \\ 1 & 8 \end{pmatrix} - \begin{pmatrix} 4 & 3 \\ 7 & 5 \end{pmatrix} = \begin{pmatrix} 6-4 & 2-3 \\ 1-7 & 8-5 \end{pmatrix}$$

$$= \begin{pmatrix} 2 & -1 \\ -6 & 3 \end{pmatrix}$$

Multiplication of Matrices

1) *Scalar multiplication.* A matric may be multiplied by a number as follows:

$$3\begin{pmatrix} 2 & 1 \\ 6 & 4 \end{pmatrix} = \begin{pmatrix} 3\times 2 & 3\times 1 \\ 3\times 6 & 3\times 4 \end{pmatrix} = \begin{pmatrix} 6 & 3 \\ 18 & 12 \end{pmatrix}$$

2) *General matrix multiplication.* Two matrices can only be multiplied together if the number of columns in the one is equal to the number of rows in the other. The multiplication is done by multiplying a row by a column as shown below.

$$\begin{pmatrix} 2 & 3 \\ 4 & 5 \end{pmatrix} \times \begin{pmatrix} 5 & 2 \\ 3 & 6 \end{pmatrix}$$

$$= \begin{pmatrix} 2\times 5 + 3\times 3 & 2\times 2 + 3\times 6 \\ 4\times 5 + 5\times 3 & 4\times 2 + 5\times 6 \end{pmatrix}$$

$$= \begin{pmatrix} 19 & 22 \\ 35 & 38 \end{pmatrix}$$

$$\begin{pmatrix} 3 & 4 \\ 2 & 5 \end{pmatrix} \times \begin{pmatrix} 6 \\ 7 \end{pmatrix}$$

$$= \begin{pmatrix} 3\times 6 + 4\times 7 \\ 2\times 6 + 5\times 7 \end{pmatrix} = \begin{pmatrix} 46 \\ 47 \end{pmatrix}$$

Matrix Notation

It is usual to denote matrices by capital letters. Thus

$$A = \begin{pmatrix} 3 & 1 \\ 7 & 4 \end{pmatrix} \quad \text{and} \quad B = \begin{pmatrix} 2 \\ 3 \end{pmatrix}.$$

Generally speaking matrix products are *non-commutative*, that is

$$A \times B \text{ does not equal } B \times A$$

If A is of order 4×3 and B is of order 3×2, then AB is of order 4×2.

Example 1

(a) Form $C = A + B$ if

$$A = \begin{pmatrix} 3 & 4 \\ 2 & 1 \end{pmatrix} \quad \text{and} \quad B = \begin{pmatrix} 2 & 3 \\ 4 & 2 \end{pmatrix}$$

$$C = \begin{pmatrix} 3 & 4 \\ 2 & 1 \end{pmatrix} + \begin{pmatrix} 2 & 3 \\ 4 & 2 \end{pmatrix} = \begin{pmatrix} 5 & 7 \\ 6 & 3 \end{pmatrix}$$

(b) Form $Q = RS$ if

$$R = \begin{pmatrix} 1 & 2 \\ 3 & 4 \end{pmatrix} \quad \text{and} \quad S = \begin{pmatrix} 3 & 1 \\ 5 & 6 \end{pmatrix}$$

$$Q = \begin{pmatrix} 1 & 2 \\ 3 & 4 \end{pmatrix}\begin{pmatrix} 3 & 1 \\ 5 & 6 \end{pmatrix} = \begin{pmatrix} 13 & 13 \\ 29 & 27 \end{pmatrix}$$

Note that just as in ordinary algebra the multiplication sign is omitted so we omit it in matrix algebra.

(c) Form $M = PQR$ if

$$P = \begin{pmatrix} 2 & 0 \\ 1 & 0 \end{pmatrix}, \quad Q = \begin{pmatrix} -1 & 0 \\ 0 & 1 \end{pmatrix}$$

and $R = \begin{pmatrix} 2 & 1 \\ 3 & 0 \end{pmatrix}$

$$PQ = \begin{pmatrix} 2 & 0 \\ 1 & 0 \end{pmatrix}\begin{pmatrix} -1 & 0 \\ 0 & 1 \end{pmatrix} = \begin{pmatrix} -2 & 0 \\ -1 & 0 \end{pmatrix}$$

$$M = (PQ)R = \begin{pmatrix} -2 & 0 \\ -1 & 0 \end{pmatrix}\begin{pmatrix} 2 & 1 \\ 3 & 0 \end{pmatrix}$$

$$= \begin{pmatrix} -4 & -2 \\ -2 & -1 \end{pmatrix}$$

Transposition of Matrices

When the rows of a matrix are interchanged with its column the matrix is said to be *transposed*. If the original matrix is A, the transpose is denoted by A^T. Thus

$$A = \begin{pmatrix} 3 & 4 \\ 5 & 6 \end{pmatrix} \quad A^T = \begin{pmatrix} 3 & 5 \\ 4 & 6 \end{pmatrix}$$

Inverting a Matrix

If $AB = I$ (I is the unit matrix) then B is called the *inverse or reciprocal* of A. The inverse of A is usually written A^{-1} and hence

$$AA^{-1} = I$$

If

$$A = \begin{pmatrix} a & b \\ c & d \end{pmatrix}$$

$$A^{-1} = \frac{1}{ad - bc} \begin{pmatrix} d & -b \\ -c & a \end{pmatrix}$$

Example 2

If $A = \begin{pmatrix} 4 & 1 \\ 2 & 3 \end{pmatrix}$ form A^{-1}

$$A^{-1} = \frac{1}{4 \times 3 - 1 \times 2} \begin{pmatrix} 3 & -1 \\ -2 & 4 \end{pmatrix}$$

$$= \frac{1}{10} \begin{pmatrix} 3 & -1 \\ -2 & 4 \end{pmatrix}$$

$$= \begin{pmatrix} 0.3 & -0.1 \\ -0.2 & 0.4 \end{pmatrix}$$

To check

$$AA^{-1} = \begin{pmatrix} 4 & 1 \\ 2 & 3 \end{pmatrix} \begin{pmatrix} 0.3 & -0.1 \\ -0.2 & 0.4 \end{pmatrix}$$

$$= \begin{pmatrix} 1 & 0 \\ 0 & 1 \end{pmatrix}$$

Equality of Matrices

If two matrices are equal then their corresponding elements are equal. Thus if

$$\begin{pmatrix} a & b \\ c & d \end{pmatrix} = \begin{pmatrix} e & f \\ g & h \end{pmatrix}$$

then $a = e$, $b = f$, $c = g$ and $d = h$.

Example 3

Find the values of x and y if

$$\begin{pmatrix} 2 & 1 \\ 3 & 4 \end{pmatrix} \begin{pmatrix} x & 2 \\ 5 & y \end{pmatrix} = \begin{pmatrix} 7 & 10 \\ 23 & 30 \end{pmatrix}$$

$$\begin{pmatrix} 2x + 5 & 4 + y \\ 3x + 20 & 6 + 4y \end{pmatrix} = \begin{pmatrix} 7 & 10 \\ 23 & 30 \end{pmatrix}$$

$$\therefore \qquad 2x + 5 = 7 \quad \text{and} \quad x = 1$$
$$4 + y = 10 \quad \text{and} \quad y = 6$$

(We could have used $3x + 20 = 23$ and $6 + 4y = 30$ if we had desired.)

Exercise 158 — All type B

1) If $A = \begin{pmatrix} 3 & 2 \\ 4 & 5 \end{pmatrix}$ and

$$B = \begin{pmatrix} 2 & 1 \\ 3 & 3 \end{pmatrix} \quad \text{form:}$$

(a) $A + B$ (d) BA (g) A^{-1}
(b) $A - B$ (e) A^T (h) B^{-1}
(c) AB (f) B^T

2) If $\begin{pmatrix} 1 & 2 \\ 3 & 4 \end{pmatrix} \begin{pmatrix} 2 \\ 3 \end{pmatrix} = k \begin{pmatrix} 16 \\ 36 \end{pmatrix}$ find k.

3) Find the values of a and b if

$$\begin{pmatrix} a & 2 \\ 3 & b \end{pmatrix} \begin{pmatrix} 3 \\ 4 \end{pmatrix} = \begin{pmatrix} 14 \\ 21 \end{pmatrix}$$

4) If $P = \begin{pmatrix} 2 & 1 \\ 3 & 5 \end{pmatrix}$ find PP^T

5) Find:
(a) PQ (b) RS (c) $PQRS$ if

$$P = \begin{pmatrix} 0 & 1 \\ 1 & 0 \end{pmatrix} \quad Q = \begin{pmatrix} 2 & 1 \\ 1 & 2 \end{pmatrix}$$

$$R = \begin{pmatrix} -1 & 2 \\ 3 & 1 \end{pmatrix} \quad S = \begin{pmatrix} 2 & 1 \\ 2 & 0 \end{pmatrix}$$

Exercise 159 — *All type B*

All the questions in this exercise have been taken from past C.S.E. examination papers.

1) Find the values of L and M in the following matrix addition:

$$\begin{pmatrix} L & 4 \\ -3 & 1 \end{pmatrix} + \begin{pmatrix} 1 & 2 \\ -2 & 4 \end{pmatrix} + \begin{pmatrix} -1 & 2 \\ M & 4 \end{pmatrix}$$

$$= \begin{pmatrix} 3 & 8 \\ -6 & 9 \end{pmatrix} \qquad (Y.R.)$$

2) If $A = \begin{pmatrix} 4 & 5 \\ 2 & 3 \end{pmatrix}$ find A^2.

3) If $A = \begin{pmatrix} 3 & 1 \\ 2 & 0 \end{pmatrix}$ and $B = \begin{pmatrix} 4 & -1 \\ 2 & 3 \end{pmatrix}$

calculate the following matrices:
(a) $A + B$ (c) AB
(b) $3A - 2B$ (d) BA (W)

4) $P = \begin{pmatrix} 2 & 1 \\ 3 & 1 \end{pmatrix}$ $Q = \begin{pmatrix} 1 & 0 \\ 0 & 1 \end{pmatrix}$

$R = \begin{pmatrix} 0 & 1 \\ 1 & 0 \end{pmatrix}$ $S = \begin{pmatrix} 1 & -2 \\ -6 & 3 \end{pmatrix}$

(a) Find each of the following as a single matrix:

$$PQ, \quad RS, \quad PQRS, \quad P^2 - Q^2.$$

(b) Find the values of a and b if $aP + bQ = S$.   (W.M.)

5) A and B are two matrices.
If $A = \begin{pmatrix} -2 & 3 \\ 4 & -1 \end{pmatrix}$ find A^2 and
then use your answer to find B, given that $A^2 = A - B$.   (W)

6) Find the value of:

$$\begin{pmatrix} 2 & 3 & 1 \\ 0 & 1 & 2 \end{pmatrix} \begin{pmatrix} 1 \\ 3 \\ -2 \end{pmatrix} \qquad (Y.R.)$$

7) If

$$\begin{pmatrix} 2 & 3 \\ 4 & 5 \end{pmatrix} \begin{pmatrix} p & 2 \\ 7 & q \end{pmatrix} = \begin{pmatrix} 31 & 1 \\ 55 & 3 \end{pmatrix}$$

find p and q.   (S)

8) If $A = \begin{pmatrix} 2 & -1 \\ 1 & 1 \end{pmatrix}$ and

$B = \begin{pmatrix} 1 & 2 \\ 1 & 1 \end{pmatrix}$, write as a single matrix

(a) $A + B$ (b) $A \times B$
(c) the multiplicative inverse of B (i.e. B^{-1}).   (A.L.)

9) If matrix $A = \begin{pmatrix} 3 & 1 \\ 2 & 4 \end{pmatrix}$ and

matrix $B = \begin{pmatrix} 4 & 2 \\ 1 & 0 \end{pmatrix}$

(a) Calculate:
(i) $A + B$ (ii) $3A - 2B$
(iii) AB

(b) (i) Eastern Airlines have 6 Tridents, 4 VC10's and 2 Jumbo Jets. Western Airlines have 3 Tridents, 6 VC10's and 1 Jumbo Jet. Write this information as a 2 by 3 matrix.
(ii) Tridents carry 150 passengers, VC10's carry 120 passengers and Jumbo Jets carry 375 passengers. Write this information as a 3 by 1 matrix.
(iii) Multiply these matrices to find a 2 by 1 matrix.
(iv) What does the 2 by 1 matrix represent?   (S)

10)
(a) The scores of five soccer clubs in the first 12 matches of the 1975–6 season are given by the matrix:

	Won	Drawn	Lost
Aston Villa	4	4	4
Birmingham	3	2	7
Derby	6	3	3
Stoke	5	2	5
Wolverhampton	2	4	6

The points awarded for a win, a draw or a lost match are given by the matrix

Won $\begin{pmatrix} 2 \\ 1 \\ 0 \end{pmatrix}$
Drawn
Lost

Calculate a matrix which shows the total number of points scored by each of these clubs, showing clearly the method used.

(b) If $A = \begin{pmatrix} 3 & 1 \\ -2 & 0 \end{pmatrix}$ and

$B = \begin{pmatrix} -1 & 3 \\ -4 & 2 \end{pmatrix}$ calculate AB

and BA.

(c) Solve the equation

$$\begin{pmatrix} 2 & 5 \\ 1 & 3 \end{pmatrix}\begin{pmatrix} x \\ y \end{pmatrix} = \begin{pmatrix} 3 \\ 1 \end{pmatrix}.$$

(W.M.)

227

Chapter 30 **Transformations**

When a point P is given a new position, the point P is said to have undergone a transformation. Thus in Fig. 30.1, the point P(2,3) has been transformed into the point P'(4, 5).

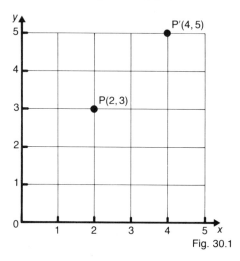

Fig. 30.1

Translation

In Fig. 30.2, the line AB has taken up the new position A'B'. Every point in AB has moved the same distance in the same direction. AB is said to be *translated* to A'B'.

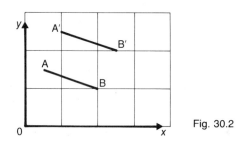

Fig. 30.2

In Fig. 30.3, every point in the line AB has been moved 1 unit to the right and 2 units upwards. Thus A(1, 2) trans-

lates to A'(2, 5) and B(5, 7) translates to B'(6, 10).

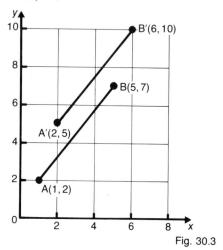

Fig. 30.3

Similarly in Fig. 30.4, the triangle XYZ has been translated to X'Y'Z'. Every point in XYZ has been moved with a displacement of 5 units to the left and 4 units downwards.

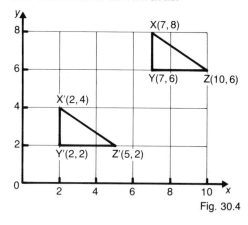

Fig. 30.4

Reflection in the *x*-axis

In Fig. 30.5, the point P is reflected in the line XOX' (the *x*-axis) so that its image is P'. The line PP' is bisected by

XOX′ and the point P is said to be reflected in the x-axis.

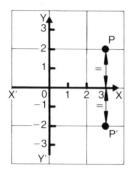

Fig. 30.5

Reflection in the y-axis

In Fig. 30.6, the point P is reflected in the line YOY′ (the y-axis) so that its image is P′. The line PP′ is bisected by YOY′ and the point P is said to be reflected in the y-axis.

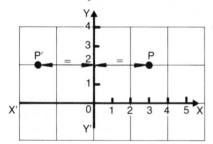

Fig. 30.6

Reflection in the Origin

In Fig. 30.7, the point P has been reflected so that its image is P′. Since $OP = OP'$ the point P is said to be reflected in the origin.

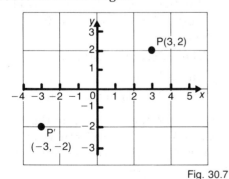

Fig. 30.7

Reflection in the Line $y = x$

If the scales on the x and y axes are the same, the line $y = x$ will be inclined at 45° to the x-axis. The reflection of the point P(4, 2) in the line $y = x$ is P′(2, 4). Note that the line $y = x$ is the perpendicular bisector of PP′ and that the effect of this transformation is to reverse the co-ordinates of P (Fig. 30.8).

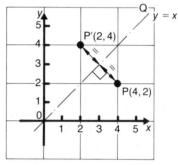

Fig. 30.8

Glide Reflection

A glide reflection in the x-axis is produced when a reflection takes place after a translation parallel to the x-axis. Thus in Fig. 30.9, the point P(2, 1) is translated to P_1(5, 1) and then reflected to P_2(5, −1). The point P has been given a *glide reflection* in the x-axis.

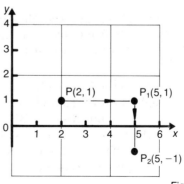

Fig. 30.9

229

In a similar way a point can be given a glide reflection in the y-axis as shown in Fig. 30.10.

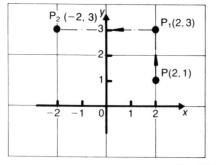

Fig. 30.10

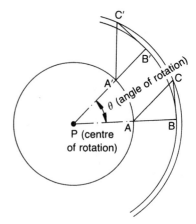

Fig. 30.11(b)

Rotation

In Fig. 30.11 (a) the point P has been given a rotation of 30° about the origin and it is transformed into the point P'. The point P has been given a *rotational transformation*.

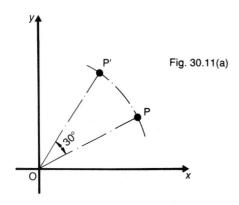

Fig. 30.11(a)

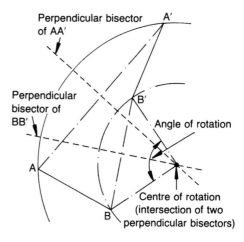

Fig. 30.11(c)

Fig. 30.11 (b) shows the triangle ABC transformed into A'B'C' by a rotation of θ degrees, the centre of rotation being P.

In Fig. 30.11 (c) the line AB has been transformed into A'B'. To find the centre of rotation join AA' and BB'. Construct the perpendicular bisectors of AA' and BB'. The point of intersection of the two bisectors is the centre of rotation.

Example 1

The triangle ABC has vertices which have the coordinates (1, 1), (3, 1) and (1, 4) respectively. Show in a single diagram:

(a) The reflection in the x-axis.

(b) The reflection in the y-axis.

(c) The reflection in the origin.

In Fig. 30.12, the reflection in the x-axis is $A_1B_1C_1$, the reflection in the y-axis is $A_2B_2C_2$ and the reflection in the origin is $A_3B_3C_3$.

230

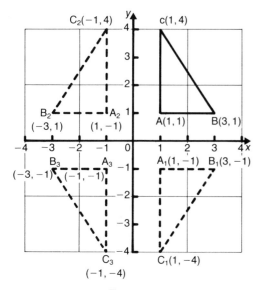

Fig. 30.12

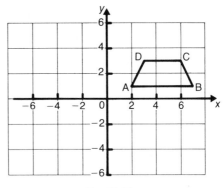

Fig. 30.14

Exercise 160 — *All type B*

1) Figure 30.13 shows the rectangle ABCD. Copy the diagram and translate ABCD so that it is displaced by:

(a) 3 units to the right and 4 units upwards

(b) 2 units to the left and 3 units downwards.

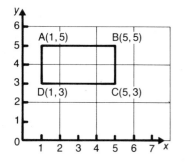

Fig. 30.13

2) Figure 30.14 shows the trapezium ABCD. Copy the diagram and show the reflection of this figure in:

(a) the x-axis

(b) the y-axis

(c) the origin

3) The triangle ABC is formed by joining the three points A(3, 2), B(5, 2) and C(3, 6).

(a) Draw the triangle ABC on graph paper.

(b) Reflect this triangle in the x-axis.

(c) State the coordinates of the transformed points A, B and C.

(d) Reflect the triangle ABC in the y-axis.

(e) State the coordinates of the points ABC after this second transformation.

(f) Reflect the triangle ABC in the origin.

(g) State the coordinates of the points A, B and C after this third transformation.

4) WXYZ is a square such that W is the point (2, 3), X is the point (4, 3) and Y is the point (4, 5).

(a) State the coordinates of the point Z.

(b) Draw the square on graph paper, using a scale of 2 cm = 1 unit on both axes.

(c) Draw the line $y = x$.

(d) Reflect WXYZ in the line $y = x$.

(e) State the coordinates of the transformed points W, X, Y and Z.

231

5) Using O as the centre of rotation, draw the image of the figure ABC shown in Fig. 30.15, after it has been given a rotation of 60°.

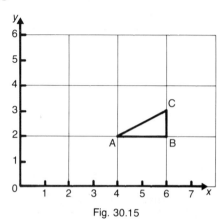

Fig. 30.15

6) Triangle ABC has vertices A(2, 3), B(4, 4) and C(3, 5). Plot these points on graph paper and join them to form triangle ABC. Show the image of ABC after it has been given a rotation of 90° about the point P(5, 1) clockwise.

7) The line AB with end points (2, 2) and (4, 2) is transformed to A'B' by a rotation such that A' is the point (8, 4) and B' is the point (8, 2). Find the coordinates of the centre of rotation and write down the angle of rotation.

Chapter 31   **Statistics**

Introduction

Statistics is the name given to the science of collecting and analysing facts. In almost all scientific and business publications, in newspapers and in Government reports these facts are presented by means of tables and diagrams. The most commonly used diagrams and charts are discussed below.

The Proportionate Bar Chart

The proportionate bar chart (Fig. 31.1) relies on heights (or areas) to convey the proportions of a whole. The bar should be of the same width throughout its length or height. This diagram is accurate, quick and easy to construct and it can show quite a large number of components without confusion. Although Fig. 31.1 shows the bar drawn vertically it may also be drawn horizontally if desired.

Example 1

Draw a proportionate bar chart for the figures below which show the way commuters in the South-east region travelled to the London area.

Type of transport	Numbers using
Private motoring	1560
Bus and underground	840
British Railways	320

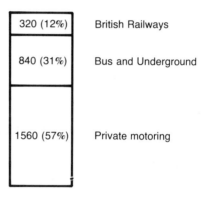

Fig. 31.1.   A proportionate bar chart

The easiest way is to draw the chart as shown in Fig. 31.1 on graph paper. However, if plain paper is used, the lengths of the component parts must be calculated and then drawn accurately using a rule.

$$\text{Total number} = 1560 + 840 + 320$$
$$= 2720$$

Suppose that the total height of the diagram is to be 6 cm. Then

1560 commuters are represented by

$$\frac{1560}{2720} \times 6 = 3.44 \text{ cm}$$

840 commuters are represented by

$$\frac{840}{2720} \times 6 = 1.85 \text{ cm}$$

320 commuters are represented by

$$\frac{320}{2720} \times 6 = 0.71 \text{ cm}$$

Alternatively, the proportions can be expressed as percentages which are calculated as shown at the top of page 234.

Type of transport	Percentage of commuters using
Private motoring	$\frac{1560}{2720} \times 100 = 57\%$
Bus and under-ground	$\frac{840}{2720} \times 100 = 31\%$
British Railways	$\frac{320}{2720} \times 100 = 12\%$

Simple Bar Charts

In these charts the information is represented by a series of bars all of the same width. The height or the length of each bar represents the magnitude of the figures. The bars may be drawn vertically or horizontally as shown in Figs. 31.2 and 31.3 which present the information given in Example 1.

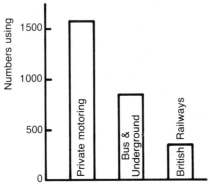

Fig. 31.2. A vertical bar chart

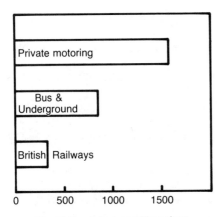

Fig. 31.3. A horizontal bar chart

Chronological Bar Charts

This type of chart compares quantities over periods of time. It is very similar to the vertical bar chart and its construction is basically the same as a graph.

Example 2

The information below gives the number of television colour sets sold in Southern England during the period 1970–75.

Year	Number of sets sold (thousands)
1970	77.2
1971	84.0
1972	91.3
1973	114.6
1974	130.9
1975	142.5

Draw a chronological bar chart to represent this information.

When drawing a chronological bar chart, time is always marked off along the horizontal axis. The chart is drawn in Fig. 31.4 and it clearly shows how the sales of TV sets has increased over the period illustrated.

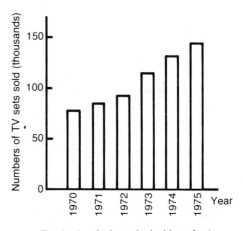

Fig. 31.4. A chronological bar chart

Pie Chart

A pie chart displays the proportions of a whole as sector angles or sector areas. The circle as a whole representing the component parts.

Example 3

Represent the information given in Example 1 in the form of a pie chart.

The first step is to calculate the sector angles. Remembering that a circle contains 360° the sector angles are calculated as shown below:

Type of transport	Sector angle (degrees)
Private motoring	$\frac{1560}{2720} \times 360 = 206°$
Bus and underground	$\frac{840}{2720} \times 360 = 111°$
British Railways	$\frac{320}{2720} \times 360 = 43°$

Using a protractor the pie chart (Fig. 31.5) can now be drawn. If desired percentages can be displayed on the diagram.

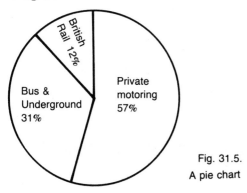

Fig. 31.5.
A pie chart

Pie charts are very useful when component parts of a whole are to be represented. Up to eight component parts can be accommodated but above this number the chart loses its effectiveness.

Exercise 161 — *All type B*

1) In Fig. 31.6, find the values of x and y.

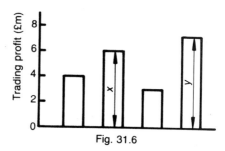

Fig. 31.6

2) Draw a proportionate bar chart for the information below which relates to expenditure per head on transport. In each case find the percentage expenditure and show it on your diagram.

Type of transport	Expenditure (£)
Private motoring	£1.10
Rail	£2.75
Other public transport	£3.15
Total	£7.00

3) The table below shows the number of people employed on various kinds of work in a factory.

Type of personnel	Number employed
Unskilled workers	45
Craftsmen	25
Draughtsmen	5
Clerical staff	10
Total	85

(a) Draw a vertical bar chart to represent this information.

(b) Draw a simple horizontal bar chart to show this data.

(c) Draw a pie chart, showing percentages, for this information.

4) The information below gives details of the temperature range used when forging various metals. Draw a horizontal bar chart to represent this data.

Metal	Temperature °C
Carbon steel	770–1300
Wrought iron	860–1340
Brass	600– 800
Copper	500–1000

5) The figures below give the World population (in millions of people) from 1750 to 1950. Draw a chronological bar chart to represent this information.

Year	Population
1750	728
1800	906
1850	1171
1900	1608
1950	2504

6) The information below gives the production of grain on a certain farm during the period from 1968–1973. Draw a chronological bar chart to represent this information.

Year	Grain production (tonnes)
1968	395
1969	410
1970	495
1971	560
1972	420
1973	515

7) The data below gives the areas of the various continents of the world.

Continent	Area (millions of square miles)
Africa	30.3
Asia	26.9
Europe	4.9
N. America	24.3
S. America	17.9
Oceania	22.8
U.S.S.R.	20.5

Draw a pie chart to depict this information.

8) Figure 31.7 is a pie chart which shows the total sales of a Departmental Store for one week. Find the correct size of each sector angle. (The diagram is NOT drawn to scale.)

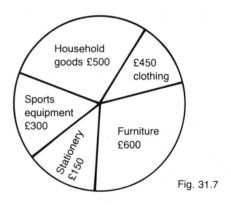

Fig. 31.7

Pictograms and ideographs

These are diagrams in the form of pictures which are used to present information to those who are unskilled in dealing with figures or to those who have only a limited interest in the topic depicted.

Example 4

The table below shows the output of bicycles for the years 1970 to 1974.

Year	Output
1970	2000
1971	4000
1972	7000
1973	8500
1974	9000

Represent this data in the form of a pictogram.

The pictogram is shown in Fig. 31.8. It will be seen that each bicycle in the diagram represents an output of 2000 bicycles. Part of a symbol is shown in 1972, 1973 and 1974 to represent a fraction of 2000 but clearly this is not a very precise way of representing the output.

It is essential that the diagram is labelled correctly and that the source of the information is stated.

A method not recommended is shown in Fig. 31.9. Comparison is difficult because the reader is not sure whether to compare heights, areas or volumes. However, if this method is used the methods shown in Examples 5 and 6 should be used.

Fig. 31.9. Sales of milk in 1950 and 1970
(millions of litres)

Output of bicycles by Thomas & Co.

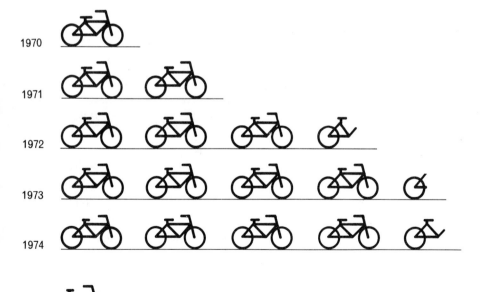

Fig. 31.8. A pictogram

Example 5

If a square of 3 cm side represents a population of 18 000, what population is represented by a square of 4 cm side?

Here the quantities are represented by the areas of squares.

The area of the square is
3 cm×3 cm = 9 square centimetres.

Hence   9 square centimetres represents a population of   18 000

and   1 square centimetre represents a population of
$$\frac{18\,000}{9} = 2000$$

The area of a square of side 4 cm is
4 cm×4 cm = 16 square centimetres.

Hence a square of 4 cm side represents a population of   2000×16 = 32 000.

Example 6

A production of 1000 tonnes of steel is represented by a cube of side 2 cm. Calculate the production of steel represented by a cube of side 3 cm.

Here, the quantities are represented by the volumes of cubes. Since the volume of a cube is
side×side×side = side^3,
volume of a cube of 2 cm
side = 2 cm×2 cm×2 cm = 8 cubic centimetres.

Therefore 8 cubic centimetres represents 1000 tonnes and 1 cubic centimetre represents
$$\frac{1000}{8} = 125 \text{ tonnes}$$

Volume of a cube of 3 cm
side = 3 cm×3 cm×3 cm = 27 cubic centimetres. Hence a cube of 3 cm side represents
125 tonnes×27 = 3375 tonnes.

238

Exercise 162 — *Questions 1–4 type A, remainder type B*

1)   Figure 31.10 is a pictogram showing the method by which first year boys come to school.

(a)   How many come by bus?

(b)   How many come by car?

(c)   Estimate the number of boys who live within 1 kilometre of the school.

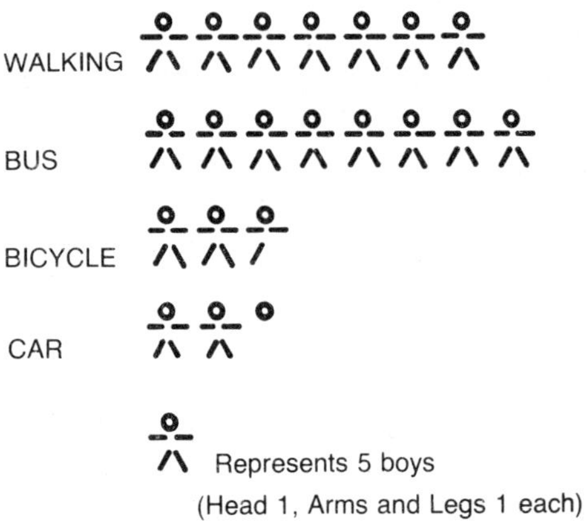

WALKING

BUS

BICYCLE

CAR

Represents 5 boys
(Head 1, Arms and Legs 1 each)

Fig. 31.10

2)   The sales of motor cars by Mortimer & Co. Ltd. were as follows:

Year	Sales
1972	2000
1973	2500
1974	3200
1975	2700
1976	3000

Represent this information in a pictogram.

3)   The table below gives the number of houses completed in the S.W. of England.

Year	Number (thousands)
1965	81
1967	69
1969	73
1971	84
1973	80

Draw a pictogram to represent this information.

4) The information below gives the production of tyres (in thousands) produced by Treadwell & Co. for the first six months of 1977.

Month	Production
January	40
February	43
March	39
April	38
May	37
June	45

Draw a pictogram to represent this information.

5) The pictogram (Fig. 31.11) is an attempt to show the sales of a company in the years 1972, 1974 and 1976. Why does the pictogram not give a true indication of the company's sales?

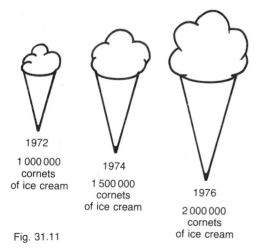

1972
1 000 000 cornets of ice cream

1974
1 500 000 cornets of ice cream

1976
2 000 000 cornets of ice cream

Fig. 31.11

6) A firm of carriers indicated their increase in parcel traffic as shown in Fig. 31.12. This indicated that they had increased eightfold. In 1970 the firm carried 1500 parcels.

(a) How many did they carry in 1972?

(b) Draw a figure in the same pattern to indicate the volume of parcel traffic in 1976 if it was 40 500 parcels.

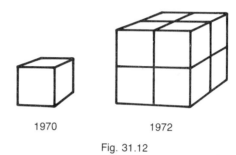

1970   1972

Fig. 31.12

7) A circle of 2 cm radius represents sales of 200 items. If sales are depicted by area what does a circle of 4 cm radius represent?

8) The volume of a sphere of diameter 3 cm represents a production of 54 000 articles. What production will a sphere of 2 cm diameter represent?

Raw Data

Raw data is collected information which is not organised numerically, that is, it is not arranged in any sort of order.

Consider the marks of 50 students obtained in a test:

4 3 5 4 3 5 5 4 3 6 5 4 5 3 4 4 5 5 7
4 3 4 3 4 5 4 3 6 1 3 6 3 2 6 6 3 5 2
7 5 7 1 7 6 5 8 6 4 3 5

This is an example of raw data and we see that it is not organised into any sort of order.

239

Frequency Distributions

One way of organising raw data into order is to arrange it in the form of a frequency distribution. The number of students obtaining 3 marks is found, the number obtaining 4 marks is found, and so on. A tally chart is the best way of doing this.

On examining the raw data we see that the smallest mark is 1 and the greatest is 8. The marks from 1 to 8 inclusive are written in column 1 of the tally chart. We now take each figure in the raw data, just as it comes, and for each figure we place a tally mark opposite the appropriate mark.

The fifth tally mark for each number is usually made in an oblique direction thereby tying the tally marks into bundles of five.

When the tally marks are complete they are counted and the numerical value recorded in the column headed 'frequency'. Hence the frequency is the number of times each mark occurs. From the tally chart below it will be seen that the mark 1 occurs twice (a frequency of 2), the mark 5 occurs twelve times (a frequency of 12) and so on.

TABLE 1

Mark	Tally	Frequency
1	11	2
2	11	2
3	1111 1111 1	11
4	1111 1111 1	11
5	1111 1111 11	12
6	1111 11	7
7	1111	4
8	1	1
	Total	50

Grouped Distributions

When dealing with a large amount of numerical data it is useful to group the numbers into classes or categories. We can then find out the number of items belonging to each class thus obtaining a class frequency. The table below shows a grouped frequency distribution for the heights of 100 male workers in a certain factory.

The first class consists of heights from 150 cm to 154 cm. Eight workers have heights belonging to this class and the class frequency is therefore 8.

TABLE 2

Height (cm)	Frequency
150–154	8
155–159	16
160–164	43
165–169	29
170–174	4
Total	100

The main advantage of grouping is that it produces a clear overall picture of the distribution. However too many groups destroy the pattern of the distribution whilst too few will destroy much of the detail contained in the raw data. Depending upon the amount of raw data, the number of classes is usually between 5 and 20.

Class Intervals

In Table 2, the first class is 150–154. These figures give the class interval. For the second class the class interval is 155–159. The end numbers 155 and 159 are called the *class limits* for the second class, 155 being the lower limit and 155 the upper limit.

Class Boundaries

In Table 2, the heights have been recorded to the nearest centimetre. The class interval 155–159 theoretically includes all the heights between 154.5 cm and 159.5 cm. These numbers are called the lower and upper class boundaries respectively.

For any frequency distribution the class boundaries may be found by adding the upper limit of one class to the lower limit of the next class and dividing the sum by two.

Example 7

The figures below show part of a frequency distribution. State the lower and upper class boundaries for the second class.

Lifetime of electric bulbs

Lifetime (hours)	Frequency
400–449	22
450–499	38
500–549	62

For the second class:

lower class boundary

$$= \frac{449+450}{2} = 449.5 \text{ hours}$$

upper class boundary

$$= \frac{499+500}{2} = 499.5 \text{ hours}$$

Width of a Class Interval

The width of a class interval is the difference between the lower and upper class boundaries. That is

width of class interval

= upper class boundary
  −lower class boundary

For Example 7,

width of second class interval
= 499.5−449.5 = 50 hours

(A common mistake is to take the class width as being the difference between the upper and lower class limits, giving in Example 7, 499–450 = 49 hours, which is incorrect.)

Discrete and Continuous Variables

A variable which can take any value between two given values is called a *continuous variable*. Thus the height of an individual which can be 158 cm, 164.2 cm or 177.832 cm, depending upon the accuracy of measurement, is a continuous variable.

A variable which can only have certain values is called a *discrete variable*. Thus the number of children in a family can only take whole number values such as 0, 1, 2, 3, etc. It cannot be $2\frac{1}{2}$, $3\frac{1}{4}$, etc., and it is therefore a discrete variable. Note that the values of a discrete variable need not be whole numbers. The sizes of shoes is a discrete variable but these can be $4\frac{1}{2}$, 5, $5\frac{1}{2}$, 6, etc.

The Histogram

The *histogram* is a diagram which is used to represent a frequency distribution. It consists of a set of rectangles whose *areas* represent the frequencies of the various classes. If all the classes have the same width then all the rectangles will be the same width and the frequencies are then represented

241

by the heights of the rectangles. Figure 31.13 shows the histogram for the frequency distribution of Table 1.

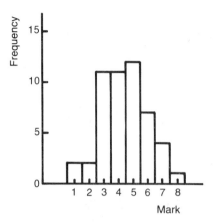

Fig. 31.13

Histogram for a Grouped Distribution

A histogram for a grouped distribution may be drawn by using the mid-points of the class intervals as the centres of the rectangles. The histogram for the distribution of Table 2 is shown in Fig. 31.14. Note that the extremes of the base of each rectangle represent the lower and upper class boundaries.

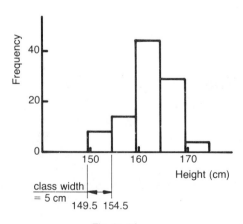

Fig. 31.14

Discrete Distributions

The histogram shown in Fig. 31.14 represents a distribution in which the variable is continuous. The data in Example 8 is discrete and we shall see how a discrete distribution is represented.

Example 8

Five coins were tossed 100 times and after each toss the number of heads was recorded. The table below gives the number of tosses during which 0, 1, 2, 3, 4 and 5 heads were obtained. Represent this data in a suitable diagram.

Number of heads	Number of tosses (frequency)
0	4
1	15
2	34
3	29
4	16
5	2
Total	100

Since the data is discrete (there cannot be 2.3 or 3.6 heads) Fig. 31.15 seems the most natural diagram to use. This

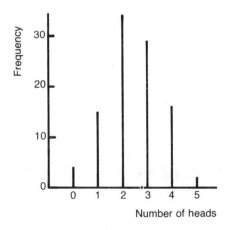

Fig. 31.15

diagram is in the form of a vertical bar chart in which the bars have zero width. Figure 31.16 shows the same data represented as a histogram. Note that the area under the diagram gives the total frequency of 100 which is as it should be. Discrete data is often represented as a histogram as was done in Fig. 31.13, despite the fact that in doing this we are treating the data as though it was continuous.

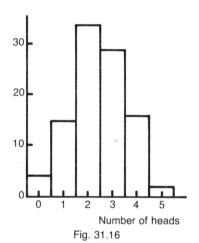

Number of heads

Fig. 31.16

Exercise 163 — *All type B*

1) The following marks were obtained by 50 students during a test:

5 4 6 5 4 6 6 5 4 7 6 5 6 4 5 5 6 6 8 5 4
2 8 6 8 3 6 4 7 7 3 4 7 4 1 7 4 5 6 4 5 8
7 6 9 7 5 4 6 2

Draw up a frequency distribution by means of a tally chart.

2) The following is a record of the percentage marks obtained by 100 students in an examination:

45 93 35 56 16 50 63 30 86 65 57 39 44
75 25 45 74 93 84 25 77 28 54 50 12 85
55 34 50 57 55 48 78 15 27 79 68 26 66
80 91 62 67 52 50 75 96 36 83 20 45 71
63 51 40 46 61 62 67 57 53 45 51 40 46
31 54 67 66 52 49 54 55 52 56 59 38 52
43 55 51 47 54 56 56 42 53 40 51 58 52
27 56 42 86 50 31 61 33 36

Draw up a tally chart for the classes 0–9, 10–19, 20–29, . . ., 90–99 and hence form a frequency distribution.

3) A large transport firm had 70 lorries in different parts of the country. It wished to compile a table showing the distance travelled by each lorry in a particular period. The following information was obtained by the inspectors who checked the speedometers and recorded the distance travelled by each lorry.

Kilometres (hundreds) which each lorry travelled

10 12 30 56 57 36 27 32 57 20 15 50 49
46 21 69 55 42 60 45 35 47 22 45 44 31
67 43 17 54 49 56 51 55 29 65 23 55 46
66 40 63 24 33 62 58 15 57 64 37 38 48
27 28 59 25 52 47 26 63 30 31 31 34 65
41 16 28 39 46

Draw up a frequency distribution for the classes 0–9, 10–19, 20–29, etc.

4) Draw a histogram of the following data which relates to the earnings of full-time girl employees in 1971.

Wage £	Frequency
12–15	2
16–19	5
17–20	8
21–23	6
24–27	2

5) Draw a histogram for the data shown below

Mass (kg)	Frequency
0–	50
5–	64
10–	43
15–	26
20–25	17

243

6) The table below shows the number of telephone calls per day received at a fire station over a given period.

Number of calls per day	Number of days (frequency)
0	75
1	62
2	32
3	16
4	9
5	6

Draw a histogram to represent this information.

7) The data below gives the diameters of machined parts:

Diameter (mm)	Frequency
14.96–14.98	3
14.99–15.01	8
15.02–15.04	12

Write down:

(a) The upper and lower class boundaries for the second class.

(b) The class width of the classes shown in the table.

(c) The class interval for the first class.

8) Classify each of the following as continuous or discrete variables:

(a) The diameters of ball bearings.

(b) The number of shirts sold per day.

(c) The mass of packets of chemical.

(d) The number of bunches of daffodils packed by a grower.

(e) The daily temperature.

(f) The lifetime of electric light bulbs.

(g) The number of telephone calls made per day by a person.

9) An industrial organisation gives an aptitude test to all applicants for employment. The results of 150 people taking the test were

Score (out of 10)	Frequency
1	6
2	12
3	15
4	21
5	35
6	24
7	20
8	10
9	6
10	1

Draw a histogram of this information.

10) The lengths of 100 pieces of wood were measured with the following results:

Length (cm)	Frequency
29.5	2
29.6	4
29.7	11
29.8	18
29.9	31
30.0	22
30.1	8
30.2	3
30.3	1

Draw a histogram of this information.

Statistical Averages

We have seen that a mass of raw data does not mean very much until it is arranged into a frequency distribution or until it is represented as a histogram.

A second way of making the data more understandable is to try and find a single value which will represent all the values in a distribution. This single representative value is called an average.

In statistics several kinds of average are used. The more important are:

(a) The arithmetic mean, often referred to as the mean.

(b) The median.

(c) The mode.

The Arithmetic Mean

This is found by adding up all the values in a set and dividing this sum by the number of values making up the set. That is,

arithmetic mean

$$= \frac{\text{sum of all the values}}{\text{the number of values}}$$

Example 9

The heights of 5 men are: 177.8 cm, 175.3 cm, 174.8 cm, 179.1 cm and 176.5 cm.

Calculate the mean height of the 5 men.

Mean = (177.8+175.3+174.8
$$+179.1+176.5)\div5$$

$$= \frac{883.5}{5} = 176.7 \text{ cm}$$

Note that the unit of the mean is the same as the unit used for each of the quantities in the set.

The Mean of a Frequency Distribution

When finding the mean of a frequency distribution we must take into account the frequencies as well as the measured observations.

Example 10

Five packets of chemical have a mass of 20.01 grammes, 3 have a mass of 19.98 grammes and 2 have a mass of 20.03 grammes. What is the mean mass of the packets?

The total mass of the ten packets
$$= (5\times20.01)+(3\times19.98)$$
$$+(2\times20.03)$$

$$= 100.05+59.94+40.06$$

$$= 200.05 \text{ grammes}$$

Mean mass

$$= \frac{\text{total mass}}{10} = \frac{200.05}{10}$$

$$= 20.005 \text{ grammes}$$

This example gives the clue whereby we may find the mean of a frequency distribution.

Example 11

Each of 200 similar engine components are measured correct to the nearest millimetre and recorded as follows:

Length (mm)	Frequency
198	8
199	30
200	132
201	24
202	6

Calculate the mean length of the 200 components.

Mean length
$$= [(198\times8)+(199\times30)+(200\times132)$$
$$+(201\times24)+(202\times6)]\div200$$

$$= \frac{1584+5970+26\,400+4824+1212}{200}$$

$$= \frac{39\,990}{200} = 199.95 \text{ mm}$$

The calculation is often set out in tabular form as shown below. This method reduces the risk of making errors when performing the calculation.

Length (mm)	Frequency	Length× frequency
198	8	1584
199	30	5970
200	132	26400
201	24	4824
202	6	1212
Total	200	39990

$$\text{mean} = \frac{\text{total of (length} \times \text{frequency)}}{\text{total frequency}}$$

$$= \frac{39990}{200} = 199.95 \text{ mm}$$

The Median

If a set of values is arranged in ascending (or descending) order of size the median is the value which lies half-way along the series. Thus the median of 3, 4, 4, 5, 6, 8, 8, 9, 10 is 6 because there are four numbers below this value and four numbers above it.

When there are an even number of values in the set the median is found by taking the mean of the middle two values. Thus the median of 3, 3, 5, 7, 9, 10, 13, 15 is $\frac{7+9}{2} = 8$.

The Mode

The mode of a set of values is the value which occurs most frequently. That is, it is the most common value. Thus the mode of 2, 3, 3, 4, 4, 4, 5, 6, 6,

7 is 4 because this number occurs three times, which is more than any of the other numbers in the set.

Sometimes, in a set of numbers, no mode exists, as for the set 2, 4, 7, 8, 9, 11 in which each number occurs once. It is possible for there to be more than one mode. The set 2, 3, 3, 3, 4, 4, 5, 6, 6, 6, 7, 8 has two modes 3 and 6, because each of these numbers occurs three times which is more than any of the other numbers.

A set of values which has two modes is called *bimodal*. If the set has only one mode it is said to be *unimodal* but if there are more than two modes the set is called *multimodal*.

Exercise 164 — *All type A*

1) Find the mean of £23, £27, £30, £28 and £32.

2) The heights of some men are as follows: 172, 170, 181, 175, 179 and 173 cm. Calculate the mean height of the men.

3) Five people earn £42 per week, 3 earn £38 per week and 2 earn £44 per week. What is the mean wage for the 10 people?

4) Calculate the mean length from the following table:

Length (mm)	Frequency
198	1
199	4
200	17
201	2
202	1

5) Calculate the mean height of 50 people from the table below:

246

Height (cm)	Frequency
160	1
161	5
162	10
163	16
164	10
165	6
166	2

6) Find the median of the numbers 5, 3, 8, 6, 4, 2, 8.

7) Find the median of the numbers 2, 4, 6, 5, 3, 1, 8, 9.

8) The marks of a student in five examinations were: 54, 63, 49, 78 and 57. What is his median mark?

9) Find the mode of the following set of numbers 3, 5, 2, 7, 5, 8, 5, 2, 7.

10) Find the mode of 38.7, 29.6, 32.1, 35.8, 43.2.

11) Find the modes of 8, 4, 9, 3, 5, 3, 8, 5, 3, 8, 9, 5, 6, 7.

Theoretical Probability

If a coin is tossed it will come down heads or tails. There are only these two possibilities. The probability of obtaining a head in a single toss of the coin is one possibility out of two possibilities. We write this

Pr (heads)

$$= \frac{\text{possibility of a head}}{\text{total possibilities}} = \frac{1}{2}$$

When we work out a probability in this way we say that we have obtained a theoretical probability.

When we roll a die (plural dice) we can get one of six possible scores, 1, 2, 3, 4, 5 or 6. The probability of scoring 3 in a single roll of the die is one possibility

out of a total of six possibilities. Hence

$$\text{Pr (three)} = \frac{1}{6}$$

There are 52 playing cards in a pack. When we cut the pack we can get one of the 52 cards, hence the total possibilities are 52. Since there are 4 aces in the pack

$$\text{Pr (ace)} = \frac{4}{52} = \frac{1}{13}$$

Example 12

Calculate the probability of cutting a king, queen or jack in a single cut of a deck of cards.

Total possibilities = 52

Possibility of cutting a king, queen or jack = 12

$$\text{Pr (king, queen or jack)} = \frac{12}{52} = \frac{3}{13}$$

The Probability Scale

When an event is absolutely certain to happen we say that the probability of it happening is 1. Thus the probability that one day each of us will die is 1.

When an event can never happen we say that the probability of it happening is 0. Thus the probability that any one of us can jump a height of 5 metres unaided is 0.

All probabilities must, therefore, have a value between 0 and 1. They can be expressed as either a fraction or a decimal. Thus

$$\text{Pr (head)} = \frac{1}{2} = 0.5$$

$$\text{Pr (ace)} = \frac{1}{13} = 0.077$$

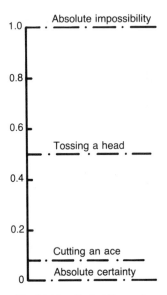

Fig. 31.17. Probability scale

Probabilities can be expressed on a probability scale (Fig. 31.17).

Total Probability

If we toss a coin it will come down either heads or tails. That is

$$\text{Pr (heads)} = \frac{1}{2}$$

$$\text{Pr (tails)} = \frac{1}{2}$$

The totaly probability, that is the probability covering all possible events, is $\frac{1}{2}+\frac{1}{2}=1$. Another way of saying this is

$$\text{Pr (success)}+\text{Pr (failure)} = 1$$

Thus the probability of cutting an ace $= \frac{1}{13}$. The probability of not cutting an ace is $1-\frac{1}{13}=\frac{12}{13}$.

Example 13

A bag contains 5 blue balls, 3 red balls and 2 black balls. A ball is drawn at random from the bag. Calculate the

probability that it will be (a) blue, (b) red, (c) not black.

(a) $\text{Pr (blue)} = \dfrac{5}{10} = \dfrac{1}{2}$

(b) $\text{Pr (red)} = \dfrac{3}{10}$

(c) $\text{Pr (black)} = \dfrac{2}{10} = \dfrac{1}{5}$

   Pr (not black)
$$= 1-\text{Pr (black)} = 1-\frac{1}{5}=\frac{4}{5}$$

Empirical Probability

Although it is possible to calculate many probabilities in the way shown above, in a great many cases we have to rely on an experiment or an enquiry in order to establish the probability of an event happening.

Suppose that we have 100 ball bearings and on examining them we find that 4 are not round. What is the probability of selecting a not-round ball bearing out of the hundred?

Total possibilities = 100

Possibilities of selecting a not-round ball bearing = 4

$$\text{Pr (not-round)} = \frac{4}{100}$$

In industry probabilities are worked out just like this and these empirical probabilities can usually be relied on. However, some probabilities, met with in every day conversation are not reliable. Suppose on 20 days we checked to see if it snowed in Gloucester and we found that on 3 of these days it did, in fact, snow. Would we be right in saying

$$\text{Pr (snow)} = \frac{3}{20}?$$

248

For a start in which part of the year were the observations taken? It must have been in the deep winter. So perhaps in December, January and February the probability might be fairly accurate but what of July and August?

Simple empirical probabilities can only be very crude measures but they are useful in conveying information in a simple direct way.

Exercise 165 — *All type B*

1) A die is rolled. Calculate the probability of:

(a) a four,

(b) a number less than four,

(c) a two or a three,

(d) an odd number.

2) 20 discs marked with the numbers 1 to 20 are placed in a box and one disc is drawn from it. Determine the probability that the number on the disc will be:

(a) a multiple of 5,

(b) odd,

(c) more than 7,

(d) less than 4.

3) A card is drawn from a deck of 52 playing cards. Find the probability that it will be:

(a) the queen of spades,

(b) a king,

(c) a picture card (i.e. an ace, king, queen or jack),

(d) the jack of hearts or the ace of clubs.

4) A letter is chosen from the word FLAGSTAFF. Find the probability that it will be:

(a) L (b) A (c) F

5) A bag contains 3 red balls, 4 blue, 6 black and 7 white. One ball is drawn from the bag. Calculate the probability that it will be:

(a) blue,

(b) red or black,

(c) not white.

6) Two dice are thrown together and their scores added. Determine the probability that the sum will be:

(a) 7, (b) less than 6,

(c) more than 8.

7) What is the least likely of (a), (b) or (c) in question 6?

8) In a factory, 200 components are checked and 15 are found to be faulty. If one component is chosen at random from the 200 components, what is the probability that it will be a good component?

Short Answer Revision Questions

1) Evaluate £2.83+46 p+8 p+£3.
(N.W.)

2) Express the number 1856.2:
(a) correct to three significant figures,
(b) in standard form. (N.W.)

3) Using ruler and compasses only construct an angle of 45°. (N.W.)

4) Evaluate $\dfrac{4.65+0.59}{46.5-5.9}$. (N.W.)

5) A man can insure the contents of his house at a rate of 38 p per £100. What will be his annual premium if he places a value of £5350 on the contents of his house? (N.W.)

6) Mr. Black and Mr. Brown form a partnership investing £1500 and £5000 respectively. They agree to share the profits in the ratio of their investments. If the profits amounted to £1300, calculate each man's share.
(N.W.)

7) The temperature, in °C, at noon on five days in January was as follows.

8°C, 12°C, 10°C, 9°C, 11°C

(a) What was the average noon temperature over the five days?
(b) What was the range of the temperatures? (N.W.)

8) Assuming the exchange rate in Denmark is 13.2 Krone to the £1 answer the following questions.
(a) The price per day of an hotel room in Denmark is 36 Krone. Calculate to the nearest 1 p the cost in £.

(b) An article costs 6.7 Krone in Denmark and 50 p in England. In which country does it cost less?
(N.W.)

9)
(a) (i) Use your table of squares to find the square of 2.831.
(ii) Use your table of square roots to find the square root of 42.63.

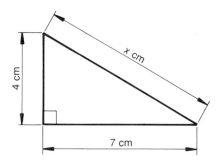

Fig. 1

(b) Use Pythagoras Theorem to work out the value of x in the right-angled triangle drawn in Fig. 1.
(W.M.)

10) A family used 240 therms of gas at 7 p per therm. They also had to pay a fixed charge of £3.50. Work out the amount of their total gas bill.

How much extra will they have to pay if the price of the gas goes up to 9 p per therm? (W.M.)

11) If 14.8×36.8 = 544.64, write down in decimal form the value of:
(a) 1.48×3.68
(b) 54.464÷14.8 (Y.R.)

12) In the following sequence all the numbers are in base seven:

$$1_7, 4_7, 12_7, 22_7, 34_7 \ldots$$

Find the next two numbers in the sequence, giving your answers in base seven. *(Y.R.)*

13) Copy Fig. 2 and draw the image of ⌐▔▔▔◞ when it is reflected in the y-axis. *(Y.R.)*

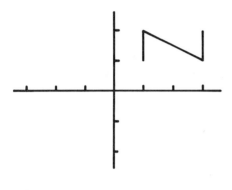

Fig. 2

14) Solve for n in the following metric conversions:

(a) $10 \text{ kg} = 10^n \text{ g}$

(b) $10\,000 \text{ m} = 10^n \text{ km}$ *(Y.R.)*

15) Calculate the smallest number whose prime factors are 5, 7 and 11. *(W.M.)*

16) Using only elements from the set $\{2, 3, 4, 5, 6\}$ for your numerator and denominator, make up:

(a) a fraction equivalent to $\frac{1}{2}$,

(b) a fraction equal to 80%,

(c) a fraction between $\frac{3}{5}$ and $\frac{4}{5}$ in value. *(W.M.)*

17) The figures below, showing the populations of seven villages, were taken at random after a census. Find the median.

1864   2467   1392   1459   2134
9803   5072 *(Y.R.)*

18) Calculate $2.5^2 - 1.3^2$. *(Y.R.)*

19) The surface area of the Earth is five hundred and ten million, one hundred thousand square kilometres.

(a) Write this as a number.

(b) Now write your answer to (a) in standard form. *(Y.R.)*

20) Find the inverse of the matrix

$$\begin{pmatrix} 1 & 1 \\ 0 & 1 \end{pmatrix}.$$ *(Y.R.)*

21) Copy the Venn diagrams in Fig. 3 and shade. *(S.W.)*

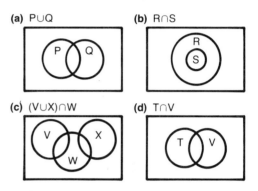

(a) P∪Q   **(b)** R∩S

(c) (V∪X)∩W   **(d)** T∩V

Fig. 3

22) Find the median of the following set of numbers:

5, 3, 7, 2, 9, 6, 12, 2, 10, 8, 2, 3. *(Y.R.)*

23) Calculate the length of the side marked x in the right-angled triangle shown in Fig. 4. *(Y.R.)*

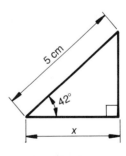

Fig. 4

24) If $A \cup B = A$, what can you say about the set B? *(Y.R.)*

25) Calculate $3\frac{2}{5} + 2\frac{1}{4}$. *(Y.R.)*

26) Write down a possible value for x if $\dfrac{2x}{5} > 10$. (Y.R.)

27) Find the value of $\dfrac{7}{12} \div \dfrac{3}{4}$ (S)

28) Find the value of $\dfrac{6^2 \times 6^3}{6^4}$. (Y.R.)

29) Write down the gradient of the line which passes through the points

$$(1, 4), (2, 5), (3, 6), (5, 8).$$ (Y.R.)

30) If $\mathbf{a} = \begin{pmatrix} 1 \\ 2 \\ 4 \\ 1 \end{pmatrix}$ and $\mathbf{b} = \begin{pmatrix} 3 \\ 0 \\ 1 \\ 4 \end{pmatrix}$

find the value of $\mathbf{b} - 2\mathbf{a}$.

(Y.R.)

31) A Pie Chart is used to show the weekly expenditure on a motor car. If the total weekly expenditure is £12 and the angle of the sector representing 'Tax and Insurance' is 60°, how much does 'Tax and Insurance' cost per week? (Y.R.)

32) In a swimming match, the times taken, to the nearest second, by 20 children to swim 1 length were as follows:

31 27 24 26 31 25 26 32 27 31
26 32 30 32 29 25 29 27 26 32

Find the frequency for each of the above times. (Y.R.)

33) Calculate 8% of £57. (Y.R.)

34) What percentage is:
(a) 650 m of 1 km?
(b) 60° of two right angles? (Y.R.)

35) What is the remainder when 6458 is divided by 9? (S)

36) If you borrow money using an Access Card you pay interest at the rate of 2% per month. How much

interest would you pay if you borrowed £15 for 1 month? (S)

37) Express 111.01_2 as a number in base 10. (Y.R.)

38) Rates are 75 p in the £1. A house has a rateable value of £300.
(a) How much does the householder pay in rates each year?
(b) 60% of the rates are spent on education. How much does the householder pay towards the cost of education? (S)

39) Write 0.028 46 correct to three significant figures. (S)

40) Multiply 3.2×10^6 by 4×10^{-3}, giving your answer in standard form. (S)

41) If $a = 1$, $b = -2$ and $c = 3$, what is the value of $\dfrac{ab - c}{c + ab}$? (S)

42) If $v^2 = 2as$,
(a) find s if $v = 8$ and $a = 40$,
(b) find v if $a = 16$ and $s = 10$.
(correct to three significant figures.) (S)

43) Find the value of 42_5 in dernary. (Y.R.)

44) $R = \{2, 4, 6, 8, 10\}$. How many subsets of R have one member only? (Y.R.)

45) From a shuffled pack of 52 cards I deal 2 cards. What is the probability of:
(a) the first card being an ace,
(b) the second card being an ace if it was known that the first card was an ace? (S)

46) Write down the largest denary number (base 10) which can be represented by six digits in the binary number system (base 2). (S)

47) Write as a single fraction:
(a) $\frac{1}{2} + \frac{1}{3}$ (b) $\frac{2}{3} \times \frac{3}{5}$ (c) $\frac{1}{4} \div \frac{2}{6}$
(A.L.)

48) For $\mathscr{E} = \{$natural numbers less than 30$\}$ and the subsets

$P = \{$square numbers$\} = \{1, 4, 9, 16, 25\}$,

$Q = \{$rectangular numbers$\} = \{4, 6, 8, 9,$ 10, 12, 14, 15, 16, 18, 20, 21, 22, 24, 25, 26, 27, 28$\}$,

$R = \{$triangular numbers$\} = \{1, 3, 6, 10,$ 15, 21, 28$\}$,

list the members of:

(a) $P \cup Q$ (c) $P \cap Q$

(b) $Q \cap R$ (d) $(P \cup Q \cup R)$

(A.L.)

49)

(a) Write in standard form:
    (i) 3010
    (ii) 0.08,

(b) calculate and give your answer in standard form:

$$3010 \times 0.08. \qquad (A.L.)$$

50) For a cylindrical can with circular base radius r cm and height h cm, the volume V cm³ is given by $V = \pi r^2 h$. [You may use $\pi = 3.14$.]

(a) If $r = 3$ cm and $h = 10$ cm find the volume.

(b) If $r = 4$ cm and $V = 140$ cm³ find the height.   (A.L.)

51) Factorise:

(a) $6x + 4y$ (c) $x^2 - x - 6$

(b) $3t^2 + t$ (A.L.)

52) What is the mode of the histogram shown in Fig. 5?

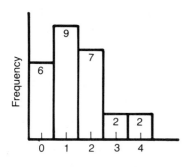

Fig. 5

53)

(a) Make an accurate drawing of the triangle ABC, where AB = 6.3 cm, AC = 4.9 cm, and angle A = 38°.

(b) What is the length of BC?

54) Write the number 0.003 61 in standard form.   (Y.R.)

55) If $f: x \rightarrow x^2 + 2x - 3$, find the value of the range when $x = 3$.   (Y.R.)

56) Find the value of $3\sqrt{169}$.   (Y.R.)

57) Find the value of $1\frac{1}{4} + 2\frac{1}{8} - \frac{5}{8}$.   (Y.R.)

58) Find the value of x which will satisfy the equation $5 - 2(x - 2) = 1$.   (Y.R.)

59) Two six-faced die are thrown together. What is the probability of a total score of exactly 11?   (Y.R.)

60) What is the mean of the numbers 7, 9, 11, 8, 10?   (Y.R.)

61) If $A * B$ means square A and add B to the answer, find the value of $7 * 4$.   (Y.R.)

62) Write down the next three terms of the following sequences:

(a) 2, 4, 6, 8,

(b) $1, -\frac{1}{2}, \frac{1}{4}, -\frac{1}{8}$.

63) The set A is defined as all the prime numbers between 10 and 30. How many members has the set A?   (Y.R.)

64) Find the exact value of 4.3×7.8.   (Y.R.)

65) Find the value of $141_5 + 42_5$ leaving your answer in base five.   (Y.R.)

66) Calculate 15% of £250.   (Y.R.)

67) Write down the gradient of the line which passes through the points (2, 4), (3, 6), (4, 8).   (Y.R.)

68) How many:

(a) pence in £4.50?

(b) metres in 1 kilometre?

(c) milligrams in 3 grams?

(d) centimetres in 9 metres?

(e) litres in 3500 millilitres?

(*W.Y.*)

69) Find the cost of:

(a) 4 pens at 25 p each.

(b) 3 metres of cloth at £1.99 per metre.

(c) 7 kg of potatoes when 3 kg cost $7\frac{1}{2}$ p.

(d) 29 litres of petrol at 13 p per litre.

(e) A piece of glass 1 metre long and 55 cm wide, when 1 m^2 of glass costs £1.00. (*W.Y.*)

70) When $a = \frac{1}{2}$, $b = \frac{1}{3}$ and $c = \frac{1}{4}$, find the value of:

(a) $a+c$ (d) $a \div c$

(b) $a \times b$ (e) $2a - b^2$

(c) $b - c$ (*W.Y.*)

71) Given that AB is a straight line 10 cm long draw AB and perform the following constructions:

(a) bisect the line AB,

(b) at A draw an angle of 60°,

(c) at B draw a circle with a *diameter* of 6 cm. (*W.Y.*)

72) Calculate $\frac{1}{2} + \frac{1}{3} + \frac{1}{4}$. (*M*)

73) Without working out any results, say why each of the following statements is incorrect.

(a) $389 \times 35 = 13611$.

(b) 197 314 is a prime number. (*M*)

74) Calculate the following 2×2 matrix products:

(a) $\begin{pmatrix} 4 & 9 \\ 3 & 7 \end{pmatrix}\begin{pmatrix} 7 & -9 \\ -3 & 4 \end{pmatrix}$

(b) $\begin{pmatrix} 7 & -9 \\ -3 & 4 \end{pmatrix}\begin{pmatrix} 4 & 9 \\ 3 & 7 \end{pmatrix}$ (*M*)

75) How many subsets of $\{v, w, x, y\}$ are there which contain just three elements? (*M*)

76) Evaluate the following:

(a) $(12^2 + 5^2)^{\frac{1}{2}}$,

(b) $(2 \times 7 \times 3 \times 2 \times 7 \times 3 \times 2 \times 3 \times 7)^{\frac{1}{3}}$,

(c) 36×3^{-2}. (*M*)

77)

(a) Find p and n when 871 is expressed in the form $871 = p \times 10^n$, where p is a positive number less than 10 but greater than 1, and n is a whole number.

(b) Find $\log 871$. (*M*)

78) A box contains 32 balloons each being one of five different colours. Show that at least 7 balloons must have the same colour. (*M*)

79) Solve the equation
$$3x + 5 = 8x - 20.$$ (*M*)

80) Express in decimal form:

(a) $2\frac{7}{10}$ (b) $13\frac{9}{100}$ (c) $3\frac{3}{25}$ (*S*)

81) If $y - 2x = 3$, find,

(a) y when $x = 2$,

(b) x when $y = 10$,

(c) x and y if $y + 2x = 7$. (*S*)

82) A rectangle is 2.2 m long and 500 mm wide. Calculate its area in square metres. (*S*)

83) Express the number 23_4 in base ten. (*S*)

84) Find the mean of the numbers 1.2, 2.3, 4.5 and 5.6. (*S*)

85) The probability that John will be selected for the school team is $\frac{13}{21}$. What is the probability that he will not be selected? (*E.M.*)

254

86) If P = {prime numbers} and F = {20, 21, 22, ..., 39}, list the members of the set $P \cap F$. *(S)*

87) The average distance from the sun to the earth is 92 956 000 miles. Write this:

(a)   to 2 significant figures,

(b)   in standard form. *(S)*

88) Multiply out $(x+3)(x-2)$ *(E.M.)*

89) How many lines of symmetry has a square? *(E.M.)*

90) A school tuckshop sold the following numbers of packets of crisps on eleven schooldays:

7, 9, 16, 24, 7, 50, 16, 32, 10, 0, 16.

Find the arithmetical mean of these numbers.

(E.M.)

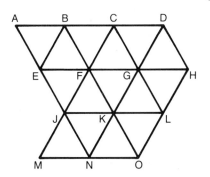

Fig. 6

91) Figure 6 consists of equilateral triangles. Using the letters given, find in the diagram:

(a)   a rhombus,

(b)   an isosceles trapezium,

(c)   a regular hexagon,

(d)   a triangle whose area is nine times as great as that of $\triangle$CFG. *(E.M.)*

92) In the Treble Chance football pool, you have to select 8 matches which you think are going to end as draws. If you select 12 matches, and 'perm any 8 from 12', the number of lines required is given by the expression:

$$\frac{12 \times 11 \times 10 \times 9 \times 8 \times 7 \times 6 \times 5}{8 \times 7 \times 6 \times 5 \times 4 \times 3 \times 2 \times 1}$$

Work out the number of lines required. (The answer is a whole number less than 500.) *(E.M.)*

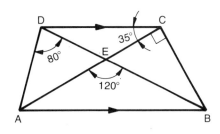

Fig. 7

93) Copy Fig. 7 (it need not be exact), and fill in the size of all the other angles in it. *(E.M.)*

94) A snail crawls 1 metre in $1\frac{1}{2}$ minutes. Find its speed in:

(a)   metres per minute,

(b)   metres per hour. *(E.M.)*

95) Use Pythagoras' Theorem or an accurate scale drawing to show that a triangle with sides 20 cm, 21 cm, and 29 cm is right-angled. Then find its area. *(E.M.)*

96) £3.00 is divided amongst fifty boys and girls, the boys getting 10 p each and the girls 5 p each. If there are x girls, write down an expression for:

(a)   the number of boys,

(b)   the total amount of money received by the girls, in pence.

Find, by algebra or by trial and error, how many girls there are. *(E.M.)*

97) There are a million millimetres in a kilometre. Using the Standard Form $A \times 10^n$, where A is a number between 1 and 10, and n is a (positive or negative) whole number, express:

(a)   50 kilometres in millimetres,

(b)   4 millimetres in kilometres. *(E.M.)*

98)

(a) What is the area of the largest circle that can be drawn inside a square of side 14 cm?

(b) What is the circumference of this circle? (Take $\pi = \frac{22}{7}$.)   (W)

99) Remove the brackets and simplify:

(a) $(3x+1)(x-4)$, (b) $(2x-3)^2$.   (W)

100) Which of the following symbols, $>$, $=$ or $\fallingdotseq$ can be correctly inserted in the following?

(a) (12) $(3\times4\times0)$

(b) (3.99×3.97) (16)

(c) $(2^3\times3^3)$ (6^3)

(d) (15^2) (8^2+7^2) (W)

Multi-Choice Revision Exercise

write down the letter corresponding to the correct answer

1) 5^4 has a value of:

    a 9   **b** 20   **c** 125   **d** 625

    e 3125   (*N.W.*)

2) The fraction of the circle which has been shaded in Fig. 1 is:

    a $\frac{5}{24}$ **b** $\frac{1}{4}$ **c** $\frac{1}{2}$ **d** $\frac{5}{8}$ **e** $\frac{17}{24}$

                                  (*N.W.*)

Fig. 1

3) Two buckets A and B, identical in shape, are such that the dimensions of A are three times as large as the corresponding dimensions of B. The ratio of the volumes of A: B is:

    a 1:9   **b** 1:27   **c** 3:1   **d** 9:1

    e 27:1   (*N.W.*)

4) $a^2 \times b \times a^4 \times b^2$ equals:

    a $a^6 b^2$ **b** $a^8 b^2$ **c** $a^3 b^3$

    d $(ab)^9$ **e** $a^6 b^3$ (*W.M.*)

5) The inverse under multiplication of the matrix $\begin{pmatrix} 5 & 7 \\ 2 & 3 \end{pmatrix}$ is:

    a $\begin{pmatrix} -3 & -7 \\ -2 & -5 \end{pmatrix}$ **b** $\begin{pmatrix} -5 & 2 \\ 7 & -3 \end{pmatrix}$

    c $\begin{pmatrix} 3 & -7 \\ -2 & 5 \end{pmatrix}$ **d** $\begin{pmatrix} 0 & 0 \\ 0 & 0 \end{pmatrix}$

                                    (*Y.R.*)

6) What is the median of the numbers:

    8, 10, 9, 6, 7, 10, 12, 8, 9, 8

    a 7.5 **b** 8 **c** 8.5 **d** 8.7 **e** 9

                                   (*W.M.*)

7) The value of y which satisfies the equation $4(y-4) = 20$ is:

    a 1 **b** 24 **c** 6 **d** 9 **e** 4

                                   (*W.M.*)

8) In the triangle shown in Fig. 2 the length of the side marked x is:

    a $7 \sin 56°$ **b** $7 \tan 56°$

    c $7 \tan 34°$ **d** $7 \cos 34°$

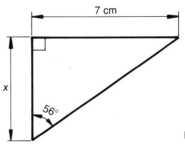

Fig. 2

257

9) What is the base of the following addition sum?

$$\begin{array}{r} 324 \\ 135 \\ \hline 503 \end{array}$$ **a** 2 **b** 3 **c** 4 **d** 5 **e** 6

10) If $2^x \times 3^2 = 144$, the value of x is:

a 7 **b** 5 **c** 4 **d** 8

11) The number of people attending a football match is quoted as 27 000, correct to 2 significant figures. The greatest possible attendance shown by this figure is:

a 27 000 **b** 27 499 **c** 27 599
d 26 999

12) The quadrilateral which has only one line of symmetry is:

a a kite **b** a parallelogram
c a rectangle **d** a rhombus

13) If $a*b = \sqrt{ab}$, the value of $4*9$ is:

a 7 **b** 36 **c** 6 **d** 49

14) If $x^2 \times 3^2 \times 1^2 = 144$, the value of x could be:

a ⁻4 **b** ⁻2 **c** 2 **d** 3.9 (Y.R.)

15) If $3x - 7 = 10$, the value of x is:

a $\dfrac{3}{17}$ **b** $\dfrac{17}{3}$ **c** 6 **d** $\dfrac{-3}{17}$

(Y.R.)

16) The sum of the interior angles of an *octagon* is:

a 360° **b** 1080° **c** 1260°
d 1440° (Y.R.)

17) The dernary number 39 written in binary is:

a 100011 **b** 100111
c 1001 **d** 10001
e 10000 (W.Y.)

18) The square root of 9.018 009 is given as 3.003. Therefore the square root of 901.800 9 is:

a 30.03 **b** 300.3 **c** 0.3003
d 3003 (Y.R.)

19) The inverse of the 2×2 matrix $\begin{pmatrix} 6 & 10 \\ 2 & 4 \end{pmatrix}$ is:

a $\begin{pmatrix} 1 & -2\frac{1}{2} \\ -\frac{1}{2} & 1\frac{1}{2} \end{pmatrix}$ **b** $\begin{pmatrix} 4 & -10 \\ -2 & 6 \end{pmatrix}$

c $\begin{pmatrix} -2 & 6 \\ -10 & 4 \end{pmatrix}$ **d** $\begin{pmatrix} 1 & 2\frac{1}{2} \\ \frac{1}{2} & 1\frac{1}{2} \end{pmatrix}$

(Y.R.)

20) The area in square units of the trapezium shown in Fig. 3 is:

a 24 **b** 40 **c** 32 **d** 30 (Y.R.)

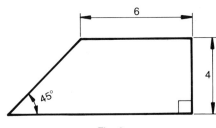

Fig. 3

21) A triangle with vertices at the points with coordinates $(-4, 4)$, $(4, 4)$ and $(0, -1)$ is:

a right-angled **b** equilateral
c isosceles **d** scalene (Y.R.)

22) 42_5 is equivalent to:

a 21_{10} **b** 10101_2 **c** 112_4
d 212_3 (Y.R.)

23) The area of a lake represented on a map is 15 cm². The scale of the map is 1 to 100. The actual area of the lake is:

a 1.5 m² **b** 15 m² **c** 150 m²
d 15 000 m² (Y.R.)

24) Given that $225 \times 35 = 7875$, then:

(i) 22.5×0.35 is:

    a 787.5   **b** 7.875   **c** 0.7875
    d 0.078 75   **e** 0.007 875

(ii) $78.75 \div 0.35$ is:

    a 0.225   **b** 2.25   **c** 22.5
    d 225   **e** 2250

(iii) $2\frac{1}{4} \times 3\frac{1}{2}$ is:

    a $5\frac{3}{4}$ **b** $6\frac{1}{8}$ **c** $6\frac{7}{8}$ **d** $7\frac{1}{8}$ **e** $7\frac{7}{8}$

(iv) 450×70 is:

    a 3.15×10^5 **b** 3.15×10^4
    c 3.15×10^3 **d** 3.15×10^2
    e 3.15×10^{-1} *(W.Y.)*

25) The inverse of the 2×2 matrix $\begin{pmatrix} 6 & 11 \\ 2 & 4 \end{pmatrix}$ is:

    a $\begin{pmatrix} 2 & -5\frac{1}{2} \\ -1 & 3 \end{pmatrix}$ **b** $\begin{pmatrix} 4 & 2 \\ -11 & 6 \end{pmatrix}$

    c $\begin{pmatrix} 3 & -5\frac{1}{2} \\ -1 & 2 \end{pmatrix}$ **d** $\begin{pmatrix} 0 & 0 \\ 0 & 0 \end{pmatrix}$

26) $\frac{3}{40}$ as a % is:

    a 3%   **b** $7\frac{1}{2}$%   **c** 40%
    d 75%   **e** 97%   *(W.Y.)*

27) A boy scored 70% in a test. If the maximum mark was 40, then the boy's mark was:

    a 4   **b** 10   **c** 28   **d** 30   **e** 35
                               (W.Y.)

28) During a sale, a shop reduced the price of everything by 10%. What was the Sale Price of an article originally priced at £4.30?

    a £0.43   **b** £3.40   **c** £3.87
    d £3.97   **e** £4.73   *(W.Y.)*

29) The value of $-6 - (-6)$ is:

    a -12 **b** 0   **c** 12   **d** 36
    e none of these   *(W.Y.)*

30) When $b = -1$, the value of $5 - b - b^2$ is:

    a 5   **b** 3   **c** 2   **d** 0
    e none of these   *(W.Y.)*

31) When $3^x = 81$, then the value of x is:

    a 2   **b** 3   **c** 4   **d** 27   **e** 78
                               (W.Y.)

32) When $\dfrac{x}{4} = \dfrac{5}{2}$, the value of x is:

    a 2   **b** 4   **c** 5   **d** 10   **e** 20
                               (W.Y.)

33) $(2x - 3) - (2 - 3x)$ is:

    a $5x - 5$ **b** $5x - 1$ **c** $x - 5$
    d $x - 1$ **e** none of these   *(W.Y.)*

34) The area of a square is x^2 cm². Its perimeter is:

    a x^4 cm   **b** $4x^2$ cm   **c** $4x$ cm
    d $2x$ cm   **e** $\dfrac{x^2}{4}$ cm   *(W.Y.)*

35) In Fig. 4 ABCD is a parallelogram, in which DE is perpendicular to BC, $DE = 5$ cm, $BC = 25$ cm and $B\hat{A}D = 45°$.

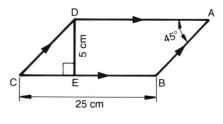

Fig. 4

(i) The size of $A\hat{B}C$ is:

    a 45°   **b** 90°   **c** 135°   **d** 145°
    e none of these

259

(ii)   The length of EC is:

    a 25 cm   **b** 20 cm   **c** 15 cm
    d 10 cm   **e** 5 cm

(iii)   The area of ABCD is:

    a 625 cm²   **b** 250 cm²
    c 125 cm²   **d** 62½ cm²
    e none of these   (W.Y.)

36)   The denary (base 10) number 37, written in binary (base 2) is:

    a 100011   **b** 100111
    c 100001   **d** 110001
    e 100101   (W.Y.)

37)   If both numbers are in binary, the average of 1011 and 111 is:

    a 1000   **b** 10010   **c** 1001
    d 10001   **e** 10000   (W.Y.)

38)   Which one of the following numbers is the product of *two consecutive* prime numbers?

    a 8 **b** 15 **c** 18 **d** 21 **e** 33
     (W.Y.)

39)   Which one of the following is irrational?

    a $\sqrt{9}$ **b** $\sqrt{1.44}$ **c** $\sqrt{0.9}$
    d $\sqrt{144}$ **e** $\sqrt{0.09}$ (W.Y.)

40)   The smallest whole number which satisfies the inequality $9-2x<5x-12$ is:

    a 1 **b** 2 **c** 3 **d** 4 **e** 5
     (W.Y.)

41)   Which one of the following triplets, *does not* represent the lengths of the sides of a right angled triangle?

    a (6, 8, 10)   **b** (8, 15, 17)
    c (5, 12, 13)   **d** (7, 23, 24)
    e (9, 40, 41)   (W.Y.)

42)   A boy obtains 60 marks out of 75 in an examination. This is equivalent

to a percentage of:

    a 60%   **b** 30%   **c** 90%
    d 125%   **e** 80%   (E.M.)

43)   (0.7)³ equals

    a 2.1   **b** 0.49   **c** 3.43
    d 0.343   **e** 0.049   (E.M.)

44)   In Fig. 5, ABC is a triangle, in which BD is the perpendicular from B to AD.   AC = 42 cm,   AD = 12 cm and   BD = 16 cm.

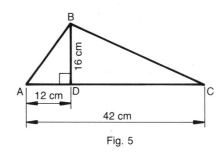

Fig. 5

(i)   Tan Â as a vulgar fraction is:
    a $\frac{4}{5}$ **b** $\frac{3}{5}$ **c** $\frac{5}{6}$ **d** $\frac{4}{3}$ **e** $\frac{3}{4}$

(ii)   Sin AB̂D as a decimal fraction is:
    a 1.6 **b** 1.3 **c** 0.8 **d** 0.75
    e 0.6

(iii)   The size of Ĉ (to the nearest degree) is:
    a 27° **b** 28° **c** 32° **d** 58°
    e 62°

(iv)   The perimeter of triangle BDC is:
    a 70 cm   **b** 80 cm   **c** 90 cm
    d 92 cm   **e** 96 cm   (W.Y.)

45)   If three angles of a quadrilateral are equal and the fourth is twice the size of the other three, find the size of a smaller angle.

    a 36° **b** 60° **c** 72° **d** 90°
    e 144°   (M)

46) The exchange rate for French Francs is 10 francs for £1 Sterling. 3653 francs changed into sterling would be:

    a £3.65   **b** £36.53   **c** £365.30
    d £3653   **e** £36530   (S.E.)

47) A transistor radio can be bought for £18.95 cash or on Hire Purchase for 9 monthly payments of £2.37 each. How much more does the Hire Purchase method cost?

    a £2.21   **b** £2.38   **c** £2.95
    d £3.32   **e** £3.71   (S.E.)

48) $5-0.003$ equals:

    a 0.002   **b** 4.003   **c** 4.007
    d 4.997   **e** 5.003   (S.E.)

49) The total wages bill for 40 men was £1180. What was the average wage?

    a £29.50   **b** £29.00   **c** £28.50
    d £27.50   **e** £27.00   (S.E.)

50) When the binary numbers $1\,0\,1$ and $1\,1$ are multiplied together the answer is:

    a $1\,0\,0\,1$ **b** $1\,0\,1\,0$ **c** $1\,0\,1\,1$
    d $1\,1\,1\,0$ **e** $1\,1\,1\,1$ (S.E.)

51) Given that $\dfrac{2}{x}=\dfrac{3}{6}$, what is the value of x?

    a 6 **b** 4 **c** 3 **d** 2 **e** 1
                                    (S.E.)

52) The length of a rectangle is twice the width. If the length is 8 cm, how long is the perimeter in centimetres?

    a 128   **b** 48   **c** 32   **d** 24
    e 12   (S.E.)

53) What is $\tfrac{1}{2}+(\tfrac{1}{2}\times\tfrac{1}{2})$?

    a $\tfrac{1}{8}$ **b** $\tfrac{1}{2}$ **c** $\tfrac{3}{4}$ **d** 1 **e** $1\tfrac{1}{2}$
                                    (S.E.)

54) $-12+8.3$ equals:

    a -4.7 **b** -4.3 **c** -3.7
    d 3.7   **e** 4.3   (S.E.)

55) Which one of the following is *not* equal to $\tfrac{1}{2}pq$?

    a $\dfrac{pq}{2}$ **b** $p\times\dfrac{q}{2}$ **c** $\tfrac{1}{2}qp$

    d $\dfrac{1}{2p}\times q$ **e** $q\times\dfrac{p}{2}$ (S.E.)

56) Given that $\tfrac{1}{3}(x+1)=6$, what is the value of x?

    a 19   **b** 17   **c** 5   **d** 3   **e** 1
                                    (S.E.)

57)

BRAZILS	ɪɪɪɪ
WALNUTS	ɪɪɪɪ 11
ALMONDS	ɪɪɪɪ 111
CHESTNUTS	ɪɪɪɪ 111
COBNUTS	ɪɪɪɪ ɪɪɪɪ 11

ɪɪɪɪ represents 5

The tally marks above show the distribution in a sample of mixed nuts. What fraction of the nuts were almonds?

    a $\tfrac{1}{8}$ **b** $\tfrac{7}{40}$ **c** $\tfrac{1}{5}$ **d** $\tfrac{1}{4}$ **e** $\tfrac{3}{10}$
                                    (S.E.)

58) Which one of the following figures, as drawn, is *not* symmetrical about a horizontal axis?

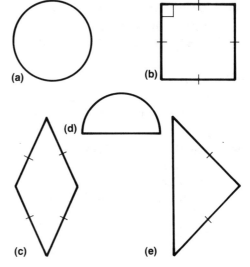

(a)   (b)   (c)   (d)   (e)

59) PQ is a straight line (Fig. 6). What are the co-ordinates of the mid-point of PQ.

    a $(-1, 3)$ **b** $(-1, -3)$
    c $(3, -1)$ **d** $(1, 3)$ **e** $(3, 1)$(S.E.)

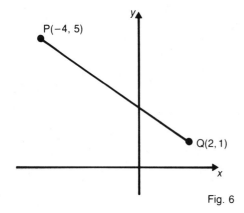

Fig. 6

60) What is 0.0063 correct to 2 decimal places?

    a 0.006   **b** 0.01   **c** 0.06
    d 0.10   **e** 0.60   (S.E.)

61) £63 is divided into two parts so that the first part is $\frac{3}{4}$ of the second. What is the value of the larger part?

    a £36   **b** £28   **c** £27   **d** £24
    e £21   (S.E.)

62) In a school's examination 480 candidates were awarded Grade 4 out of a total of 720 results. On a pie-chart showing all the grades what would be the angle at the centre for grade 4?

    a 270°   **b** 240°   **c** 210°
    d 180°   **e** 120°   (S.E.)

63) If $\frac{1}{2}p = x+y$ then p equals:

    a $2x+y$ **b** $\frac{1}{2}(x+y)$ **c** $x+2y$
    d $x+y-\frac{1}{2}$ **e** $2(x+y)$ (S.E.)

64) ABCD is a trapezium (Fig. 7). Angle D is a right-angle and BE is perpendicular to DC   AB = 12 cm, DC = 18 cm,   AD = 8 cm. The value of tan C is:

    a $\frac{4}{9}$ **b** $\frac{2}{3}$ **c** $\frac{4}{3}$ **d** $\frac{4}{5}$

                       (A.L.)

262

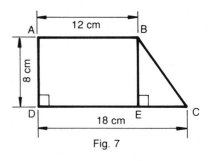

Fig. 7

65) $4\times10^2\times2\times10^{-4}$ is equal to:

    a 8×10^2 **b** 8×10^{-2}
    c 8×10^{-8} **d** 6×10^6 **e** 6×10^{-2}
                          (S.E.)

66) What is the number missed out in the following series?   14, −3, *, −37

    a 11   **b** −14   **c** −17   **d** −20
    e −26   (S.E.)

67) Using the given triangle (Fig. 8) which one of the following ratios equals sin 60°?

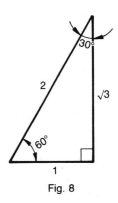

Fig. 8

    a cos 30°   **b** sin 30°   **c** cos 60°
    d tan 30°   **e** tan 60°   (S.E.)

68) Figure 9 shows a rectangular sheet of thin metal from which a

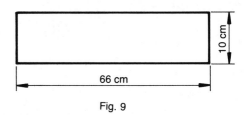

Fig. 9

cylinder, 10 cm high, is to be made with no overlap. What would be the radius of this cylinder in centimetres?

Circumference of a circle, $C = 2\pi r$. Take π as $\frac{22}{7}$.

    a 3.3   **b** 6.6   **c** 10.5   **d** 21
    e 38   (*S.E.*)

69) What is the ratio of the areas of the two triangles shown in Fig. 10?

    a 1:6   **b** 1:2   **c** 1:4   **d** 1:9
    e 1:3   (*W.M.*)

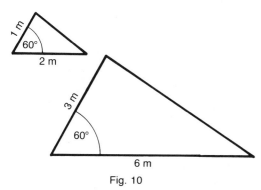

Fig. 10

70) A regular polygon, centre O, can be sub-divided into isosceles triangles identical to △POQ (Fig. 11). How many such triangles are there in the polygon?

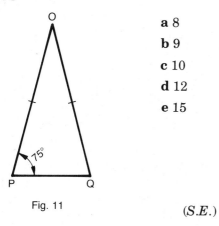

    a 8
    b 9
    c 10
    d 12
    e 15

Fig. 11   (*S.E.*)

71) Which ONE of the following points lies on the straight line $y = 2x - 5$?

    a (1, 3)   **b** (2, 5)   **c** (3, −1)
    d (3, 0)   **e** (3, 1)   (*S.E.*)

72) The value of 0.6×0.04 is:

    a 0.24   **b** 0.64   **c** 0.024
    d 2.4   **e** 0.0024   (*W.M.*)

73) In the number 460.23 the actual value represented by the digit 3 is:

    a 3   **b** $\frac{3}{10}$ **c** 30   **d** $\frac{3}{1000}$

    e $\frac{3}{100}$ (*W.M.*)

74) On the map drawn to a scale of 2 cm representing 1 km the actual area represented by a square of side 4 cm is:

    a 2 km²   **b** 4 km   **c** 1 km²
    d 4 km²   **e** 8 km   (*W.M.*)

75) If $\dfrac{1}{v} = \dfrac{1}{f} - \dfrac{1}{u}$ then the value of v when $f = 2$ and $u = 3$ is:

    a −1   **b** +5   **c** +6   **d** −6
    e +1   (*W.M.*)

76) If £120 is divided in the ratio 2 to 3 then the smaller share is:

    a £48   **b** £80   **c** £72   **d** £60
    e £40   (*W.M.*)

77) If 20% of a sum of money is £400 then the whole sum of money is:

    a £2000   **b** £80   **c** £20
    d £40 000   **e** £8000   (*W.M.*)

78) If $P \times +4 = -20$, then the value of P is:

    a −5   **b** −80   **c** −16
    d −24   **e** +16   (*W.M.*)

79) The total surface area of a cube of edge 3 cm is:

    a 27 cm²   **b** 27 cm³   **c** 54 cm
    d 54 cm²   **e** 36 cm²   (*W.M.*)

80) 24_5 is equivalent to:

    a 40_3 **b** 112_3 **c** 11000_2
    d 120_{10} **e** 31_4 (*W.M.*)

81) How many lines of symmetry, in the plane of the paper, has the triangle shown in Fig. 12?

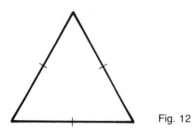

Fig. 12

a 5   **b** 4   **c** 2   **d** 3   **e** 1

(N.W.)

82) Calculate the average of 1, 2, 5, 7 and 15.

a 6   **b** 30   **c** 7   **d** 15   **e** 4

(N.W.)

83) Evaluate $13^2 - 12^2$.

a 25   **b** 5   **c** 1^2 **d** 125   **e** 2

(N.W.)

84) The pie chart (Fig. 13) illustrates how a group of children travel to school. What percentage walk to school?

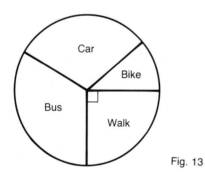

Fig. 13

a 50%   **b** 20%   **c** 25%
d 10%   **e** 30%   (N.W.)

85) If O is the centre of the circle (Fig. 14), what is the area of the shaded part?

a $\dfrac{3\pi r^2}{4}$ **b** $\dfrac{\pi r^2}{2}$ **c** $\dfrac{\pi r^2}{4}$

d πr **e** $\dfrac{\pi r}{2}$ (N.W.)

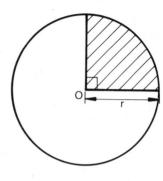

Fig. 14

86) Find the value of x in the equation $5x + 1 = 31$.

a 31   **b** 5   **c** $6\frac{2}{5}$ **d** 25   **e** 6

(N.W.)

87) Find the value of the angle marked X (Fig. 15).

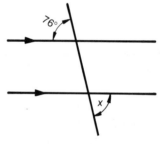

Fig. 15

a 104°   **b** 94°   **c** 90°   **d** 76°
e 114°   (N.W.)

88) Add $(2x+y)$ and $(x-2y)$.

a $3x+y$ **b** $x-y$ **c** $x-3y$
d $x+3y$ **e** $3x-y$ (N.W.)

89) Simplify $\dfrac{2^3 \times 2^4}{2^2}$

a 2^4 **b** 2^3 **c** 2^2 **d** 2^6 **e** 2^5

(N.W.)

90) A sum of money was divided in the ratio of 2:3 between two children. What fraction of the money was received by the child who received the smaller amount?

a $\frac{2}{5}$ **b** $\frac{3}{5}$ **c** $\frac{1}{2}$ **d** $\frac{2}{3}$ **e** $\frac{3}{2}$ (N.W.)

91) Evaluate $2002_3 - 202_3$.

a 100_3 **b** 101_3 **c** 1100_3
d 1010_3 **e** 1001_3 (N.W.)

264

92) Evaluate $1001_2 \times 101_2$.

a 100111_2 **b** 111001_2
c 101101_2 **d** 11001_2
e 111010_2 (*N.W.*)

93) Evaluate $1010_2 \div 101_2$.

a 101_2 **b** 11_2 **c** 10_2 **d** 100_2
e 1_2 (*N.W.*)

94) When $\dfrac{t+2}{2} + \dfrac{t+3}{3}$ is simplified, the result is:

a $\dfrac{5t+5}{6}$ **b** $\dfrac{5t+12}{6}$

c $\dfrac{2t+5}{5}$ **d** $\dfrac{t^2+6}{6}$

e $\dfrac{2t+5}{6}$ (*M*)

95) The cosine of $60° = \frac{1}{2}$. What is the value of $28 - 20 \cos 60°$?

a 18   **b** 10   **c** 4   **d** 24   **e** 8.

96) Assuming $\sqrt{1.44}$ to be 1.2 and $\sqrt{14.4}$ to be 3.795, it follows that $\sqrt{0.0144}$ is:

a 0.3795   **b** 0.12   **c** 0.037 95
d 0.012   **e** 0.003 795   (*M*)

97) In three triangles ABC, DEF and XYZ: triangles ABC and DEF are equiangular but not congruent; triangles DEF and XYZ are congruent. It follows that triangles:

a ABC and DEF are equal in area

b ABC and XYZ are similar

c ABC and XYZ are congruent

d ABC and XYZ are equal in area

e DEF and XYZ are equal in area   (*M*)

98) The area of a triangle, the sides of which are 5 cm, 4 cm and 3 cm long, is

a 30 cm²   **b** 15 cm²   **c** 12 cm²
d 10 cm²   **e** 6 cm²   (*M*)

99) The largest angle of any triangle

a must always be an acute angle

b can sometimes be an acute angle

c can never be a right angle

d can sometimes be a right angle

e must always be an obtuse angle   (*M*)

100) In a trapezium, the lengths of the parallel sides are 4 cm and 6 cm, and the perpendicular distance between these sides is 3 cm, so that the area is

a 15 cm²   **b** 18 cm²   **c** 30 cm²
d 36 cm²   **e** 77 cm²   (*M*)

Longer Questions

The following questions have all been taken from Paper 1 of past C.S.E. examination papers.

The questions which follow are all Type B.

1) A record player costs £30 but is offered for sale at a reduction of $\frac{1}{4}$ of this price.

(a) What is the sale price? I actually pay for the record player by making a deposit of £5 followed by 6 monthly payments of £3.50.

(b) How much will the record player cost by paying for it in this way?

In the same shop records are offered for sale at a reduction of 15%.

(c) How much will I have to pay for a record which would have cost £2.50? *(S)*

2)
(a) Find the value of each of the following expressions when $a = 5$, $b = 4$, $x = 3$, $y = 6$.

   (i) $3a + 2b$,
   (ii) $a + b - (x + y)$,
   (iii) $\dfrac{ay}{(a-x)}$,
   (iv) $2ax + by$,
   (v) $ab^2 - y^2 + x^2$,

(b) If $S = ut + \frac{1}{2}at^2$, find S when $a = 10$, $t = 5$ and $u = 12$. *(S)*

3)
(a) From the following set of numbers
$$\{24, 33, 45, 61, 63, 27, 49\}$$
write down:

   (i) an even number
   (ii) an odd number
   (iii) a prime number
   (iv) a perfect square
   (v) a number exactly divisible by 7
   (vi) how many numbers are exactly divisible by 9
   (vii) a pair of numbers which multiplied together give 1485.

(b) What is, 1011_2
$$101_2 +$$
_____

_____

Give your answer as a base 2 number.
Convert your answer to a base 10 number.

(c) What is, 10101_2
$$1011_2 -$$
_____

_____

Give your answer as a base 2 number only. *(S)*

4) Use a slide rule, logarithms, or otherwise, to calculate

(a) 15.8×80.7
(b) $(14.7)^3$
(c) $\sqrt{44.5}$
(d) $498 \div 3.14$ *(S)*

266

5) Which of the symbols $<, =, >$ can be correctly inserted in the following?

(i) $\sqrt{1.21}$ 1.1

(ii) $\sqrt{12.1}$ 3.5

(iii) $9^2 - 3^2$ 6^2

(iv) $12^2 \div 3^2$ 4^2 *(W)*

6) ABC is a right-angled triangle (Fig. 1). $\hat{B} = 90°$, $\tan C = \frac{4}{3}$ and $AB = 12$ cm.

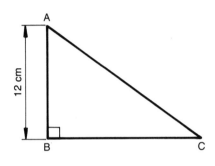

Fig. 1

(a) Calculate the length of BC and of AC.

(b) Find the value of $\sin C$ and of $\cos A$.

(c) Find, from tables, the size of $\hat{C}$.   *(W)*

7) Consider the number 3.26:

(a) Write this number
    (i) to the nearest whole number,
    (ii) correct to one decimal place.

(b) If $\log 3.26 = 0.513$, what is $\log 32.6$?

(c) Find the value of $(3.26)^{-1}$.

(d) Use tables to find the square root of 0.326.

(e) Find the value of
$$\frac{(3.26)^4 \times (3.26)^2}{(3.26)^6}.$$
        (S)

8) AOB is a sector of a circle, centre O, radius 8 cm (Fig. 2).

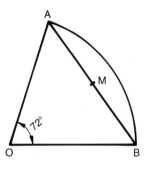

Fig. 2

Angle $AOB = 72°$.
M is the mid point of the chord AB.
Take $\pi = 3.14$.

(a) How many sectors like this can be cut from a complete circle?

(b) Calculate the length of the arc AB to the nearest centimetre.

(c) If OM is joined, what is the size of angle AMO?

(d) The area of the triangle AOB can be found from the formula
$$\text{Area} = \tfrac{1}{2} \times 8^2 \times \sin 72°.$$
Calculate this area to the nearest square centimetre.

(e) Calculate the length of the chord AB.   *(S)*

9)

Sale price	Rate of commission
First £500	5%
Next £4500	$2\frac{1}{2}$%
All over £5000	$1\frac{1}{2}$%

The table shows the basis on which an estate agent charges commission for selling a house.

(a) Find 5% of £500.

(b) Find the commission on £4500 at $2\frac{1}{2}$%.

(c) What is the total commission on a house sold for £5000?

(d) What is the total commission on a house sold for £10 000?

(e) If the estate agent earns a commission of £182.50 for how much was the house sold? (S)

10) Write down the special names given to the quadrilaterals that have the following properties:

(i) equal diagonals that bisect each other at 90°;

(ii) unequal diagonals that bisect each other at 90°;

(iii) unequal diagonals that bisect each other at angles that are not equal to 90°. (W)

11) ABC and DEF are two similar triangles with Â = D̂ = 90°, and Ĉ = F̂ (Fig. 3).

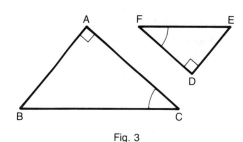

Fig. 3

(a) Without using trigonometrical ratios complete the following statements:

(i) $\dfrac{AB}{BC} =$

(ii) $\dfrac{AB}{DE} =$

(b) Given AB = 5 cm, AC = 10 cm and DF = 5 cm write down the numerical value of:

(i) the ratio of $\dfrac{BC}{EF}$,

(ii) the ratio

$\dfrac{\text{area of triangle ABC}}{\text{area of triangle DEF}}$. (W)

12)
(a) What is the value of 9.35×10^4?

(b) Express 0.00638 in standard form.

(c) Use your slide rule or 3-figure tables to find the value of:

(i) $2.6 \times 3.8 \times 4.25$.

(ii) $\sqrt{15.6}$. (Y.R.)

13) Figure 4 (not drawn to scale) represents two solid blocks from a child's building outfit. Each block is a right prism.

Prism A is a rectangular block, 10 cm long, its uniform cross section being a square of side 5 cm.

Prism B is a triangular prism, 10 cm long, its uniform cross section being a right-angled triangle of sides 3 cm, 4 cm and 5 cm. (M)

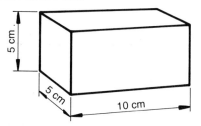

Solid A

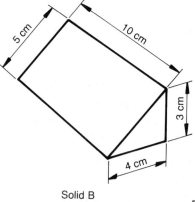

Solid B

Fig. 4

(a) Find the total surface area of the rectangular block, solid A.

(b) Find the total surface area of solid B.

(c) Find the volume of solid A. (M)

268

14) Which of the diagrams (Fig. 5).

(a) are nets for a cube?

(b) possess rotational symmetry of order greater than one?

(c) have a line of symmetry?

(d) are nets for a tetrahedron? (Y.R.)

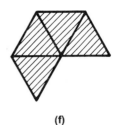

(f)

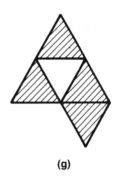

(g)

Fig. 5

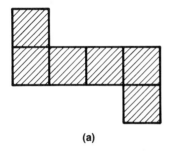

(a)

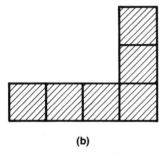

(b)

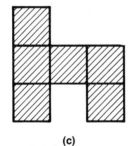

(c)

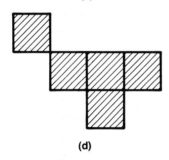

(d)

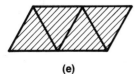

(e)

15) A new car costs £2000. In its first year it loses 25% of its value at the beginning of the year. Every year after the first it loses another 15% of its value at the start of the year. Calculate its value after:

(a) 1 year,

(b) 2 years,

(c) 3 years

to the nearest pound. (S)

16) $A = (3 \quad 4)$. $B = \begin{pmatrix} 3 \\ 4 \end{pmatrix}$.

Calculate the matrix products

(a) AB.

(b) BA. (S)

17) $\xi = \{\text{whole numbers}\}$. $A = \{11, 19, x, 15, 12\}$.

(a) What is the value of $n(A)$?

(b) Write down all the possible values of x if x is the median member of set A.

(c) Find x if the mean of the members of set A is 12. (S)

18) The goals scored by a football team in 60 matches were as follows.

4 1 3 2 0 1 1 1 1 0 2 5 0 0 4 1 1 0 1 1 5
1 2 1 1 0 2 1 2 0 1 2 3 1 1 1 0 1 2 0 1 0
2 0 1 3 0 0 2 0 1 2 1 0 2 1 1 2 4 0

(a) Arrange this information in a frequency table using classes of 0 goals, 1 goal, 2 goals, 3 goals and more than 3 goals.

(b) Draw a pie-chart to represent this information.

(c) What is the mode of the above distribution?   (N.W.)

19) Calculate the mean shoe size of the distribution shown in Fig. 6.

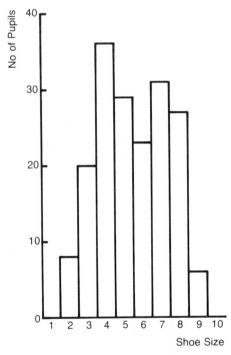

Fig. 6

20)

(a) Write 1101_2 as a denary (base 10) number.

(b) Write $\frac{3}{4}$ as a bicimal.

(c) Calculate in base 2: 111×101.

(d) Decide which base is used in the calculation:

$$12 + 31 + 23 = 1*1$$

and find the missing number.   (S.W.)

270

The questions which follow are all Type C

21)

(a) Solve the following equations:

   (i) $5x + 3x = 16$

   (ii) $6x - 2x = 5x - 2$

   (iii) $3x + 2(x - 5) = 20$

   (iv) $\frac{x}{5} + 2x = \frac{x}{2} + 17$.

(b) A cuboid has a square end, sides x cm and a length y cm (Fig. 7).

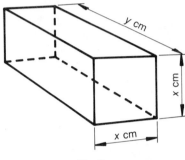

Fig. 7

   (i)   What is the volume of the cuboid in terms of x and y?

   (ii)   What is the volume of the cuboid if $x = 6$ and $y = 9$?
          (S)

22) In Fig. 8, which is not drawn to scale, the equation of the line AQ is $y = \frac{1}{2}x + 1$ and OM = 5.

(a) Calculate:

   (i)   the length of QM,

   (ii)   the area of AOMQ.

(b) Write down the coordinates of the point where the line QA meets the line $y = 0$.   (W.M.)

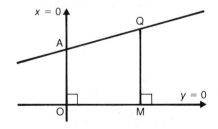

Fig. 8

23)

(a) Copy the diagrams shown in Fig. 9 and

  (i) shade the region A,

  (ii) shade the region (A ∩ B) ∪ C.

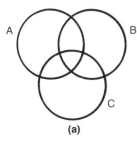

(a)

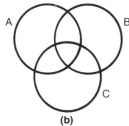

(b)

Fig. 9

(b) Describe in terms of A, B, C and using the and/or '∩', the region shaded in Fig. 10.

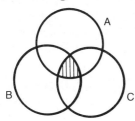

Fig. 10

(c) How many axes of symmetry has

  (i) a square

  (ii) a rectangle

  (iii) an equilateral triangle

  (iv) a circle? (S)

24)

(a) Given $A = \dfrac{(a+b)}{2}h$.

  (i) If $a = 7$, $b = 9$, $h = 5$ calculate the value of A.

  (ii) If $A = 12$, $h = 4$, $a = 2$ calculate the value of b. (W)

(b) Using the *binary scale only* calculate:

  (i) 1011×1011,

  (ii) $10001111 \div 1101$.

(c) (i) Change 73 (base 10) to base 2.

  (ii) Change 11011 (base 2) to base 10. (W)

25) In Fig. 11, AB is parallel to DC.

$$AB = 5.5 \text{ cm}$$
$$DC = 12.5 \text{ cm}$$

The perpendicular distance between AB and DC is 4.0 cm.

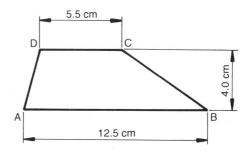

Fig. 11

(a) Give the correct geometrical name for the quadrilateral ABCD.

(b) Calculate the area of ABCD.

(c) If all the measurements were doubled, how many times bigger than the original area would the new area be?

(d) If angle BCD = 123°, what is the size of angle ABC? (W)

(e) In Fig. 12 ABCD is the cross section of a right solid prism $(x-y)$ cm long. The area of ABCD is $(x+y)$ cm². What is the volume of the prism? (Give your answer in terms of x and y without brackets.) (S)

271

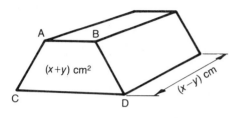

$(x+y)$ cm^2

A B

$(x-y)$ cm

C D

Fig. 12

26)

(a) Convert 11011 base 2 to base 10.

(b) Add the numbers 121_3, 20_3 and 212_3. Give your answer in base 3.

(c) $101\times101 = 10201$. In what base is this *not* true?

(d) Convert 34 base 5 to base 6.

(e) The denary number 94 is the same as the three figure number 2*4 in another base. Find the value of *. *(S)*

27) Figure 13 represents an open cylindrical can of internal height 21 cm and internal diameter 6 cm.

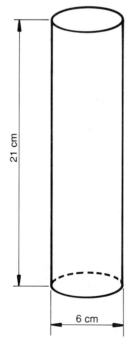

21 cm

6 cm

Fig. 13

Figure 14 represents a solid cuboidal block of copper 3 cm long, 3 cm wide and 4 cm deep.

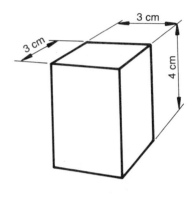

3 cm

3 cm

4 cm

Fig. 14

(a) Find the volume of the block.

(b) If the mass of 1 cm^3 of copper is 8 grammes, what is the mass of the block in grammes?

(c) Water is poured into the can until it is one-third full. Find the volume of water poured in. $\left(\text{Take } \pi \text{ as } \dfrac{22}{7}\right)$.

(d) What will be the increase in height of the water after the block has been lowered into the can until it rests on the bottom?

(e) Another cuboidal block with height 8 cm and square base has a volume of 50 cm^3. Find the length of one side of the base. *(S)*

28)

(a) Expand and simplify
$$(2a+4)(2a-4).$$

(b) Factorise $x^2+11x+24$.

(c) If $y = x^2-10x-24$, find the value of y when:

    (i) $x = 0$,

    (ii) $x = 13$,

    (iii) $x = -2$. *(Y.R.)*

29) ABC is a triangle with a right angle at C. DE is parallel to BC. AE = 1 cm, EC = 2 cm, BC = 2.1 cm (see Fig. 15).

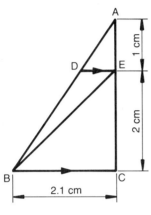

Fig. 15

(a) State the ratio of AD to AB.

(b) Find the area of triangle ABC.

(c) Calculate the size of angle BAC.

(d) Calculate the length AB.

(e) Triangle ABC has a perpendicular height in common with triangle ABE. Name another triangle with this same perpendicular height. (S)

30) An investigation was carried out into the reasons for absence or for late arrival at a school on a particular Monday morning. The results of the investigation were as follows:

Missed the bus	25%
Sickness	38%
Overslept	11%
Had a cold	21%
Bicycle had puncture	5%

(a) On the graph paper draw a bar chart to illustrate these statistics. Use a scale of 2 cm to represent 5% on the vertical axis.

(b) If the information had been represented on a pie chart, calculate the angle at the centre which would have been required for the sector representing 'Sickness'.

(c) If 1200 pupils attended this school and, on that particular morning, 20% were absent or arrived late, calculate how many pupils missed the bus. (Y.R.)

31)
(a) Copy and complete the table of values given below for the function $y = 5-x$, where x is a real number.

x	−3	−2	−1	0	1	2	3	4	5
y						4	3	2	1	0

(b) Plot these points and join them up to form a straight line.

(c) Copy and complete the table of values given below for the function $y = x^2-1$, where x is a real number.

x	−3	−2	−1	0	1	2	3
y							

(d) Plot these points on same axes as for (b). Join them up to form a smooth curve.

(e) Write down the coordinates of the points of intersection of the two graphs. (Y.R.)

32) Draw lines PQ = 6 cm and AB = 4 cm long.

(a) Using ruler and compasses only, construct:

(i) an angle of 90° at Q,

(ii) an angle of 60° at P.

Thus, complete triangle PQR so that angle PQR = 90°, angle PQR = 60°.

(b) Using any method you wish, construct a second triangle with AB = 4 cm as base, so that triangle ABC is similar to triangle PQR.

(c) What is the ratio of PR to AC?

(d) What is the ratio of the area of the triangle PQR to that of triangle ABC? (M)

273

33) In Fig. 16 (not drawn to scale) WXYZ is a parallelogram. Angle WYX = 90° and WN is perpendicular to ZY. WY = 40 mm, XY = 9 mm.

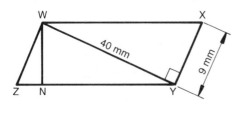

Fig. 16

(a) Name two angles equal in size to angle ZWN.

(b) Calculate the size of angle XWY.

(c) Calculate the length of WX.

(d) Calculate the length of WN.

(e) Calculate the area of the parallelogram WXYZ. (M)

34) In the triangle ABC, AB = 25 m, AB̂C = 90°, BD̂C = 90° and tan C = 1.25 (Fig. 17).

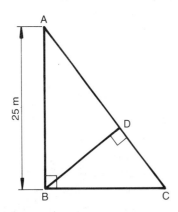

Fig. 17

(i) Calculate the length of BC.

(ii) Find the size of Ĉ in degrees and minutes.

(iii) Calculate the length of DC correct to the nearest metre.

35) Figure 18 shows AB and BC which are adjacent sides of a regular polygon with nine sides.

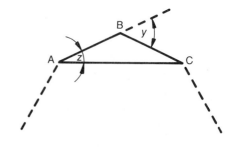

Fig. 18

Calculate:

(a) the angle $y°$,

(b) the angle $z°$. (S.W.)

36)

$$A = \begin{pmatrix} 2 & 1 \\ 0 & 3 \\ -1 & 4 \end{pmatrix}$$

$$B = \begin{pmatrix} 3 & 1 & 5 \\ 0 & -2 & 4 \end{pmatrix}$$

$$C = \begin{pmatrix} 3 \\ 2 \\ 5 \end{pmatrix}$$

(a) Calculate the following, where possible. (If impossible, say so.)
   (i) A+B.
   (ii) BC.
   (iii) AB.

(b) If BA = K, what will be the order of the matrix K?

37)
(a) If $a = 30.2$, find $\log a$.
(b) If $\log b = 0.5441$, find b.
(c) Calculate $a×b$.
(d) (i) Solve the following equation:
$$10^{1.4800} × 10^{1.5441} = 10^x.$$
   (ii) Find the number, the logarithm of which is equal to x. (Y.R.)

274

38) The diagram Fig. 19, which is not drawn to scale, represents a

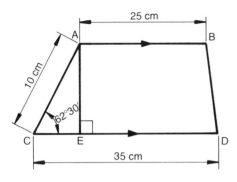

25 cm

A B

10 cm

62°30'

C E

35 cm

D

Fig. 19

trapezium ABCD. AB is parallel to DC, AB = 25 cm, DC = 35 cm, AD = 10 cm, angle ADE = 62° 30' and AE is perpendicular to DC.

Calculate:

(a) angle DAE,

(b) the length of AE,

(c) the length of EC,

(d) the area of the trapezium ABCD.
(Y.R.)

39) On a certain brand of matches it states on the box that the average contents is 36 matches. The contents of 9 different boxes were counted with the following results:

32, 37, 35, 29, 37, 32, 40, 37, 36.

(a) What is the mode for this set of figures?

(b) What is the median number of matches in a box?

(c) Calculate the mean number of matches to a box.

(d) What is the probability of selecting a box from this sample which will contain 32 matches? (Y.R.)

40) Figure 20 shows the numbers of children, classified by weight, in groups at intervals of 2 kilograms.

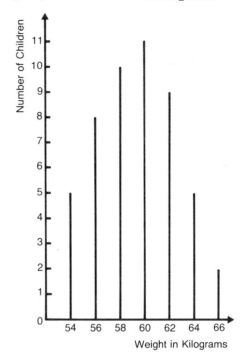

Fig. 20

(a) Calculate the total number of children.

(b) What is the modal weight of the children?

(c) Calculate the mean weight, correct to the nearest kilogram, of the children. (M)

41)
(a) Taking 2 cm to represent 1 unit on each axis, draw axes 0x, 0y, taking values of x from −5 to +5 and values of y from −6 to +6.

(b) Plot the points (1, 2), (3, 6) and (5, 1). Join these points to form a triangle.

(c) Draw the reflection of this triangle in the x axis. Write down the coordinates of the vertices of the new triangle. (Y.R.)

Answers

Exercise 1

1) 457   3) 7777   5) 705   7) 5090
2) 9536   4) 3008   6) 30 028   8) 4904
9) 125 906   11) 95 827 000
10) 3 800 007   12) 300 000 009
13) two hundred and twenty five
14) eight thousand three hundred and twenty one
15) three thousand and seventeen
16) three thousand nine hundred and sixty
17) one thousand eight hundred and seven
18) twenty thousand and four
19) seventeen thousand
20) one hundred and ninety eight thousand, three hundred and seventy six
21) two hundred thousand and five
22) seven million, three hundred and sixty five thousand, two hundred and thirty one
23) twenty seven million, three hundred and nine

Exercise 2

1) 351   3) 58 190   5) 126 331
2) 4570   4) 8 579 649

Exercise 3

1) 32   2) 335   3) 14   4) 1558
5) 9226

Exercise 4

1) 11   2) 32   3) 36   4) 18

Exercise 5

1) 6   3) 54   5) 63   7) 81
2) 35   4) 32   6) 15   8) 42

Exercise 6

1) 928   3) 1 010 829   5) 1 022 656
2) 9334   4) 4 483 887

Exercise 7

1) 246   3) 433 remainder 3
2) 56   4) 1842 remainder 1
5) 624 remainder 5

Exercise 8

1) 546 remainder 4   5) 903 remainder 1
2) 1264   6) 1701
3) 309 remainder 1   7) 59 817
4) 909 remainder 2   8) 5923

Exercise 9

1) 13   6) 15   11) 5   15) 14
2) 10   7) 45   12) 10   16) 21
3) 57   8) 74   13) 7   17) 17
4) 7   9) 13   14) 7   18) 13
5) 35   10) 20

Exercise 10

1) (a) 2×12, 4×6, 8×3, 24×1
   (b) 2×28, 4×14, 7×8, 56×1
   (c) 2×21, 3×14, 6×7, 42×1
2) 2, 3, 4, 6, 12; 12, 18, 24
3) 12, 15, 18, 21, 24, 27, 30, 33, 36, 39
4) (a) $2 \times 2 \times 2 \times 3$ (c) $2 \times 2 \times 2 \times 7$
   (b) $2 \times 2 \times 3 \times 3$ (d) $2 \times 2 \times 3 \times 11$
5) 23 and 29
6) (a) 6   (b) 720   (c) 24
7) (a) 30   (b) 118   (c) 12

Exercise 11

1) 192, 768   4) 6, 2
2) 13, 16   5) 48, 96
3) 29, 35

Exercise 12

1) 26   6) 4656
2) 5   7) 68103
3) (a) 30 (b) 48   8) b
4) 80   9) 45
5) 409
10) (a) 24   (d) 49 or 63
    (b) any except 24   (e) 45 and 63
    (c) 61   (f) 33 and 45
11) 162   19) 4
12) c   20) 621
13) d   21) 114
14) b   22) (a) $(1+4) \times 8$
15) 1980   (b) $16-(2+6)$
16) 5   23) 4799
17) 224 and 448   24) e
18) (a) 6, 8 (b) 7, 9   25) (a) b (b) b

277

ANSWERS TO CHAPTER 2

Exercise 13

1) $\frac{21}{28}$ 3) $\frac{25}{30}$ 5) $\frac{8}{12}$ 7) $\frac{24}{64}$
2) $\frac{12}{20}$ 4) $\frac{7}{63}$ 6) $\frac{4}{24}$ 8) $\frac{25}{35}$

Exercise 14

1) $\frac{1}{2}$ 4) $\frac{3}{5}$ 7) $\frac{5}{7}$ 9) $\frac{2}{3}$
2) $\frac{3}{5}$ 5) $\frac{7}{8}$ 8) $\frac{18}{35}$ 10) $\frac{2}{3}$
3) $\frac{1}{8}$ 6) $\frac{3}{4}$

Exercise 15

1) $3\frac{1}{2}$ 4) $1\frac{1}{11}$ 7) $\frac{51}{10}$ 9) $\frac{127}{20}$
2) 2 5) $2\frac{5}{8}$ 8) $\frac{26}{3}$ 10) $\frac{31}{7}$
3) $2\frac{1}{5}$ 6) $\frac{19}{8}$

Exercise 16

1) 24 4) 24 7) 160 9) 420
2) 60 5) 40 8) 120 10) 5040
3) 12 6) 100

Exercise 17

1) $\frac{1}{2}, \frac{7}{12}, \frac{2}{3}$ and $\frac{5}{6}$ 4) $\frac{3}{5}, \frac{5}{8}, \frac{13}{20}$ and $\frac{3}{4}$
2) $\frac{3}{4}, \frac{6}{7}, \frac{7}{8}$ and $\frac{9}{10}$ 5) $\frac{9}{14}, \frac{11}{16}, \frac{7}{10}$ and $\frac{3}{4}$
3) $\frac{11}{20}, \frac{3}{5}, \frac{7}{10}$ and $\frac{13}{16}$ 6) $\frac{3}{8}, \frac{2}{5}, \frac{5}{9}$ and $\frac{4}{7}$

Exercise 18

1) $\frac{5}{6}$ 5) $2\frac{1}{8}$ 9) $13\frac{23}{56}$
2) $\frac{13}{10} = 1\frac{3}{10}$ 6) $1\frac{47}{120}$ 10) $10\frac{2}{3}$
3) $1\frac{1}{8}$ 7) $4\frac{15}{16}$ 11) $11\frac{5}{16}$
4) $\frac{11}{20}$ 8) $14\frac{4}{15}$ 12) $10\frac{13}{15}$

Exercise 19

1) $\frac{1}{6}$ 4) $\frac{1}{2}$ 7) $1\frac{1}{5}$ 10) $\frac{51}{160}$
2) $\frac{2}{15}$ 5) $\frac{1}{24}$ 8) $\frac{7}{8}$ 11) $\frac{41}{80}$
3) $\frac{1}{6}$ 6) $2\frac{2}{7}$ 9) $2\frac{19}{40}$

Exercise 20

1) $1\frac{3}{8}$ 4) $\frac{2}{3}$ 7) $2\frac{21}{80}$ 9) $3\frac{7}{8}$
2) $\frac{7}{20}$ 5) $8\frac{13}{80}$ 8) $8\frac{23}{32}$ 10) $3\frac{31}{100}$
3) $6\frac{7}{8}$ 6) $12\frac{9}{40}$

Exercise 21

1) $\frac{8}{15}$ 3) $\frac{10}{27}$ 5) $4\frac{9}{10}$ 7) $1\frac{32}{45}$
2) $\frac{15}{28}$ 4) $1\frac{19}{36}$ 6) $6\frac{2}{3}$ 8) $2\frac{53}{56}$

Exercise 22

1) $1\frac{1}{3}$ 4) $1\frac{1}{2}$ 7) $6\frac{3}{4}$ 10) 100
2) 4 5) $\frac{1}{24}$ 8) $8\frac{1}{4}$ 11) 3
3) $\frac{7}{16}$ 6) 4 9) 12 12) 2

Exercise 23

1) $\frac{3}{5}$ 3) $1\frac{1}{3}$ 5) $\frac{2}{3}$ 7) $1\frac{1}{5}$
2) 8 4) $1\frac{1}{2}$ 6) $\frac{25}{26}$ 8) $3\frac{5}{6}$

Exercise 24

1) $3\frac{13}{14}$ 4) $\frac{5}{6}$ 7) $1\frac{2}{5}$ 9) $\frac{1}{6}$
2) 5 5) $\frac{2}{3}$ 8) $\frac{2}{3}$ 10) $\frac{3}{25}$
3) $2\frac{1}{2}$ 6) $2\frac{1}{2}$

Exercise 25

1) (a) $\frac{9}{10}$ (b) $\frac{39}{40}$
2) (a) $\frac{7}{12}, \frac{2}{3}, \frac{7}{8}$ (b) $1\frac{17}{24}$ (c) $\frac{5}{9}$
3) $\frac{2}{3}$ 4) 495
5) (a) $1\frac{1}{2}$ (b) 1 (c) $2\frac{1}{3}$
6) $\frac{7}{10}$ 8) $1\frac{1}{12}$
7) 1 hour 9) $\frac{3}{8}$
10) (a) $\frac{5}{6}$ (b) $\frac{2}{5}$ (c) $\frac{5}{8}$
11) c 13) e 15) d 17) e
12) a 14) c 16) c
18) (a) $\frac{7}{12}$ (b) $\frac{1}{20}$ 19) $5\frac{13}{20}$ 20) $2\frac{3}{4}$

ANSWERS TO CHAPTER 3

Exercise 26

1) 0.7 7) 8.06 13) $437\frac{25}{100}$
2) 0.37 8) 24.0209 14) $\frac{4}{1000}$
3) 0.589 9) 50.008 15) $\frac{36}{1000}$
4) 0.009 10) $\frac{2}{10}$ 16) $400\frac{29}{1000}$
5) 0.03 11) $4\frac{6}{10}$ 17) $\frac{1}{1000}$
6) 0.017 12) $3\frac{58}{100}$ 18) $\frac{329}{10000}$

Exercise 27

1) 3 5) 54.852 9) 0.812
2) 11.5 6) 4.12 10) 5.4109
3) 24.04 7) 15.616
4) 58.616 8) 0.339

Exercise 28

1) 41, 410, 4100 3) 0.46, 4.6, 46
2) 24.2, 242, 2420 4) 3.5, 35, 350
5) 1.486, 14.86, 148.6
6) 0.017 53, 0.1753, 1.753
7) 48.53 9) 1700.6
8) 9 10) 5639.6

Exercise 29

1) 0.36, 0.036, 0.0036
2) 6.4198, 0.641 98, 0.064 198
3) 0.007, 0.0007, 0.000 07
4) 51.04, 5.104, 0.5104
5) 0.0352, 0.003 52, 0.000 352
6) 0.054
7) 0.002 05 9) 0.000 008 6
8) 0.004 10) 0.062 742 8

Exercise 30

1) 743.0266 4) 7.411 25
2) 0.951 534 5) 0.001 376
3) 0.2888

Exercise 31

1) 1.33   3) 189.74   5) 43.2
2) 0.016   4) 4.1066

Exercise 32

1) 24.8658, 24.87, 25
2) 0.008 357, 0.008 36, 0.0084
3) 4.9785, 4.98, 5
4) 22
5) 35.60
6) 28 388 000, 28 000 000
7) 4.1498, 4.150, 4.15
8) 9.20

Exercise 33

1) $200 \times 0.005 = 1$
2) $32 \times 0.25 = 8$
3) $0.7 \times 0.1 \times 2 = 0.14$
4) $80 \div 20 = 4$
5) $0.06 \div 0.003 = 20$
6) $30 \times 30 \times 0.03 = 27$
7) $\dfrac{0.7 \times 0.006}{0.03} = 0.14$
8) $\dfrac{30 \times 30}{10 \times 3} = 30$

Exercise 34

1) 0.25   8) 0.4531   15) 0.356
2) 0.75   9) 1.8333   16) 0.232
3) 0.375   10) 2.4375   17) 0.525
4) 0.6875   11) 0.333   18) 0.384
5) 0.5   12) 0.778   19) 0.328
6) 0.6667   13) 0.133   20) 0.567
7) 0.6563   14) 0.189

Exercise 35

1) $\frac{1}{5}$ 4) $2\frac{11}{20}$ 7) 0.0001
2) $\frac{9}{20}$ 5) $\frac{3}{400}$ 8) 0.001 875
3) $\frac{5}{16}$ 6) $2\frac{1}{8}$

Exercise 36

1) 56.8
2) (a) 53.02   (b) 1.67
3) (a) 7.5   (b) 7.5
4) 0.003
5) 0.0285
6) (a) 5.93   (b) 5.9
7) (a) 0.2   (b) 0.3   (c) 0.1̇
8) 4.55
9) 0.14
10) (a) 1.08   (b) 108   (c) 12   (d) 0.12
11) (a) 973   (b) 7.42   (c) 0.027
12) a
13) (a) 3.1   (b) 12.57
14) e
15) d

16) b
17) c
18) c
19) a
20) b
21) c
22) d
23) a
24) b
25) 0.8524
26) 2.20, 2.02, 0.22, 0.022
27) (a) b   (b) b
28) b
29) 10, 8
30) (a) 5.4464   (b) 3.68

ANSWERS TO CHAPTER 4

Exercise 37

1) 68 p, 63 p, $58\frac{1}{2}$ p
2) 216 p, $359\frac{1}{2}$ p, 1768 p
3) £0.35, £0.78$\frac{1}{2}$, £0.06, £0.03
4) £2.46, £9.83$\frac{1}{2}$, £265.32
5) (a) £10.06   (c) £5.42$\frac{1}{2}$ (e) £2.00$\frac{1}{2}$
   (b) £215.58   (d) £2.35
6) (a) £2.24   (c) £68.61$\frac{1}{2}$ (e) £2.09$\frac{1}{2}$
   (b) £7.93   (d) £0.78

Exercise 38

1) £1.80   4) £168.84   7) £1.30$\frac{1}{2}$
2) £6.37$\frac{1}{2}$ 5) 13 p   8) £2.16$\frac{1}{2}$
3) £16.98$\frac{1}{2}$ 6) 21$\frac{1}{2}$ p

Exercise 39

1) £1.80   7) £1.95   11) a
2) 12   8) 363   12) a
3) (a) £12.27   (b) £7.07
4) £22.43   9) 21   13) e
5) 29 p   10) d   14) e
6) £4.85; 55 p   15) c

ANSWERS TO CHAPTER 5

Exercise 40

1) $\frac{8}{3}$ 4) $\frac{3}{5}$ 7) $\frac{25}{4}$ 10) $\frac{6}{1}$
2) $\frac{2}{3}$ 5) $\frac{2}{3}$ 8) 150 m
3) $\frac{3}{1}$ 6) $\frac{3}{20}$ 9) £192

Exercise 41

1) £500 and £300   5) 15, 22.5 and 37.5 kg
2) £64 and £16   6) 84, 294, 462 mm
3) £50, £40 and £30   7) £6258 and £4470
4) £280   8) £3.60

Exercise 42

1) £4.80
2) £4.24
3) $87\frac{1}{2}$p, £48.12$\frac{1}{2}$
4) £1.75
5) 33.17 litres
6) $18\frac{1}{3}$, $36\frac{2}{3}$, 2, 40, 1
7) £224
8) 7 hours

Exercise 43

1) $13\frac{1}{2}$ days
2) $3\frac{1}{3}$ days
3) 160 rev/min
4) 6
5) 20 men

Exercise 44

1) 60.45
2) 2975
3) 54.40
4) £131.18
5) £5.97
6) 5944.48
7) $44.71
8) £3.43
9) SK9.00 = £1
10) (a) 840
(b) 804 francs
(c) 36 francs
(d) £4.34

Exercise 45

1) c
2) $17\frac{1}{2}$p
3) d
4) a
5) (a) c   (b) a
6) 9
13) 4 hours
14) (a) 300 days
(b) 60
15) 8
7) £1.74
8) 24
9) $262.50
10) £267.29
11) £250 and £150
12) £15
(c) 100 days
(d) 6 days

ANSWERS TO CHAPTER 6

Exercise 46

1) 70
2) 55
3) 36
4) 80
5) 62
6) 25
7) 90
8) 95

Exercise 47

1) 70
2) 73
3) 68
4) 81.3
5) 92.7
6) 33.3
7) 81.9

Exercise 48

1) 0.32
2) 0.78
3) 0.06
4) 0.24
5) 0.315
6) 0.482
7) 0.025
8) 0.0125
9) 0.0395
10) 0.201

Exercise 49

1) (a) 10
(b) 24
2) (a) 12.5
(b) 20
3) 60%; 27
6) (a) £7.20
7) (a) 2.083% are bad
(b) 3.077% are absent
(c) 87.76% eat lunches
8) 39 643
(c) 6
(d) 2.4
(c) 16
(d) 16.29
4) 115 cm
(b) £13.20
9) 150 kg
(e) 21.315
(f) 2.516
(e) 45.45
5) $88\frac{2}{3}$ cm
(c) £187.50
10) 600

Exercise 50

1) 25%
2) (a) 20%   (b) $16\frac{2}{3}$%
3) (a) $13\frac{1}{3}$%
(b) 9.95%
4) 10%
5) 20%
6) $33\frac{1}{3}$%
7) $12\frac{1}{2}$%
8) 17.65%

Exercise 51

1) £12.60
2) £28.50
3) 18 p
4) £4.25
5) £265.05

Exercise 52

1) 48%
2) £2.89
3) 20%
4) £0.52
5) 25%
6) 32 p
7) 525 g
8) £12
9) £72.54
10) £26.60
11) d
12) c
13) b
14) c
15) c
16) a
17) 8%
18) £5.85
19) (a) b   (b) b   (c) c
20) (a) £1.20   (b) £120   (c) £110.40

ANSWERS TO CHAPTER 7

Exercise 53

1 22.24
2) 115
3) £28.30
4) 324
5) 12.2 kg
6) £38.40
7) 97.6
8) 14 years 6 months
9) 76
10) 9.13 p

Exercise 54

1) c
2) (a) 7.9 kg   (b) 10.3 kg
3) 16 years 7 months
4) 11 runs
5) 25
6) 3.4
7) e
8) 12.5
9) £48
10) £60

ANSWERS TO CHAPTER 8

Exercise 55

1) 2.25
2) 4.41
3) 73.96
4) 9.923
5) 58.98
6) 27.35
7) 18.18
8) 62.67
9) 64.27
10) 75.76
11) 529
12) 1648
13) 9 566 000
14) 12 610
15) 9628
16) 0.000 361
17) 0.5317
18) 0.000 017 80
19) 0.080 32
20) 0.000 000 334 6

Exercise 56

1) 1.844
2) 2.862
3) 2.294
4) 3.039
5) 2.649
6) 1.735
7) 5.916
8) 9.445
9) 7.292
10) 9.110
11) 8.901
12) 7.072
13) 30
14) 26.94
15) 84.51
16) 298.3
17) 62.81
18) 29 890
19) 0.3921
20) 0.041 21
21) 0.1987
22) 0.027 98
23) 0.044 47

Exercise 57

1) 10	3) 49	5) 120	7) 336
2) 15	4) 24	6) 30	8) 2520

Exercise 58

1) $\frac{2}{3}$	5) $\frac{9}{10}$	9) $\frac{4}{5}$	13) 3
2) $\frac{3}{4}$	6) $\frac{2}{3}$	10) $\frac{1}{6}$	14) 9
3) $\frac{5}{7}$	7) $\frac{5}{8}$	11) 13	15) 6
4) $\frac{2}{3}$	8) $\frac{5}{7}$	12) 12	

Exercise 59

1) 0.2941	6) 0.028 57	11) 6.506
2) 0.1221	7) 0.011 21	12) 588.9
3) 0.1900	8) 0.018 81	13) 25.34
4) 0.1082	9) 0.001 111	14) 1277
5) 0.1426	10) 0.000 14	15) 505.6

Exercise 60

1) 0.004 283	6) 7.458	11) 0.2230
2) 53.12	7) 0.001 023	12) 0.3465
3) 0.000 016	8) 0.005 163	13) 13.73
4) 0.3449	9) 5.801	14) 0.0654
5) 0.2311	10) 9.881	

Exercise 61

1) (a) 45.56	8) 0.49	15) 39
(b) 2.598	9) (a) 2.343	16) 0.273 67
2) 100	(b) 0.094	17) $2\times3\times5$
3) No	10) a	18) e
4) 1.77	11) d	19) (a) 1.1
5) 9.87	12) a	(b) 0.3
6) 26	13) 30	(c) $2\frac{1}{2}$
7) d	14) c	20) 25

ANSWERS TO CHAPTER 9

Exercise 62

1) 15	3) -32	5) -24	7) -18
2) -12	4) 14	6) 26	8) 23

Exercise 63

1) -5	3) 5	5) -1	7) -4
2) -9	4) 5	6) 0	8) 7

Exercise 64

1) 2	3) 14	5) 1	7) -5
2) 3	4) 4	6) -5	8) 16

Exercise 65

1) -42	3) 42	5) -48	7) 120
2) -42	4) 42	6) 4	8) 9

Exercise 66

1) -3	5) -2	9) -2	13) -8
2) -3	6) -1	10) 12	14) -3
3) 3	7) 2	11) -1	
4) 3	8) -1	12) -2	

Exercise 67

1) 5 and 198

2) -9

3) Rational: 1.57, $\frac{1}{4}$, -5.625, $\sqrt{9}$, 6.76 and $-3\frac{1}{2}$
   Irrational: $\sqrt{15}$

4) 9.5782, -7.38, $\sqrt{8}$ and $7\frac{2}{3}$

Exercise 68

1) 13, 16	6) 64, 81
2) 29, 35	7) 2, -2
3) $-6, -8$	8) 2.0736, 2.488 32
4) 3, 5	9) 0.1875, $-0.093\,75$
5) $\frac{1}{108}, \frac{1}{324}$	10) $-1.4641, 1.610\,51$

Exercise 69

1) e	4) -0.2	7) a	10) d
2) b	5) 36, 49	8) $\frac{1}{27}$	11) $-\frac{1}{8}, \frac{1}{16}, -\frac{1}{32}$
3) 9	6) b	9) -2	

12) (a) 0, $-1\frac{1}{3}$ (b) 162,486

ANSWERS TO CHAPTER 10

Exercise 70

1) $7x$	6) $8xyz$
2) $4x-3$	7) $\frac{xy}{z}$
3) $5x+y$	
4) $\frac{x+y}{z}$	8) $3x-4y$
5) $\frac{x}{2}$	

Exercise 71

1) 9	6) 6	11) 33	16) 5
2) 3	7) 45	12) 33	17) 5
3) 3	8) 30	13) 28	18) 7
4) 18	9) 23	14) 1	
5) 45	10) 26	15) $\frac{3}{4}$	

Exercise 72

1) 4	5) 1152	9) 3
2) 81	6) 74	10) 18.96
3) 54	7) 20	
4) 32	8) 3024	

Exercise 73

1) a^{11}	8) m^7	15) L^2
2) z^{11}	9) 2^4	16) x^{12}
3) y^{12}	10) x^{15}	17) a^{15}
4) 2^8	11) a^4	18) $9x^8$
5) 3^8	12) q^8	19) 2^6
6) $\frac{3}{32}a^6$	13) m	20) 10^6
7) a^3	14) l^2	21) a^3b^6

22) $a^4b^8c^{12}$

23) $25x^{10}y^{15}z^5$

24) $\frac{35m^{10}}{45n^{15}}$

25) $\frac{1}{10}, \frac{1}{4}, \frac{1}{81}, \frac{1}{25}$

26) 32, 625, 2, 3

27) $3^6, 3^{15}, 3^{12}, 3^{17}$

28) $a^{1/5}, a^{2/3}, a^{4/7}, a^3$

Exercise 74

1) $18x$
2) $2x$
3) $-3x$
4) $-6x$
5) $-5x$
6) $5x$
7) $9a$
8) $12m$
9) $5b^2$
10) ab
11) $14xy$
12) $-3x$
13) $-6x^2$
14) $7x-3y+6z$
15) $9a^2b-3ab^3+4a^2b^2+11b^4$
16) $1.2x^3+0.3x^2+6.2x-2.8$
17) $9pq-0.1qr$
18) $-0.4a^2b^2-1.2a^3-5.5b^3$
19) $10xy$
20) $12ab$
21) $12m$
22) $4pq$
23) $-xy$
24) $6ab$
25) $-24mn$
26) $-12ab$
27) $24pqr$
28) $60abcd$
29) $2x$
30) $-\dfrac{4a}{7b}$
31) $\dfrac{-5a}{8}$
32) $\dfrac{a}{b}$
33) $\dfrac{2a}{b}$
34) $2b$
35) $3xy$
36) $-2ab$
37) $2ab$
38) $\dfrac{7ab}{3}$
39) a^2
40) $-b^2$
41) $-m^2$
42) p^2
43) $6a^2$
44) $5X^2$
45) $-15q^2$
46) $-9m^2$
47) $9pq^2$
48) $-24m^3n^4$
49) $-21a^3b$
50) $10q^4r^6$
51) $30mnp$
52) $-75a^3b^2$
53) $-5m^5n^4$

Exercise 75

1) $3x+12$
2) $2a+2b$
3) $9x+6y$
4) $\dfrac{x}{2}-\dfrac{1}{2}$
5) $10p-15q$
6) $7a-21m$
7) $-a-b$
8) $-a+2b$
9) $-3p+3q$
10) $-7m+6$
11) $-4x-12$
12) $-4x+10$
13) $-20+15x$
14) $2k^2-10k$
15) $-9xy-12y$
16) $ap-aq-ar$
17) $4abxy-4acxy+4dxy$
18) $3x^4-6x^3y+3x^2y^2$
19) $-14P^3+7P^2-7P$
20) $2m-6m^2+4mn$
21) $5x+11$
22) $14-2a$
23) $x+7$
24) $16-17x$
25) $7x-11y$
26) $\dfrac{7y}{6}-\dfrac{3}{2}$
27) $-8a-11b+11c$
28) $7x-2x^2$
29) $3a-9b$
30) $-x^3+18x^2-9x-15$

Exercise 76

1) $2(x+3)$
2) $4(x-y)$
3) $5(x-1)$
4) $4x(1-2y)$
5) $m(x-y)$
6) $x(a+b+c)$
7) $\dfrac{1}{2}\left(x-\dfrac{y}{4}\right)$
8) $5(a-2b+3c)$
9) $ax(x+1)$
10) $\pi r(2r+h)$
11) $3y(1-3y)$
12) $ub(b^0-a)$

Exercise 77

1) x^2+3x+2
2) x^2+4x+3
3) $x^2+9x+20$
4) $2x^2+11x+15$
5) $3x^2+25x+42$
6) $5x^2+21x+4$
7) $6x^2+16x+8$
8) $10x^2+17x+3$
9) $21x^2+41x+10$
10) x^2-4x+3
11) x^2-6x+8
12) $x^2-9x+18$
13) $2x^2-9x+4$
14) $3x^2-11x+10$
15) $4x^2-33x+8$
16) $6x^2-16x+8$
17) $6x^2-17x+5$
18) $21x^2-29x+10$
19) x^2+2x-3
20) $x^2+5x-14$
21) $x^2-2x-15$
22) $2x^2+x-10$
23) $3x^2+13x-30$
24) $3x^2+23x+30$
25) $6x^2+x-15$
26) $12x^2+4x-21$
27) $6x^2-x-15$
28) $3x^2+5xy+2y^2$
29) $2p^2-7pq+3q^2$
30) $6v^2-5uv-6u^2$
31) $6a^2+ab-b^2$
32) $5a^2-37a+42$
33) $6x^2-xy-12y^2$
34) x^2+2x+1
35) $4x^2+12x+9$
36) $9x^2+42x+49$
37) x^2-2x+1
38) $9x^2-30x+25$
39) $4x^2-12x+9$
40) $4a^2+12ab+9b^2$
41) $x^2+2xy+y^2$
42) $P^2+6PQ+9Q^2$
43) $a^2-2ab+b^2$
44) $9x^2-24xy+16y^2$
45) $M^2-4MN+4N^2$
46) x^2-1
47) x^2-9
48) x^2-49
49) $4x^2-25$
50) $9x^2-49$
51) $4x^2-1$
52) a^2-b^2
53) $9x^2-4y^2$
54) $25a^2-4b^2$

Exercise 78

1) $(x+3)(x+1)$
2) $(x+4)(x+2)$
3) $(x+5)(x+4)$
4) $(x-1)(x-2)$
5) $(x-2)(x-4)$
6) $(x-3)(x-4)$
7) $(x+5)(x-3)$
8) $(x+7)(x-4)$
9) $(x+7)(x-1)$
10) $(x-4)(x+3)$
11) $(x-7)(x+2)$
12) $(x-y)^2$
13) $(x-3)^2$
14) $(x+5)^2$
15) $(3x-2)^2$
16) $(x+3)(x-3)$
17) $(m+5)(m-5)$
18) $(2x+5)(2x-5)$
19) $(x+y)(x-y)$
20) $(2a+3b)(2a-3b)$
21) $(x-3)$
22) $(x-7)$
23) $(2x+5)$
24) $(5x-3)$
25) $(x+1)$
26) $(x-1)$
27) $(3p-5)$
28) $(2x+3)(x+5)$
29) $(3m+7)(m-4)$
30) $2(2x+1)(x-3)$
31) $(5a-3)(2a+5)$
32) $(3x+1)(7x+10)$
33) $(2p+3)(13p-3)$
34) $(2x+3)^2$
35) $(3x+1)^2$

Exercise 79

1) $\dfrac{b}{c}$
2) $\dfrac{9s^2}{2t}$
3) $\dfrac{8acz}{3y^3}$
4) $\dfrac{9qs}{pr}$
5) $\dfrac{21b^2}{10ac}$

282

Exercise 80

1) $\dfrac{47x}{60}$

2) $\dfrac{a}{36}$

3) $\dfrac{1}{2q}$

4) $\dfrac{32}{15y}$

5) $\dfrac{9q-10p}{15pq}$

6) $\dfrac{9x^2-5y^2}{6xy}$

7) $\dfrac{15xz-4y}{5z}$

8) $\dfrac{40-11x}{40}$

9) $\dfrac{19m-n}{7}$

10) $\dfrac{a+11b}{4}$

11) $\dfrac{8n-3m}{3}$

12) $\dfrac{5x-2}{20}$

13) $\dfrac{x-14}{12}$

14) $\dfrac{13x-21}{30}$

Exercise 81

1) 7

2) -4

3) $\frac{1}{2}$

4) 25

5) 12

6) 4

7) 12

8) 1

9) 14 884

10) 19

Exercise 82

1) (a) c (b) e (c) a

2) e

3) e

4) b

5) e

6) a

7) b

8) d

9) e

10) e

11) c

12) (a) 13 (b) 30 (c) 28 (d) 4

13) -5

14) 14

15) $4a-2b-2c = 2(2a-b-c)$

16) d

17) b

18) (a) 1 (b) 64 (c) -8 (d) $\frac{1}{5}$

19) (a) $6(4+y)$ (b) $(y+10)(y-10)$
    (c) $(x+4)(x+3)$

20) b

21) e

22) $4x^2-12xy+9y^2$

23) 3

24) (a) $\frac{1}{1000}$ (b) 0.001

25) (a) 6 (b) 3

26) 1

27) (a) $9x$ (b) $-3x$
    (c) 2 (d) $18x^2$

28) (a) $2ab(c-3d)$ (b) $(4-c)(a-b)$

29) 144

30) $(x-4)(x-1)$

31) $\dfrac{4}{3x}$

32) (a) -24 (b) 15 (c) 0

33) $3(a+b)(a-b)$

34) $5(2-3x^2)$

35) (a) $(3x-4)(3x+4)$ (b) $x(9x-16)$
    (c) $(x-11)(x+2)$

ANSWERS TO CHAPTER 11

Exercise 83

1) $x = 5$

2) $t = 7$

3) $q = 2$

15) $x = 2$

16) $x = 6$

17) $m = 2$

29) $m = -1.5$

30) $x = \dfrac{15}{28}$

31) $m = 1$

4) $x = 20$

5) $q = -3$

6) $x = 3$

7) $y = 6$

8) $m = 12$

9) $x = 2$

10) $x = 3$

11) $p = 4$

12) $x = -2$

13) $x = -1$

14) $x = 4$

18) $x = -8$

19) $d = 6$

20) $x = 5$

21) $x = 3$

22) $m = 5$

23) $x = -\dfrac{29}{5}$

24) $x = 2$

25) $x = \dfrac{45}{8}$

26) $x = -2$

27) $x = -15$

28) $x = \dfrac{50}{47}$

32) $x = 2.5$

33) $t = 6$

34) $x = 4.2$

35) $y = -70$

36) $x = \dfrac{5}{3}$

37) $x = 13$

38) $x = -10$

39) $m = \dfrac{25}{26}$

40) $y = \dfrac{9}{7}$

ANSWERS TO CHAPTER 12

Exercise 84

1) (a) 1.96×10 (b) 3.85×10^2
   (c) 5.9876×10^4 (d) 1.5×10^6
   (e) 1.3×10^{-2} (f) 3.85×10^{-3}
   (g) 6.98×10^{-4} (h) 2.385×10^{-2}

2) (a) 150 (b) 47 000
   (c) 3 600 000 (d) 9450
   (e) 0.25 (f) 0.004
   (g) 0.000 08 (h) 0.04

3) (a) 2.1×10^3 (b) 9.95×10^3
   (c) 8.58×10^4

4) (a) 2.1×10^{-2} (b) 8.72×10^{-3}
   (c) 2.11×10^{-4}

Exercise 85

1) 0.5563

2) 0.6812

3) 0.5340

4) 0.9238

5) 0.9624

6) 0.6218

7) 0.9194

8) 0.7865

9) 0.4588

10) 0.7557

Exercise 86

1) (a) 1 (b) 4 (c) 4 (d) 2
   (e) 5 (f) 1 (g) 0 (h) 2
   (i) 3 (j) 2

2) (a) 0.8451, 1.8451, 2.8451, 3.8451, 4.8451
   (b) 0.4914, 1.4914, 2.4914, 3.4914, 6.4914
   (c) 1.6839, 5.6839, 0.6839, 2.6839
   (d) 3.8974, 0.8974, 1.8974, 4.8974
   (e) 0.0013, 1.0013, 3.0013, 2.0013

Exercise 87

1) 2.089, 208.9, 20 890, 20.89

2) 1884, 1.884, 18 840, 1 884 000

3) 3.969, 39.69, 39 690, 396.9

4) 7850, 7.850, 785.0, 78 500

5) 2.399 6) 18.32 7) 1473 8) 365.6

Exercise 88

1) 362.1	**5)** 1.941	**9)** 71.93
2) 17 970	**6)** 2.599	**10)** 9.338
3) 148 900	**7)** 9.907	**11)** 25.67
4) 3783	**8)** 1.566	**12)** 1.898

Exercise 89

1) 393.2	**5)** 49.82	**9)** 2.486
2) 863.4	**6)** 1.213	**10)** 1.888
3) 1.596	**7)** 1.647	**11)** 15.19
4) 102.1	**8)** 2.398	**12)** 56 130

Exercise 90

1) 0.4498, $\bar{1}.4498$, $\bar{2}.4498$, $\bar{3}.4498$
2) 0.6625, $\bar{1}.6625$, $\bar{3}.6625$, $\bar{5}.6625$
3) $\bar{2}.9898$, $\bar{4}.9898$, $\bar{1}.9898$
4) $\bar{5}.7690$, $\bar{2}.7690$, $\bar{4}.7690$

5) 0.2714	**8)** 0.030 70
6) 0.006 606	**9)** 0.000 000 034 03
7) 0.000 3537	**10)** 0.1052

Exercise 91

1) 0	**6)** $\bar{2}$	**11)** $\bar{1}$	**16)** 5
2) 1	**7)** $\bar{3}$	**12)** $\bar{3}$	**17)** 0
3) $\bar{4}$	**8)** $\bar{9}$	**13)** $\bar{3}$	**18)** 3
4) $\bar{4}$	**9)** $\bar{3}$	**14)** $\bar{3}$	**19)** $\bar{3}$
5) 1	**10)** $\bar{2}$	**15)** 3	**20)** 3

Exercise 92

1) 0.1	**13)** 4.4	**24)** $\bar{2}.1$
2) 2.3	**14)** 2.3	**25)** $\bar{2}.9$
3) $\bar{2}.9$	**15)** $\bar{2}.9172$	**26)** $\bar{1}.5$
4) 0.1	**16)** 0.2340	**27)** $\bar{4}.5$
5) 1.1	**17)** $\bar{9}.1650$	**28)** $\bar{2}.5$
6) $\bar{2}.7$	**18)** 5.1	**29)** $\bar{1}.8$
7) $\bar{4}.1$	**19)** $\bar{3}.2$	**30)** 1.8
8) $\bar{2}.0$	**20)** 0.4	**31)** 6.9094
9) $\bar{2}.2$	**21)** 2.3	**32)** $\bar{1}.6204$
10) 1.1	**22)** $\bar{2}.5$	**33)** $\bar{4}.5424$
11) $\bar{1}.2$	**23)** 4.2	**34)** 2.1238
12) $\bar{4}.5$		

Exercise 93

1) $\bar{2}.8$	**5)** $\bar{1}.0$	**9)** $\bar{1}.5$
2) $\bar{9}.3$	**6)** $\bar{1}.3$	**10)** $\bar{2}.7$
3) $\bar{1}.4$	**7)** $\bar{1}.3$	**11)** 0.047 20
4) $\bar{4}.4$	**8)** $\bar{1}.6$	**12)** 0.2992

13) 0.000 001 814	**17)** 0.9305
14) 0.5069	**18)** 0.000 474 8
15) 0.4119	**19)** 0.4894
16) 0.092 10	**20)** 0.000 019 24

Exercise 94

1) (a) 1.8727 (b) 5.572 (c) 5565
(d) 8.637
2) **e** **3)** **d**
4) 2.106 **5)** 702.3
6) (a) 1275 (b) 3177 (c) 6.671
(d) 158.6
7) **a** **8)** **c** **9)** **a** **10)** **c**
11) (a) 510 100 000 (b) 5.101×10^8
12) $n = 6$
13) (a) 134.0 (b) 4912 (c) $\bar{1}.0031$
(d) 8.877
14) **c**
15) (a) 1.4800 (b) 3.500 (c) 105.7
(d) $x = 3.0241$; 1057

ANSWERS TO CHAPTER 13

Exercise 95

1) £126	**9)** £0.30
2) £20	**10)** £66
3) 4 years	**11)** £14.56
4) 5 months	**12)** (a) £189
5) $2\frac{1}{2}$ years	(b) £275
6) 7%	(c) £3200
7) 9%	(d) £10 010
8) £320	(e) £1701

ANSWERS TO CHAPTER 14

Exercise 96

1) (a) 5630 (b) 680 (c) 17 698 (d) 5.92 (e) 0.68 (f) 6.895 (g) 0.073 (h) 45.97 (i) 0.798 (j) 0.005
2) (a) 9.753 (b) 0.259 (c) 0.058 (d) 0.029 85 (e) 0.790 685
3) (a) 468 (b) 78.2 (c) 516 000 (d) 389.7 (e) 8.8
4) (a) 1234 (b) 580 000 (c) 258 (d) 3890 (e) 52
5) (a) 0.530 (b) 35 (c) 0.002 473 (d) 0.597 600
6) (a) 56 (b) 0.096 (c) 8 630 (d) 81 (e) 0.584
7) 18.2 tonnes **8)** 19 400 kg

Exercise 97

1) 4507	**4)** 19.7675	**7)** 14.01 km
2) 1.393	**5)** 4.25 kg	**8)** 42.45 m
3) 6.2 cm	**6)** 74 kg	

Exercise 98

1) 39.95 m	**5)** 36
2) 505.6 m	**6)** 1 053 kg
3) 18.98 m	**7)** 6
4) 51 pieces; 42 cm	**8)** 12.6 m

Exercise 99

1) 172 cm
2) 7.5 kg
3) 40
4) 15.048 m
5) 5
6) (a) 2000 m
   (b) 2056 m
   (c) 6.72 m
7) (a) 3000
   (b) 900
   (c) 3.5
8) a
9) 13; 25 cm
10) $\frac{9}{20}$
11) 250
12) 356
13) 1.45 m
14) 14.1 tonne
15) 0.8 kg
16) c
17) e
18) c

ANSWERS TO CHAPTER 15

Exercise 100

1) (a) 56 cm²
   (b) 220 mm²
   (c) 630 m²
2) 1.036 m²
3) 1.7424 m²
4) 28.42 m²
5) 62 m²
6) 174 m²
7) (a) 53.55 m²
   (b) 37.23 m²
   (c) 16.32 m²
8) (a) 1200 mm²
   (b) 275 mm²
   (c) 259.5 mm²
   (d) 774 mm²
   (e) 1050 mm²
   (f) 1094 mm²

Exercise 101

1) 6 m
2) 8.3 m
3) 10 m²
4) 5.5 m
5) 60 cm
6) 144 cm²; 12 cm
7) 2400
8) 66 m²

Exercise 102

1) 56 cm²
2) 0.0455 m²
3) 4 m
4) 7.2 m
5) 23.4 cm²

Exercise 103

1) 108 cm²
2) 22.125 cm²
3) 13.416 cm²
4) 9.617 cm²
5) 10 cm

Exercise 104

1) 40 cm²
2) 94.24 cm²
3) 10 cm
4) 30.615 cm²
5) 198 mm²

Exercise 105

1) 132 cm
2) 2200 mm
3) 270.2 m
4) 19.86 cm
5) 88 cm
6) 267.1 mm
7) 26.47 m
8) 4400 mm
9) 88 m
10) 10.18 m
11) 30.16 m
12) 2 m
13) 35 cm
14) 304.3 mm

Exercise 106

1) 616 cm²
2) 385 000 mm²
3) 24.99 m²
4) 1386 cm²
5) 47.55 m²
6) 30 670 mm²
7) 141.4 cm²
8) 581.3 mm²
9) 116.3 m²
10) 289.8 m²

Exercise 107

1) 3.142 cm; 6.284 cm²
2) 15.71 cm; 78.55 cm²
3) 3.142 cm; 4.713 cm²
4) 3.959 m; 5.345 m²
5) 238.3 mm; 9292.5 mm²
6) 39.10 cm²

Exercise 108

1) 21.45 cm²
2) 5.363 cm²
3) 13.728 cm²
4) 15.45 cm²
5) 211.9 cm²

Exercise 109

1) $x = 5$cm
2) $x = 140$ cm
3) (a) $4x+8$
   (b) $4x+8 = 20$
   (c) $x = 3$ cm
4) 30 m by 33 m
5) (a) $(4x+14)$ cm
   (b) $[x(x+7)]$ cm²
   (c) $x(x+7) = 18$
6) $4x^2+8x+3$

Exercise 110

1) 162 cm²
2) 55 cm²
3) c
4) 5.5 cm
5) d
6) 12.56 cm
7) 60 cm²
8) (a) (i) 18.84 cm
       (ii) 28.26 cm²
       (iii) 36 cm
       (iv) 111.36 cm
   (b) $(8\pi x +12x)$ cm
9) 7.2 cm²
10) 28 cm
11) 62.8 cm²
12) d
13) (a) 12.56 m²
    (b) 63.98 m
    (c) 86.13 m²
    (d) 69.57 m²

ANSWERS TO CHAPTER 16

Exercise 111

1) 140 cm³
2) 225 000 mm³
3) 7700 cm³
4) 31 420 mm³
5) 73.28 cm³
6) 0.0087 m³
7) 3.855 cm³
8) 300 cm³
9) 23.1 m³
10) 22 622 cm³

Exercise 112

1) 47.5 m²
2) 1960 cm²
3) 77.4 m²
4) 4.522 m²
5) 15.91 m²
6) 86.28 m²
7) 82.92 m²

Exercise 113

1) 50.27 cm³; 62.84 cm²
2) 150.8 cm²; 199.5 cm³
3) 20.78 cm³
4) 288 cm³
5) 523.7 cm³; 314.2 cm²
6) 1527 cm³
7) 30 470 cm³; 4210 cm²
8) 4295 cm³

Exercise 114

1) 2800 litres
2) 39 600 litres
3) 9.426 m³
   9426 litres
4) 7.855 litres
5) 15.375 litres
6) 384 mℓ; 96
7) 31.81 mℓ; 15.7
8) 9000 litres
9) 11.31 litres
10) 3.620 litres
11) 150 seconds
12) (a) 0.053 m³/s
    (b) 3181ℓ/min
13) 1 800 000ℓ/min
14) 35.35 m³;
    707 000 s
15) 3.82 cm/min

Exercise 115

1) 600 g
2) 1600 kg
3) 9.12 kg
4) 100.7 kg
5) 14 139 kg
6) 17.50 kg
7) 1080 kg
8) 452.4 kg
9) 300.9 kg
10) 1591 kg

Exercise 116

1) 5 cm
2) 7.638 m
3) 3.118 cm
4) 5 cm²
5) 2.5 mm
6) 10.61 m
7) 2474 m
8) 6.542 cm
9) 2 211 000
10) 6.365 cm
11) 8 cm
12) 40 cm²

Exercise 117

1) 38.5 cm²
2) No
3) $x = 10$ cm
4) 25.30 cm
5) 113 cm³;
   524 cm³
6) 27 cm³
7) 9.35 cm
8) 66 900 mm²;
   10 500 mm²
9) 46.1 cm²
10) 22.7 kg;
    13.10 kg

Exercise 119

1) (b) 9 cm
   (d) 6480 cm³
   (c) 3456 cm²
3) 560 cm³
4) (a) 4200 cm²
   (c) (i) 154 cm²
   (b) 6600 cm²
   (ii) 46.2ℓ
5) (a) 4500 cm²
   (b) 450 000 cm³
6) (a) 240 m²
   (b) (i) 30 cm×20 cm×15 cm
    (ii) 9000 cm³
   (c) 12
   (d) 0.786

286

7) (a) 6 cm
   (c) 39.25 cm³
   (e) 29 m
   (b) 2.5 cm
   (d) 6.5 cm
8) (a) 1570 cm³
   (c) 1 kg
   (b) 113 cm³
9) (a) 176 cm²
   (c) (i) 32.34 kg
   (d) 7 cm
   (b) $l = 10.5$ cm
   (ii) £67.91
10) (a) (i) 81 000 cm³
    (b) 271 s
   (ii) 25 cm

ANSWERS TO CHAPTER 17

Exercise 120

2) 254
4) £1.71
5) 63, 9.5
6) 0.7, 2.5

Exercise 121

1) (a) 10, 14, 18, 22
   (b) 18, 30, 42, 54
2) (a) 9
   (b) 36
3) (a) 11
   (b) $x \rightarrow 3x - 1$
4) (a) 2, 0; 3, −2; 4, −4; 5, −6
   (b) 2, 4; 3, 8; 4, 16; 5, 32
5) (a) $x \rightarrow 4x + 1$
   (b) 17, 33
6) 1, 0; 2, 0; 3, 2; 4, 6
7) $x \rightarrow 2x$

Exercise 122

1) (a) 4
   (b) 2
   (c) 44
   (d) $\frac{1}{4}$
2) (a) 17
   (b) −23
   (c) −7
3) (a) 1
   (b) 21
   (c) 0
   (d) 5
   (e) 33
4) −1; 53; −1
5) $6\frac{1}{2}$; $-3\frac{1}{2}$
6) $\frac{3}{2}$; $\frac{1}{4}$; $-\frac{7}{2}$

Exercise 124

1) 2.0
2) 0.44
3) 0.51
4) 0.03
5) 6.4

ANSWERS TO CHAPTER 18

Exercise 125

1) $<$
2) $=$
3) $>$
4) $=$
5) $>$
6) $=$
7) $>$
8) $<$
9) $>$
10) $<$

Exercise 127

1) $x > 5$
2) $x < 8$
3) $x \geqslant 2$
4) $x \leqslant 2$
5) $x > 1$
6) $x \geqslant 4$
7) $x > 4$
8) $x \geqslant -\frac{3}{4}$
9) $x < 8\frac{1}{2}$
10) $x \geqslant 2$

ANSWERS TO CHAPTER 19

Exercise 129

1) 8 h 51 min
2) 6 h 23 min
3) 10 h 24 min
4) 3 h 54 min
5) 7 h 45 min
6) 17 h 40 min
7) 6 h 37 min
8) 11 h 47 min
9) 7 h 31 min
10) 12 h 6 min
11) (a) 8.06 and 9.06. Time is 13 hours 39 min
    (b) 12.30 Wed.

Exercise 130

1) 75 km/h
2) 4 hours
3) 350 km
4) 26 km/h
5) 75 km/h
6) 80 km/h
7) 5 hours
8) 38.4 km/h
9) 40 km/h
10) 2 h 45 min
    211.75 km

Exercise 131

1) (a) 50 km/h
   (b) 100 km
   (c) 3 hours
2) 180 km, $\frac{2}{3}$ hour
3) 45.7 km/h
4) 35 km, 10 km/h
5) 22.1 km/h

ANSWERS TO CHAPTER 20

Exercise 132

1) 135°
2) 54°
3) 60°
4) 63°
5) 18°
6) 135°
7) 288°
8) 288°
9) 108°
10) 90°
11) 28° 37'
12) 69° 23'
13) 14° 22' 34"
14) 62° 48' 11"
15) 179° 11' 25"
16) 21° 3'
17) 22° 48'
18) 7° 43' 56"
19) 5° 54' 50"
20) 36° 58' 11"

Exercise 133

1) 20°
2) 100°
3) 35°
4) 70°, 110°, 110°, 70°
5) 65°
6) 80°
7) d
8) a
9) b
10) a
11) b, d
12) c
13) c
14) 54°
15) $x = 130°$
16) 65°
17) 230°, 32°
18) b, d
19) b, d

ANSWERS TO CHAPTER 21

Exercise 134

1) $x = 49$; $y = 131$
2) $x = 77$; $y = 81$
3) $x = 63$; $y = 98$
4) $x = 37$; $y = 127$
5) $x = 140$; $y = 60$
6) $x = 80$; $y = 70$

Exercise 135

1) $a = 10$
2) $b = 22.4$
3) $c = 2.65$
4) (a) 3.87
   (b) 4.24
   (c) 5.29
5) (a) 7.42
   (b) 3.71
   (c) 6.54
6) (a) 60
   (b) 40
   (c) 40
7) (a) $x = 70$
       $y = 40$
       $z = 35$
   (b) $x = 110$
       $y = 70$
       $z = 70$

Exercise 136

1) c
2) b, c, d
3) RQ = 7; SX = 4; $\angle$ SXP = 97°
4) PY = 6
5) BC = 5; $\angle$ BCA = 42°
6) ADF ≡ DFE ≡ FEC ≡ BED
   DGH ≡ GJE ≡ HGJ ≡ HJF

Exercise 137

1) {AFI} {CK} {BDM} {HJ}
2) b
3) b, d
4) d
5) a, d
6) c
7) a, b
8) b
9) BC = 32
10) EC = 4.5
    AB = $8\frac{1}{3}$

Exercise 138

1) 72 cm^2
2) a
3) b
4) b
5) c

ANSWERS TO CHAPTER 22

Exercise 139

1) $x = 143$
2) $x = 93$
3) $x = 39$, $y = 105$
4) d
5) a
6) a
7) b
8) 65
9) 100
10) Yes, Yes, Yes

Exercise 140

1) (a) 540
   (b) 1080
   (c) 1440
   (d) 1800
2) (a) 108
   (b) 135
   (c) 144
   (d) 150
3) 131
4) 12
5) 72
6) 8
7) a
8) b
9) c
10) b

ANSWERS TO CHAPTER 23

Exercise 141

1) Square 4. Rhombus 2. Isosceles
   trapezium 1. Isosceles triangle 1.
   Equilateral triangle 3. Regular hexagon 6.
2) Line symmetry: b, e, g, h, i
   Point symmetry: b, d, g, h, i.
3) (b) 2   (d) 2   (g) 8   (h) 4
4) (a) 6   (b) 1   (c) 8
5) (a) 9   (b) ∞   (c) 1   (d) 2
6) (a) 1, 1, 1, 2, 0, 1, 0, 1, 2
   (c) 0, 0, 0, 2, 0, 2, 0, 0, 2

Exercise 142

1) (a) 0.5	(b) 0.707	(c) 0.9272
2) (a) 19.5	(b) 48.6	(c) 46.1
3) (a) 0.2079	(b) 0.3123	(c) 0.9646
(d) 0.1285	(e) 0.9990	(f) 0.0032
4) (a) 9	(b) 66	(c) 81° 6′
(d) 4°36′	(e) 78° 55′	(f) 47° 41′
(g) 2° 52′	(h) 15° 40′	
5) (a) 3.381	(b) 10.13	(c) 25.94
6) (a) 41.8	(b) 40.8	(c) 22.4
7) 28.3	9) 21.6	11) 44.7, 44.7,
8) 0.794	10) 7.47	90.6

Exercise 143

1) (a) 0.965 9	(b) 0.911 4	(c) 0.201 1
(d) 1.000	(e) 0.286 3	(f) 0.766 3
2) (a) 24	(b) 70	(c) 14° 42′
(d) 64° 36′	(e) 16° 32′	(f) 89° 31′
(g) 74° 52′	(h) 61° 58′	
3) (a) 9.33	(b) 2.64	(c) 5.29
4) (a) 60.7	(b) 69.3	(c) 53.3

5) 66.1°, 66.1°, 47.8°, 3.84
6) 2.88
7) 1.97
8) $\angle$ BAC = 92°, BC = 8.74,
9) BD = 4.53, AD = 2.11, AC = 2.39
   BC = 5.65

Exercise 144

1) (a) 0.324 9	(b) 0.634 6	(c) 1.361
(d) 0.822 9	(e) 0.200 4	(f) 2.658
2) (a) 24	(b) 73	(c) 4° 24′
(d) 21° 42′	(e) 19° 38′	(f) 39° 34′
(g) 62° 33′	(h) 0° 56′	
3) (a) 4.35	(b) 9.29	(c) 4.43
4) (a) 59°	(b) 15.9°	(c) 22.7°
5) 7.70	7) 33.3	9) 2.09
6) 2.78	8) 2.86	

Exercise 145

1) (a) $\bar{1}$.679 4	(b) $\bar{1}$.983 7	(c) $\bar{1}$.995 8
(d) $\bar{1}$.959 9	(e) $\bar{1}$.992 7	(f) $\bar{1}$.094 3
2) (a) 57° 2′	(b) 22° 25′	(c) 75° 7′
(d) 11° 42′	(e) 80°	(f) 88°
3) (a) 45° 42′	(b) 18° 30′	(c) 58°
4) 9.29	6) 17° 42′	
5) 46° 12′	7) 5.81	

Exercise 146

1) 0.948 4   0.334 4
2) $\frac{3}{5}$; $\frac{4}{5}$
3) $\frac{5}{13}$; $\frac{5}{12}$
7) 0.743 1
8) 0.454 0

Exercise 147

1) d	3) 3.716	
2) d	4) 36° 52′	

288

5) (a) $\frac{3}{5}$	(b) $\frac{4}{5}$	(c) $\frac{4}{3}$
6) (a) 45.56	(b) 2.598	(c) 3.003
(d) 0.599 5	(e) $\bar{1}$.004 6	
7) (a) BC = 4	(b) 53.2	(c) 203.2
(d) 18.5	(e) 7.4	

8) cos A = 0.96,   tan (90−B) = $\frac{3}{4}$ = 0.75
9) c

10) (a) 26	(b) $\frac{12}{13}$	(c) 50°
11) (a) 20	(b) 51° 20′	(c) 12.49
12) (a) 5	(b) 12	(c) $\frac{12}{5}$ = 2.4
(d) 67.4°	(e) 13.9	
13) (a) 18.09	(b) 14.78	(c) 56.52
14) (a) 5	(b) 53.1	(c) 6.25

ANSWERS TO CHAPTER 26

Exercise 148

1) (a) 51 km   (b) 63 km   (c) 63 km
2) (a) (i) 66 km   (ii) 35 km   (b) (i) 64 km
   (ii) 48 km   (iii) 75 km
3) (a) (i) 25 km   (ii) 38 km   (iii) 34 km
   (b) via Bolton, 13 km and 9 km shorter
4) (i) 84 km   (ii) 101 km   (iii) 100 km
   (iv) 75 km; via Whitchurch and Broxton.
   Shorter by 9 km, 26 km and 25 km
5) (a) 85 km   (b) 82 km   (b) is shorter by
   3 km.

ANSWERS TO CHAPTER 27

Exercise 149

1) A = {5, 7, 9, 11, 13, 15}
2) X = {Tuesday, Thursday}
3) B = {2, 4, 6, 8, 10}
4) P = {2, 3, 5, 7, 11, 13, 17, 19, 23}
5) Q = {3, 6, 9, 12, 15, 18, 21, 24, 27, 30, 33}
6) {multiples of 5 less than 26}
7) {family}
8) {prime numbers greater than 2 but less than 18}

Exercise 150

1) infinite	6) null
2) finite	7) finite
3) infinite	8) null
4) finite	9) n(A) = 4
5) infinite	10) n(B) = 10

Exercise 151

1) P = {2, 4, 6, 8, 10}   7 ∉ P
2) Q = {1, 4, 9, 16, 25, 36}   18 ∉ Q
3) R = {17, 14, 11, 8, 5, 2}   9 ∉ R
4) S = {a, b, c, d, e, f}   ∅ ∉ S
5) T = {5, 7, 11, 13, 17, 19, 23, 29}   9 ∉ T

6) True	7) True	8) True
9) False	10) False	

Exercise 152

1) (a) {3, 5, 9, 11, 13, 15} (b) {6, 8, 12}
   (c) {3, 5, 11, 13} (d) {6, 8, 12}
2) 16 3) **c** and **d**
4) No. $A \subset C \subset B$
5) {a}, {b}, {c}, {d}, {a, b}, {a, c}, {a, d}, {b, c}, {b, d},
   {c, d}, {a, b, c}, {a, c, d}, {a, b, d}, {b, c, d}
6) $g \subset a$; $h \subset b$; $e \subset c$; $f \subset d$
8) **a**, **d**, **g**

Exercise 153

1) (a) {a, e, i, o, u}
   (b) {u, v, w, x, y, z}
   (c) {b, c, d, f, g, h, j, k, l, m, n, p, q, r, s, t, v,
       w, x, y, z}
2) {triangle, quadrilateral, pentagon, hexagon,
   septagon, octagon}
3) (a) {2, 3, 5, 7, 11, 13, 17, 19}
   (b) {3, 6, 9, 12, 15, 18}
   (c) {2, 3, 5, 7}
4) (a) {Nov, Dec, Jan, Feb}
   (b) {Sept, Oct}
5) {1, 4, 9, 16, 25}

Exercise 154

1) {2, 3, 4, 5, 6, 7, 8, 9, 11}
2) {2, 4, 7, 8}
3) {5, 6, 7, 8}
4) {3, 5, 6, 9, 11}
5) {2, 3, 4, 9, 11}
6) {7, 8}
7) {2, 4, 5, 6, 7, 8}
8) {3, 9, 11}
9) $\notin$ 13) $\subset$ 17) $\notin$
10) $\cap$, =   14) $\supset$ 18) $\subset$
11) $\in$ 15) $\neq$ 19) =
12) =   16) $\subset$, $\subset$ 20) $\subset$
21) {3, 4, 6, 7, 8, 9, 10}
22) {6, 8}
23) {3, 4, 6, 7, 8, 9, 10}
24) {6, 8}   25) $A \supset B$
26) {2, 3, 4, 5, 6, 7, 8, 9, 10, 11, 12, 13, 14, 15,
    16}
27) {3, 4, 6, 8}
28) {10, 12, 13, 14, 15}
29) $\emptyset$
30) {3, 4, 6, 8, 10, 12, 13, 14, 15}

31) 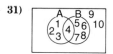   33)

32) 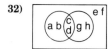   34)

---

35)

36) (a) B (b) $A \cap B$
    (c) $(A \cup B)'$ or $A' \cap B'$
    (d) $B \cap A'$ (e) $A \cup B$
    (f) $(A \cap B)'$ or $A' \cup B'$
    (g) $A \cap B'$

37)

ANSWERS TO CHAPTER 28

Exercise 155

1) (a) 10111   (c) 111101
   (b) 101010   (d) 111001
2) (a) 22   (b) 57   (c) 90   (d) 55
3) (a) 0.8125 (b) 0.4375   (c) 0.1875
4) (a) 0.011   (b) 0.0101   (c) 0.111
5) (a) 0.0010101
   (b) 10010.0111011
   (c) 1101100.1011010
6) (a) 1110   (e) 1.0011
   (b) 100110   (f) 1.11000
   (c) 111000   (g) 1101.0010
   (d) 1100100   (h) 10010.00
7) (a) 101   (c) 1110   (e) 10.001
   (b) 100   (d) 1.110
8) (a) 110   (d) 101011111
   (b) 100011   (e) 100011110
   (c) 1101110
9) (a) 11   (c) 101   (e) 1101
   (b) 100   (d) 1010
10) (a) 10111.101   (c) 10.0001
    (b) 10011.00001   (d) 1.00101

Exercise 156

1) (a) 111_3 (d) 1242_5 (g) 161_8
   (b) 1120_3 (e) 435_6 (h) 1304_6
   (c) 11211_3 (f) 1213_4
2) (a) 100_3 (c) 1100_3 (e) 4422_8
   (b) 3_4 (d) 13_4 (f) 134_5
3) (a) 214   (c) 137   (e) 187
   (b) 69   (d) 313
4) (a) 36_8 (c) 2523_6 (e) 5551_8
   (b) 121_3 (d) 54606_7 (f) 322242_5
5) (a) 1032_8 (e) 21201_5
   (b) 122_3 (f) 2330_8
   (c) 11110_3 (g) 1100100_2
   (d) 120_8
6) (a) 12_3 (c) 3_4 (e) 17_8
   (b) 3_5 (d) 115_6 (f) 253_7
7) (a) 223.02_4 (d) 11.400_6
   (b) 3.0021_5 (e) 102.20112_3
   (c) 33.3762_9

Exercise 157

1) 23   4) 0.11_2 7) 3
2) Base 2   5) 1200_3 8) 13_4
3) 22   6) 31_6 9) 100001_2
10) Base 5, 2
11) $27\frac{3}{4}$ 17) 102_4, 41_5,
12) 32.2_4 10110_2,
13) (a) 24 212_3
(b) $\frac{3}{25}$ 18) (a) 1005.1_6
14) (a) 1111001_2 (b) 505.3_6
(b) 1011_2 19) (a) 2051.43_6
15) 1010_3 (b) 5.72_8
16) 8   20) (a) 21.22_4
              (b) $(13.2)_4$

ANSWERS TO CHAPTER 29

Exercise 158

1) (a) $\begin{pmatrix} 5 & 3 \\ 7 & 8 \end{pmatrix}$ (e) $\begin{pmatrix} 3 & 4 \\ 2 & 5 \end{pmatrix}$

(b) $\begin{pmatrix} 1 & 1 \\ 1 & 2 \end{pmatrix}$ (f) $\begin{pmatrix} 2 & 3 \\ 1 & 3 \end{pmatrix}$

(c) $\begin{pmatrix} 12 & 9 \\ 23 & 19 \end{pmatrix}$ (g) $\begin{pmatrix} \frac{5}{7} & -\frac{2}{7} \\ -\frac{4}{7} & \frac{3}{7} \end{pmatrix}$

(d) $\begin{pmatrix} 10 & 9 \\ 21 & 21 \end{pmatrix}$ (h) $\begin{pmatrix} 1 & -\frac{1}{3} \\ 1 & \frac{2}{3} \end{pmatrix}$

2) $k = \frac{1}{2}$ 3) $a = 2,\ b = 3$

4) $\begin{pmatrix} 5 & 11 \\ 11 & 34 \end{pmatrix}$

5) (a) $\begin{pmatrix} 1 & 2 \\ 2 & 1 \end{pmatrix}$ (c) $\begin{pmatrix} 18 & 5 \\ 12 & 1 \end{pmatrix}$

(b) $\begin{pmatrix} 2 & -1 \\ 8 & 3 \end{pmatrix}$

Exercise 159

1) $L = 3,\ M = -1$

2) $\begin{pmatrix} 26 & 35 \\ 14 & 19 \end{pmatrix}$

3) (a) $\begin{pmatrix} 7 & 0 \\ 4 & 3 \end{pmatrix}$ (c) $\begin{pmatrix} 14 & 0 \\ 8 & -2 \end{pmatrix}$

(b) $\begin{pmatrix} 1 & 5 \\ 2 & -6 \end{pmatrix}$ (d) $\begin{pmatrix} 10 & 4 \\ 12 & 2 \end{pmatrix}$

4) (a) $PQ = \begin{pmatrix} 2 & 1 \\ 3 & 1 \end{pmatrix}$

$RS = \begin{pmatrix} -6 & 3 \\ 1 & -2 \end{pmatrix}$

$PQRS = \begin{pmatrix} -11 & 4 \\ -17 & 7 \end{pmatrix}$

$P^2 - Q^2 = \begin{pmatrix} 6 & 3 \\ 9 & 3 \end{pmatrix}$

(b) $a = -2,\ b = 5$

5) $A^2 = \begin{pmatrix} 16 & -9 \\ -12 & 13 \end{pmatrix}$

$B = \begin{pmatrix} -18 & 12 \\ 16 & -14 \end{pmatrix}$

6) $\begin{pmatrix} 9 \\ -1 \end{pmatrix}$

7) $p = 5;\ q = -1$

8) (a) $\begin{pmatrix} 3 & 1 \\ 2 & 2 \end{pmatrix}$ (c) $\begin{pmatrix} -1 & 2 \\ 1 & -1 \end{pmatrix}$

(b) $\begin{pmatrix} 1 & 3 \\ 2 & 3 \end{pmatrix}$

9) (a) (i) $\begin{pmatrix} 7 & 3 \\ 3 & 4 \end{pmatrix}$ (iii) $\begin{pmatrix} 13 & 6 \\ 12 & 4 \end{pmatrix}$

(ii) $\begin{pmatrix} 1 & -1 \\ 4 & 12 \end{pmatrix}$

(b) (i) $\begin{pmatrix} 6 & 4 & 2 \\ 3 & 6 & 1 \end{pmatrix}$

(ii) $\begin{pmatrix} 150 \\ 120 \\ 375 \end{pmatrix}$ (iii) $\begin{pmatrix} 2130 \\ 1545 \end{pmatrix}$

(iv) The number of passengers that each airline can carry

10) (a) $\begin{pmatrix} 12 \\ 8 \\ 15 \\ 12 \\ 8 \end{pmatrix}$

(b) $AB = \begin{pmatrix} -7 & 11 \\ 2 & -6 \end{pmatrix}$

$BA = \begin{pmatrix} -9 & -1 \\ -16 & -4 \end{pmatrix}$

(c) $x = 4,\ y = -1$

ANSWERS TO CHAPTER 30

Exercise 160

3) (c) $(3, -2)$, $(5, -2)$, $(3, -6)$
(e) $(-3, 2)$, $(-5, 2)$, $(-3, 6)$
(g) $(-3, -2)$, $(-5, -2)$, $(-3, -6)$
4) (a) $(2, 5)$
(e) $(3, 2)$, $(3, 4)$, $(5, 4)$, $(5, 2)$
7) $(6, 0)$, $90°$ clockwise

ANSWERS TO CHAPTER 31

Exercise 161

2) Private motoring 15.7%; rail 39.3%; other 45%
3) Unskilled workers 52.9%; craftsmen 29.4%; draughtsmen 5.9%; clerical staff 11.8%
8) Clothing 81°; furniture 108°; stationery 27°; sports equipment 54°; household goods 90°

Exercise 162

1) (a) 40 (b) 11 (c) 35
6) (a) 12 000
7) 800 items
8) 16 000 articles

Exercise 163

7) (a) 15.015 and 14.985 mm
  (b) 0.03 mm (c) 14.96–14.98 mm
8) Discrete: (b), (d), (g)

Exercise 164

1) £28   **5)** 163.1 cm   **9)** 5
2) 175 cm   **6)** 5   **10)** no mode
3) £41.20   **7)** 4.5   **11)** 3 and 8
4) 199.92 mm   **8)** 57

Exercise 165

1) (a) $\frac{1}{6}$ (b) $\frac{1}{2}$ (c) $\frac{1}{3}$ (d) $\frac{1}{2}$
2) (a) $\frac{1}{5}$ (b) $\frac{1}{2}$ (c) $\frac{13}{20}$ (d) $\frac{3}{20}$
3) (a) $\frac{1}{52}$ (b) $\frac{1}{13}$ (c) $\frac{4}{13}$ (d) $\frac{1}{26}$
4) (a) $\frac{1}{9}$ (b) $\frac{2}{9}$ (c) $\frac{1}{3}$
5) (a) $\frac{1}{5}$ (b) $\frac{9}{20}$ (c) $\frac{13}{20}$
6) (a) $\frac{1}{6}$ (b) $\frac{5}{18}$ (c) $\frac{5}{18}$
7) (a)
8) $\frac{37}{40}$

SHORT ANSWER REVISION QUESTIONS

1) £6.37
2) (a) 1860   (b) 1.8562×10^3
4) 0.1291
5) £20.33
6) £300 and £1000
7) (a) 10°C   (b) 4°C
8) (a) £2.73   (b) England
9) (a) (i) 8.015   (ii) 6.529
  (b) 8.062 cm
10) £20.30; £4.80
11) (a) 5.4464   (b) 3.68
12) 51_7 and 100_7
14) $n = 3; n = 1$
15) 385
16) (a) $\frac{2}{4}$ (b) $\frac{4}{5}$ (c) $\frac{2}{3}$
17) 2134
18) 4.56
19) (a) 510 100 000   (b) 5.101×10^8
20) $\begin{pmatrix} 1 & -1 \\ 0 & 1 \end{pmatrix}$
22) 5.5
23) 3.716 cm
25) $5\frac{13}{20}$
26) $x > 25$
27) $\frac{7}{9}$
28) 6
29) 1
30) $\begin{pmatrix} 1 \\ -4 \\ -7 \\ 2 \end{pmatrix}$
31) £2
33) £4.56
34) (a) 65%   (b) $33\frac{1}{3}\%$

35) 5
36) £0.30
37) 7.25
38) (a) £225   (b) £135
39) 0.0285
40) 1.28×10^4
41) -5
42) (a) 0.8   (b) 17.9
43) 22
44) 6
45) (a) $\frac{1}{13}$ (b) $\frac{3}{51}$
46) 63
47) (a) $\frac{5}{6}$ (b) $\frac{2}{5}$ (c) $\frac{5}{8}$
48) (a) {1, 4, 6, 8, 9, 10, 12, 14, 15, 16, 18, 20, 21, 22, 24, 25, 26, 27, 28}
  (b) {6, 10, 15, 21, 28}
  (c) {4, 9, 16, 25}
  (d) {1, 3, 4, 6, 8, 9, 10, 12, 14, 15, 16, 18, 20, 21, 22, 24, 25, 26, 27, 28}
49) (a) (i) 3.010×10^3 (ii) 8×10^{-2}
  (b) 2.408×10^2
50) (a) 282.6 cm³   (b) 2.787
51) (a) $2(3x+2y)$ (b) $t(3t+1)$
  (c) $(x-3)(x+2)$
52) 1
53) (b) 3.9 cm
54) 3.61×10^{-3}
55) 12
56) 39
57) $2\frac{3}{4}$
58) 4
59) $\frac{1}{18}$
60) 9
61) 53
62) (a) 10, 12, 14   (b) $\frac{1}{16}, -\frac{1}{32}, \frac{1}{64}$
63) 6
64) 33.54
65) 233_5
66) £37.50
67) 2
68) (a) 450   (b) 1000   (c) 3000
  (d) 900   (e) 3.5
69) (a) £1.00   (b) £5.97   (c) $17\frac{1}{2}$p
  (d) £3.77   (e) £0.55
70) (a) $\frac{3}{4}$ (b) $\frac{1}{6}$ (c) $\frac{1}{12}$
  (d) 2   (e) $\frac{8}{9}$
72) $1\frac{1}{12}$
74) (a) $\begin{pmatrix} 1 & 0 \\ 0 & 1 \end{pmatrix}$ (b) $\begin{pmatrix} 1 & 0 \\ 0 & 1 \end{pmatrix}$
75) 4
76) (a) 13   (b) 42   (c) 4
77) (a) 8.71×10^2 (b) 2.9400
79) $x = 5$
80) (a) 2.7   (b) 13.09   (c) 3.12
81) (a) 7   (b) 3.5   (c) $x = 1, y = 5$
82) 1.1 m²
83) 11
84) 3.4
85) $\frac{8}{21}$
86) {23, 29, 31, 37}

87) (a) 93 000 000   (b) 9.2956×10[7]

88) x^2+x-6

89) 4

90) 17

91) (a) ABFE   (b) EBCG
(c) FCDHLK   (d) ADN

92) 495

93) $\angle$ BAC = 35°, $\angle$ EBA = 25°, $\angle$ DEC = 120°,
$\angle$ DEA = $\angle$ CEB = 60°, $\angle$ DAE = 40°,
$\angle$ CDE = 25°, $\angle$ CBE = 30°

94) (a) $\frac{2}{3}$ (b) 40

95) 210 cm²

96) (a) $50-x$ (b) $5x$ (c) 40

97) (a) 5×10[7]   (b) 4×10[-6]

98) (a) 154 cm²   (b) 44 cm

99) (a) $3x^2-11x-4$ (b) $4x^2-12x+9$

100) (a) >   (b) ≏   (c) =   (d) none

MULTI-CHOICE REVISION EXERCISE

1) d   2) a   3) e   4) e   5) c   6) c   7) d
8) c   9) e   10) c   11) b   12) a   13) c
14) a   15) b   16) b   17) b   18) a
19) a   20) c   21) c   22) c   23) b
24) (i) b   (ii) d   (iii) e   (iv) b
25) a   26) b   27) c   28) c   29) b
30) a   31) c   32) d   33) a   34) c
35) (i) c   (ii) e   (iii) c
36) e   37) c   38) b   39) c
40) d   41) d   42) e   43) d
44) (i) d   (ii) e   (iii) b   (iv) b
45) c
46) c   47) b   48) d   49) a   50) e
51) b   52) d   53) c   54) c   55) d
56) b   57) c   58) d   59) a   60) b
61) a   62) b   63) e   64) c   65) b
66) d   67) a   68) c   69) d   70) d
71) e   72) c   73) e   74) d   75) c
76) a   77) a   78) a   79) e   80) b
81) d   82) a   83) a   84) c   85) c
86) e   87) d   88) e   89) e   90) a
91) c   92) c   93) c   94) b   95) a
96) b   97) b, e   98) e   99) b, d   100) a

ANSWERS TO LONGER QUESTIONS

1) (a) £22.50   (b) £26   (c) £2.12½

2) (a) (i) 23   (ii) 0   (iii) 15   (iv) 54
(v) 53   (b) 185

3) (a) (i) 24   (ii) 27, 33, 45, 49, 61 or 63
(iii) 61   (iv) 49   (v) 49 or 63
(vi) 27, 45 and 63   (vii) 33 and 45
(b) 10000₂   (c) 1010₂

4) (a) 1275   (b) 3176   (c) 6.671   (d) 158.6

5) (i) $\sqrt{1.21}=1.1$ (ii) $\sqrt{12.1}<3.5$
(iii) $9^2-3^2>6^2$ (iv) $12^2\div3^2=4^2$

6) (a) 9 cm and 15 cm   (b) $\frac{4}{5}$; $\frac{4}{5}$ (c) 53° 8'

7) (a) (i) 3   (ii) 3.3   (b) 1.513
(c) 0.3067   (d) 0.5710   (e) 1

8) (a) 5   (b) 10 cm   (c) 36°   (d) 30 cm²
(e) 9.405 cm

9) (a) £25   (b) £112.50   (c) £137.50
(d) £212.50   (e) £8000

10) (i) square   (ii) rhombus   (iii) parallelogram

11) (a) (i) $\dfrac{AB}{BC}=\dfrac{ED}{EF}$
(ii) $\dfrac{AB}{DE}=\dfrac{BC}{EF}=\dfrac{AC}{DF}$
(b) (i) $\frac{1}{2}$ (ii) 4

12) (a) 93 500   (b) 6.38×10[-3]
(c) (i) 42.0   (ii) 3.95

13) (a) 250 cm²   (b) 132 cm²   (c) 250 cm³

14) (a) a, d   (b) a, e   (c) none   (d) e, g

15) (a) £1500   (b) £1275   (c) £1084

16) (a) 25   (b) $\begin{pmatrix} 9 & 12 \\ 12 & 16 \end{pmatrix}$

17) (a) 5   (b) 13, 14   (c) 3

18) (a) 0, 16; 1, 25; 2, 11; 3, 3; more than 3, 5
(c) 1

19) 5.3

20) (a) 13   (b) 0.11₂   (c) 100011₂
(d) Base 5, 2

21) (a) (i) 2   (ii) 2   (iii) 6   (iv) 10
(b) x^2y (c) 324

22) (a) (i) 3.5   (ii) 11.25   (b) (−2, 0)

23) (b) A ∩ B ∩ C
(c) (i) 4   (ii) 2   (iii) 3   (iv) ∞

24) (a) (i) 40   (ii) 4   (b) (i) 1111001₂
(ii) 1011₂   (c) (i) 1001001₂   (ii) 27

25) (a) Trapezium   (b) 36 cm²   (c) 4
(d) 57°   (e) x^2-y^2

26) (a) 27   (b) 1200₃   (c) 2   (d) 31₆   (e) 3

27) (a) 36 cm³   (b) 288 g   (c) 198 cm³
(d) 1.272 cm   (e) 2.5 cm

28) (a) $4a^2-16$ (b) $(x+8)(x+3)$
(c) (i) −24   (ii) 15   (iii) 0

29) (a) $\frac{1}{3}$ (b) 3.15 cm²   (c) 35°
(d) 3.662 cm   (e) △BEC

30) (b) 136.8°   (c) 240

31) (e) (−3, 8) and (2, 3)

32) (c) $\frac{3}{2}$ (d) $\frac{9}{4}$

33) (a) $\angle$ NYW, $\angle$ XWY   (b) 12° 41'
(c) 41 mm   (d) 8.782 mm   (e) 360.1 mm²

34) (i) 20 m   (ii) 51° 20'   (iii) 12.50 m

35) (a) 40°   (b) 20°

36) (a) (i) Not possible   (ii) $\begin{pmatrix} 36 \\ 16 \end{pmatrix}$

(iii) $\begin{pmatrix} 6 & 0 & 14 \\ 0 & -6 & 12 \\ -3 & -9 & 11 \end{pmatrix}$ (b) 2×2

37) (a) 1.4800   (b) 3.500   (c) 105.7
  (d) (i) $x = 3.0241$ (ii) 1057
38) (a) 73° 44′   (b) 8.870 cm   (c) 4.618 cm
  (d) 266.1 cm^2

39) (a) 37   (b) 36   (c) 35   (d) $\frac{2}{9}$
40) (a) 50   (b) 60 kg   (c) 59.36 kg
41) (c) $(1, -2), (3, -6), (5-1)$

Glossary

Acute angle. An angle less than 90°.
Acute angled triangle. One which has all its angles less than 90°.
Alternate angles. These are the internal angles on opposite sides of the transversal which cuts two parallel lines (see diagram). $a = b$ and $c = d$ are the alternate angles.

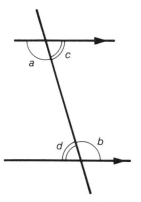

Altitude of a triangle. This is the height of the triangle, i.e. the perpendicular distance between any vertex and its opposite side.
Amount. This is the total formed by adding the interest to the principal, i.e. the sum of money invested.
Angle. This is the amount of opening between two straight lines. It is measured either in degrees, minutes and seconds or in radians.
Angle sum of a polygon. The sum of the interior angles of a polygon is $(2n-4)$ right angles, where n is the number of sides. The sum of the exterior angles is 360°, no matter how many sides the polygon has.
Arc. This is a part of the circumference of a circle. If the arc subtends an angle of θ degrees at the centre of the circle, its length is

$$2\pi r \times \frac{\theta}{360}$$

where r is the radius of the circle.

Area. The area of a plane figure is measured by seeing how many square units it contains. The standard unit of area is the square metre.
Average. The three kinds of average are the arithmetical mean, the mode and the median.
Average speed. This is found by dividing the total distance travelled by the total time taken. That is

$$\text{average speed} = \frac{\text{distance travelled}}{\text{time taken}}$$

Axes of a graph. These are two lines drawn at right angles to each other. The vertical axis is usually called the y-axis. The horizontal axis is called the x-axis.

Bar charts are used in statistics. They represent information by means of bars all having the same width. The height (or length) of each bar represents the magnitude of the figures in the data.
Base of logarithm. If $N = a^x$ then $x = \log_a N$. a is said to be the base of the logarithm.
Binary system. This number system uses the base 2 and only the digits 0 and 1 are used. Numbers containing a binary point are called *bicimals*.
Binomial expressions contain two algebraic terms, e.g. $x+y$ or $a-b$.

Cancelling means dividing the top and bottom of a fraction by the same amount.
Capacity. This is the amount of liquid which a container will hold. It is usually measured in litres.
Cartesian coordinates. These are the perpendicular distances of a point on a graph measured from the x and y axes respectively. They are sometimes called rectangular coordinates.
Characteristic. This is the whole number part of a logarithm.
Chord. This is a straight line which joins two points on the circumference of a circle.

Circle. This is the locus of points which are equidistant from a fixed point (which is the centre of the circle).

Circumference. This is the perimeter of a circle. It is calculated from the formula $C = 2\pi r$, where r is the radius of the circle.

Coefficient of x. This is the number which multiplies x. Thus in the term $3x$, 3 is the coefficient of x.

Column matrix. This is a matrix which has only one column.

Complementary angles are angles whose sum is 90°.

Congruent triangles are triangles which are identical in size and shape.

Continuous variable. A variable which can take any value between two given end values is called a continuous variable.

Corresponding angles are the angles a and l, b and m, c and p, d and q in the diagram. They are formed by a transversal and a pair of parallel lines.

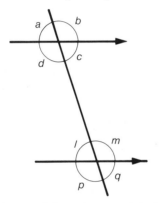

Cosine of an angle is a trigonometrical ratio which equals

$$\frac{\text{side of the triangle opposite to the angle}}{\text{hypotenuse of the triangle}}$$

Counting numbers are positive whole numbers.

Cube of a number. This is a number multiplied by itself three times. Thus seven cubed is $7 \times 7 \times 7$ and is written 7^3.

Decimal places. In a number, the number of figures following the decimal point gives the number of decimal places.

Decimal system. A number system which uses the base 10 and the digits 0, 1, 2, 3, 4, 5, 6, 7, 8 and 9. It is sometimes called the denary system.

Denominator. This is the bottom part of a fraction and it tells how many parts the whole has been divided into.

Diagonal matrix. This is a square matrix in which all the elements are zero except for those in the diagonal.

Difference. The difference of two numbers is the smaller number subtracted from the larger number.

Difference of two squares refers to the factors of $a^2 - b^2 = (a+b)(a-b)$.

Digits. These are the numbers 0, 1, 2, 3, 4, 5, 6, 7, 8 and 9.

Directed numbers are numbers with a sign attached. $+5$ is a positive directed number whilst -4 is a negative directed number.

Discount is the amount a dealer takes off his selling price when payment is made in cash. A discount of 5% means that the customer pays only 95% of the selling price.

Discrete variable. This is a variable which can only take certain values.

Dividend. This is the number to be divided. Thus in $265 \div 15$, 265 is the dividend.

Divisor. This is the number by which the dividend is divided. Thus in $18 \div 6$, 6 is the divisor.

Dollar. The American unit of currency. 1 Dollar = 100 cents.

Drachma. The Greek unit of currency. 1 drachma = 100 lepta.

Element. In a set it is the different objects, numbers, etc. making up the set. In a matrix it is one of the numbers making up the array which forms the matrix.

Equilateral triangle. One which has all its sides and angles equal. Each angle of the triangle equals 60°.

Even number. A number which is divisible by 2.

Exchange rate. The rate at which one currency may be changed into a second currency. £1 = \$2.00 is a typical exchange rate.

Factor. This is a number or an algebraic expression which will divide exactly into another number or algebraic expression. Thus 3 is a factor of 6 and m is a factor of $m(p+q)$.

Factorial. Factorial 5 is written 5! and it equals $5 \times 4 \times 3 \times 2 \times 1$. Similarly factorial 3 is 3! which equals $3 \times 2 \times 1$.

Finite set. This is a set in which all the elements can be listed.

Franc. The unit of currency of France, Belgium and Switzerland. 1 franc = 100 centimes.

Frequency. This is the number of times an event occurs.

Function. y is a function of x if the value of y depends upon the value allocated to x. Thus if $y = x^2 + 3x - 7$ then y is a function of x. This is usually written $y = f(x)$.

Gradient of a straight line. This is the value of m in the equation $y = mx + c$ which is the equation of a straight line. c is the intercept on the y-axis.

Grouped distribution. When the information comprising the raw data is grouped into classes or categories a grouped distribution is formed.

Glide reflection is a transformation in which a reflection takes place after a translation.

Hexagon. A polygon with six sides.

Histogram. A diagram used in statistics to represent a frequency distribution. The area of each bar in the diagram is proportional to the class frequency.

Hypotenuse. The side of a right angled triangle which lies opposite to the right angle. It is the longest side of the triangle.

Imaginary number. Numbers like $\sqrt{-1}$ and $\sqrt{-7}$ are said to be imaginary because it is impossible to find their value.

Improper fraction. This is a fraction which has its numerator greater than its denominator. It is sometimes called a top heavy fraction.

Index. This is the power to which a quantity is raised. Thus in 5^4, the index indicating the power is 4.

Inequalities. Statements such as 20 pence is less than £1 and 9 is greater than 5 are called inequalities.

Infinite set. This is a set in which it is impossible to list all the elements. Thus the set of even numbers is an infinite set.

Irrational number. A number which cannot be expressed as a vulgar fraction is called an irrational number. Numbers such as $\sqrt{5}$ and $\sqrt{7}$ are irrational.

Inscribed circle. The inscribed circle of a triangle just touches each of the sides of the triangle internally. Its centre is found by bisecting the angles of the triangle.

Integers are whole numbers. They include positive and negative numbers and zero.

Interest is money paid to an investor for lending money.

Intersection. The intersection of the sets A and B is the set of elements which are contained in both A and B. Thus if $A = \{1, 2, 3, 4\}$ and $B = \{2, 4, 6, 8\}$ then $A \cap B = \{2, 4\}$.

Invert of a matrix. If $AA^{-1} = I$, I being the unit matrix, then A^{-1} is called the invert of A.

Inverse proportion. If $y = \dfrac{k}{x}$, k being a constant, then x is inversely proportional to y.

Isometries are transformations in which size and shape do not change.

Isosceles triangle is one which has two equal sides. The angles which lie opposite to the equal sides are also equal.

Kilogramme. This is the standard unit of mass. 1000 grammes = 1 kilogramme.

Linear equation. This is the same as a simple equation and is of the type $y = mx + c$, m and c being constants. It is so called because its graph is a straight line.

Lira. The unit of currency used in Italy. 1 lira = 100 centissimi.

Litre. The standard unit of capacity. 1000 cubic centimetres = 1 litre.

Logarithm. If $N = a^x$ then $x = \log_a N$. x is said to be the logarithm of N to the base a.

Lowest Common Multiple. The L.C.M. of a set of numbers is the smallest number into which each of the numbers in the set will divide exactly.

Mantissa. The decimal part of a logarithm.

Mapping. If $y = 4x$ the values of y are called the range and the corresponding values of x are called the domain. Values of the domain are mapped onto the range, often in the form of a graph.

Matrix. This is an arrangement of numbers into rows and columns. A 2×3 matrix has 2 rows and 3 columns.

Mean. This is usually called the arithmetic mean. Its value is found by dividing the sum of the quantities by the number of quantities.

Median. This is a statistical average. When numbers are arranged in ascending (or descending) order the median is the middle value of the set. If there is an even number of quantities the median is found by taking the mean of the two middle values.

Median of a triangle. This is the line joining a vertex to the mid-point of its opposite side.

Mediator. This is the perpendicular bisector of a straight line.

Metre. This is the standard unit of length. 1 metre = 100 centimetres = 1000 millimetres. 1000 metres = 1 kilometre.

Mixed number consists of a whole number and a fraction. Thus $3\frac{2}{3}$ and $5\frac{3}{4}$ are both mixed numbers.

Mode. This is a statistical average. It is the most frequently occurring value in a set of quantities. If there are several modes the set is said to be multimodal. If there are two modes the set is bimodal. If there is only one mode the set is unimodal.

Multiple. The number $84 = 7 \times 12$. 84 is a multiple of 7 (it is also a multiple of 12). Likewise 18 is a multiple of 2, 3, 6 and 9 because each of these numbers will divide into 18 exactly.

Net. This is a plane figure which can be folded to form a solid figure. In Technical Drawing a net is called a development.

Null set. This is a set with no elements. It is represented by the symbol ø (the Danish letter oe).

Number line. This is a way of representing positive and negative numbers in a diagram.

Numerator. This is the top part of a fraction and it indicates how many equal parts are to be taken. Thus in the fraction $\frac{3}{4}$, the whole is divided into 4 and 3 of these equal parts are to be taken.

Obtuse angle. This is an angle with a value greater than 90° but less than 180°.

Octagon. A polygon with eight sides.

Octal. A number system using the base 8.

Ordered pair. In an ordered pair the numbers are stated in a certain order. The cartesian coordinates of a point on a graph form an ordered pair.

Origin. The intersection of the x and y axes on a graph. The origin has the coordinates (0,0).

Parallelogram. This is a quadrilateral with opposite sides parallel. In effect it is a rectangle pushed out of square.

Pentagon. A polygon with 5 sides.

Percentage. A fraction with a denominator of 100. Thus

$$25\% = \frac{25}{100}.$$

Pictogram is used in statistics. It is a pictorial way of presenting information.

Pie chart is a statistical diagram consisting of a circle divided up into sectors. The proportions of the whole are then represented by the sector angles or sector areas.

Plane. A flat surface.

Polygon. Any closed figure bounded by straight lines. A convex polygon has no interior angle greater than 180°. A re-entrant polygon has at least one angle greater than 180°. A regular polygon has all its sides and angles equal.

Powers. The power of a number indicates the number of times that the number is to be multiplied by itself. Thus $3^5 = 3 \times 3 \times 3 \times 3 \times 3 = 729$.

Prime numbers have only themselves and 1 as factors. 2, 3, 5, 7, 11, 13, etc. are prime numbers.

Principal. This is the sum of money which has been invested.

Probability has a value between 0 (the absolute impossibility) and 1 (the absolute certainty). It is calculated from

$$Pr = \frac{\text{possibility of the event occurring}}{\text{total possibilities}}$$

Product. The result of a multiplication. The product of 5 and 7 is $5 \times 7 = 35$.

Pythagoras' theorem states that in a right angled triangle the square on the hypotenuse is equal to the sum of the squares on the other two sides.

Quadratic equation is of the type $ax^2 + bx + c = 0$, where a, b and c are constants. The solution is given by

$$x = \frac{-b \pm \sqrt{b^2 - 4ac}}{2a}$$

Quadrilateral is any four sided figure.

Quotient is the result of a division.

Radian. An angle may be measured in radians. 1 radian is the angle subtended at the centre of a circle by an arc whose length is equal to the radius of the circle. 2π radians = 360° and 1 radian = 57.3° (approx.).

Rate per cent is the rate of interest paid per annum.

Ratio is a comparison between two similar quantities. The ratio of 5 cm to 2 m is $5:200$ or $1:40$.

Rational number is one which can be expressed as a vulgar fraction. Thus 0.375 and 0.3̇ are rational numbers because they represent the fractions $\frac{3}{8}$ and $\frac{1}{3}$.

Raw data is collected information which has not been organised into any sort of order.

Real numbers are rational and irrational numbers but not imaginary numbers.

Rectangle. A quadrilateral with all its angles equal to 90°.

Reciprocal of a number is $\dfrac{1}{\text{number}}$. Thus
the reciprocal of 2 is $\frac{1}{2} = 0.5$.

Reflection is a transformation in which a point is reflected in a line which acts as a mirror.

Reflex angle is greater than 180° but less than 360°.

Right angle is equal to 90° or $\frac{1}{4}$ of a revolution.

Right angled triangle has one angle equal to 90°.

Rotational transformation is an isometry with an invariant point which is the centre of rotation.

Scale of a graph is the number of units to a unit length along the axes. Thus a scale might be 1 cm = 10 units or 1 cm = 5 m/s.

Scalene triangle has each of its three sides of different length.

Sector of a circle is bounded by an arc and two radii. Its area is given by

$$A = \pi r^2 \times \frac{\theta}{360},$$

where $\theta°$ is the angle subtended at the centre of the circle by the arc.

Set. This is a collection of objects, numbers, etc. with one or more common properties, e.g. the set of even numbers.

Sequence is a set of numbers which are connected by some definite law. Thus 2, 5, 8, 11, ... form a sequence because each number is formed by adding 3 to the previous number.

Significant figures are the figures used to give a required degree of accuracy when stating a number. For instance, 587 = 590 correct to 2 significant figures.

Similar triangles are triangles which are equiangular.

Simple equation is another name for a linear equation. Simple equations are of the type $y = mx + c$ where m and c are constants.

Sine of an angle is a trigonometrical ratio which equals

$$\frac{\text{side opposite to the angle}}{\text{hypotenuse}}$$

Square of a number. This is a number multiplied by itself. Thus the square of 2 is $2^2 = 2 \times 2$.

Square metre. This is the standard unit of area. It is the area contained in a square whose side is 1 metre.

Square root of a number is the number whose square equals the given number. Thus the square root of 9 is $\sqrt{9} = 3$.

Standard form. When a number is expressed in the form $A \times 10^n$ where A is a number between 1 and 10 and n is an integer, the number is said to be expressed in standard form. Thus $5\,200\,000 = 5.2 \times 10^6$.

Subsets. The set $\{2, 3\}$ is contained in the set $\{1, 2, 3, 4, 5\}$. $\{2, 3\}$ is said to be a subset of $\{1, 2, 3, 4, 5\}$.

Substitution. This is the process of finding the numerical value of an algebraic expression for given values of the symbols which appear in the expression.

Sum. This is the result of an addition. Thus the sum of 5 and 7 is $5 + 7 = 12$.

Supplementary angles are angles whose sum is 180°.

Tangent of an angle is a trigonometrical ratio. It equals

$$\frac{\text{side opposite to the angle}}{\text{side adjacent to the angle}}$$

Transformation means mapping a shape onto its image.

Translation is a transformation in which every point of a shape is moved the same distance in the same direction.

Transpose of a matrix. If the rows and columns of a matrix are interchanged the matrix is said to be transposed.

Transversal is a straight line which cuts two parallel lines.

Trapezium is a quadrilateral with two sides parallel.

Union. The union of the sets A and B is the set of all the elements contained in both sets. If $A = \{1, 2, 3, 4\}$ and $B = \{2, 4, 6, 8\}$ then $A \cup B = \{1, 2, 3, 4, 6, 8\}$.

Universal set is the set from which all subsets are formed.

Venn diagram. This is a method of representing sets.

Volume is measured by seeing how many cubic units are contained in a solid figure. The standard unit of volume is the cubic metre.

Index

301